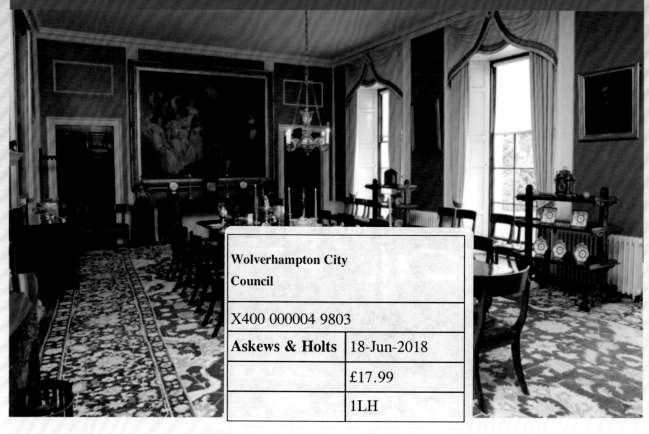

HUDSON^s

The definitive guide to heritage in the United Kingdom

Published by Specialist Guides Ltd,
26 Eldon Business Park, Chilwell, Nottingham NG9 6DZ
Email: info@specialistguides.com   www.visitheritage.co.uk

Front cover: Alnwick Castle, Northumberland

2018

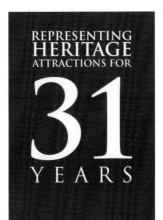

REPRESENTING HERITAGE ATTRACTIONS FOR

31 YEARS

WOODLAND ©HAREWOOD HOUSE TRUST

KEY TO SYMBOLS

Hudson's is organised by region according to this map.
We use the symbols on this key to include as much information
as possible. We indicate ownership so if you are a member of
a heritage organisation, you know if you can have privileged
access, but please check first.

- ⓘ Information
- 🚻 Toilets
- Baby Changing
- € Accepts Euros
- ❄ Open All Year
- Ⓟ Parking Available
- ♿ Suitable for Disabled People
- 🚲 Cycling Routes
- 🐕 Dogs Welcome
- Accommodation
- 🎧 Audio Tours
- Guided Tours
- Educational/School Visits
- ☕ Café / Tearoom / Refreshments
- 🍽 Restaurant
- 🛍 Shop
- Plant Sales
- Private or Corporate Venue
- Special Events
- Weddings
- 🎥 In the Movies

- Member of the Historic Houses Association but does not give free access to Friends
- Ⓕ Member of the HHA giving free access under the HHA Friends Scheme
- Owned by National Trust
- Owned by National Trust Scotland
- In the care of Historic Scotland
- In the care of English Heritage
- In the care of Cadw, the Welsh Government's historic environment service
- Royal Horticultural Society Partner Garden
- NIEA In the care of Northern Ireland Environment Agency
- In the care of the Landmark Trust

- ✦ Hudson's Heritage Awards – Winner 2017
- ✧ Hudson's Heritage Awards – Highly Commended 2017

VISITORS IN CENTRAL LOBBY
©HOUSES OF PARLIAMENT

NEW PLACE, SHAKESPEARE BIRTHPLACE TRUST
©MARTIN NEEVES

©HAREWOOD HOUSE TRUST

Welcome to
HUDSON^s

Welcome to our family and the new look to Hudson's!

Hudson's is part of Visit Heritage which aims to raise the profile of Heritage sites across our fair lands. We are the only totally independent representation of all that is Heritage in UK, and we are very proud to fill that space.

You will have already noticed that this year the Hudson's book looks and feels different. Inside you will meet a new Mrs Hudson who will bring to life our UK Heritage by sharing her perspectives and suggestions around hidden gems. We are also seeking to keep you informed of some of the lesser known places, and people, that are no less interesting and have made an important contribution to our past. You will notice in the section '100 Years of Women & Suffrage', we are tipping our hats to some of the great ladies in our history.

We aim to encourage you to go and explore Great Britain and its unrivalled history. Please visit and get close to places which helped form the world we now know. Discover the past and help those hundreds of people and organisations that are working to maintain our unique Heritage for generations to discover.

Look out for the exciting new publications we will be introducing that focus on specific aspects of Heritage. In future years, copies of Hudson's annual book will also adopt a theme, and we hope this will ensure you are kept informed of things that are available for you in the world of UK Heritage.

Please also visit the website at visitheritage.co.uk to get the full effect of what we can offer. Have a wonderful 2018 and be sure to spend some of your valuable time appreciating some of the wonderful Heritage available in these beautiful lands.

Paul

Paul Bridle

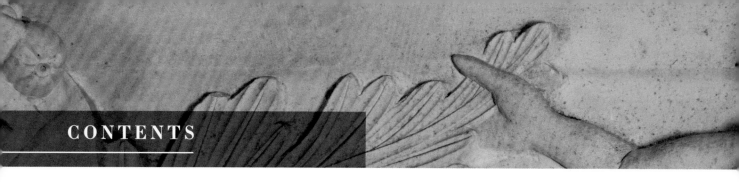

CONTENTS

We want Hudson's to make discovering Britain's heritage easy for you but please check opening times before you visit to avoid disappointment. Many heritage places open regularly but others only occasionally or only for special events.

THE STAIRCASE, FAIRFAX HOUSE, YORK
©FAIRFAX HOUSE TRUST

NATIVE AMERICAN FIGURES IN THE OVERMANTEL DATING FROM AROUND 1560 AT WOLFETON HOUSE, DORSET ©DAVE PENMAN

THE ANTIQUE PASSAGE, CASTLE HOWARD, YORKSHIRE
©ANDY BULMER

Contributors:

Mark Pearsall is The National Archives' Family History specialist. He is the author of a number of publications on Family History.

Mark Francis is General Manager of Burgh House in Hampstead and co-ordinator of Shh, London's Small Historic Houses.

Sheila Charrington is the owner of Layer Marney Tower with her husband, Nick; Chairman of Invitation to View and was a participant on Channel 4's Four in a Campbed.

James Miller is an art consultant and ex-Deputy Chairman of Sotheby's International. He is the founder of website Northamptonshire Surprise.

Dr Adam Bowett is a furniture historian and chairman of the Chippendale Society, co-ordinators of Chippendale 300.

Derek Tarr is an enthusiastic rambler and has been planning walks to heritage places for Hudson's for the last six years.

Sarah Greenwood is editor of Hudson's and has spent a lifetime working with historic attractions.

Hudson's team:

Publisher: **Paul Bridle**

Editorial: **Sarah Greenwood**

Publishing & Production Manager: **Kylie Woolgar**

Creative team: **Alex Fajfric; Kylie Woolgar; Neil Jones**

Bookings: **Antonia Buxton; Rachel Price-Hood**

Advertising: **Hall-McCartney Ltd, Baldock SG7 5SH**

Web team: **Antonia Buxton; Rachel Price-Hood**

Social media: **Edwina Holmes**

Printer: **Biddles, King's Lynn, Norfolk PE32 1SF**

Distribution: **Compass International Publishing Services, Brentford TW8 9DF**

Address: **Unit 26 Eldon Business Park, Chilwell, Nottingham NG9 6DZ Tel: 0203 3880 5059**
email: **info@specialistguides.com**

Thanks to all private owners, local authorities, English Heritage, Historic Royal Palaces, Historic England, Historic Environment Scotland, the National Trust, the National Trust for Scotland, the Royal Collection, the Landmark Trust, Heritage Open Days for their information and for keeping Hudson's accurate and up-to-date. All images are copyright to Specialist Guides Ltd or to the organisation or property depicted unless otherwise stated. All rights reserved.

MARK THE YEAR

You can have a great historic day out anytime but sometimes it's fun to mark the anniversary year of great men and women of the past or historic events. You may even find a special event being put on. We've added a few ideas to our regional pages and here, year by year, is what to look out for. Join us online for special events at www.visitheritage.com.

CHIPPENDALE
300
1718 - 2018

A celebration of Britain's greatest furniture maker

Thomas Chippendale 1718

Celebrate our greatest furniture maker 300 years after his birth in 1718. See superb examples of his work all over Britain. For each region, we have highlighted places where you can see furniture and interiors by the master and look out for special exhibitions to mark the anniversary. Read more about Chippendale on page 250.

Humphrey Repton 1818

Join the Gardens Trust in celebrating the gardens of Humphry Repton 200 years after his death. Following in the footsteps of landscape designer Capability Brown, Repton created settings for country houses, using his famous Red Books to demonstrate how he would marry the open landscape style of the 18th century with elements of formal gardens. Turn to each region to find gardens on which Repton worked so that you can see his landscapes for yourself. Read more about Repton on page 80.

CELEBRATING HUMPHRY REPTON · 1752 ~ 1818 ·

MIRROR BY THOMAS CHIPPENDALE AT BURTON CONSTABLE HALL

DETAIL OF CHIPPENDALE CABINET, DUMFRIES HOUSE

First World War Armistice 1918

The Great War, in which 17 million soldiers and civilians died, finally came to an end on 11 November 1918. Many heritage places have been exploring their connections with the First World War since 2014. We have recognised their efforts with two awards, for the Yorkshire Country Houses Partnership's series of exhibitions titled Duty Calls and for Dunham Massey's recreation of the Stamford Hospital. Take the chance to understand the impact of the war in 2018 and watch out for 1000 Beacons of Light lit across the country in November to mark the armistice, many hosted by heritage places in the care of English Heritage.

Women & Suffrage 1918

The struggle of the militant Suffragettes and of non-militant suffragists came to an end with the introduction of limited votes for women with the Representation of the People Act 1918. The act allowed women of property over 30 to vote and was a precursor of the Equal Franchise Act of 1928 which gave all women over 21 the vote. Hudson's features a selection of influential women through the centuries including suffragettes whose history you can explore at heritage places.

PLUS

- the execution of Sir Walter Raleigh of Sherborne Castle 1618
- the birth of novelist Emily Bronte at Bronte Parsonage Museum 1818
- the Exhibiton of the North June-Sept makes this a great year to visit the North East
- European Year of Cultural Heritage 2018 celebrates shared identity and heritage across European nations

10

BEDROOM OF CAPT TOMMY AGAR-ROBARTES AT LANHYDROCK, CORNWALL
© NICOLA BURFORD

SUFFRAGETTE MONTAGE © GREATER MORPETH DEVELOPMENT TRUST

2019

William Talman 1619

Visit the architectural masterpieces of William Talman, pupil of Sir Christopher Wren, 300 years after his death in 1719. His career culminated in his work for William III as Comptroller of the Royal Works, collaborating on the interior and gardens of Hampton Court Palace. Talman also worked on private commissions which we have highlighted in our regional sections so you can explore this influential architect of the English Baroque.

PLUS

- birth of Queen Victoria at Kensington Palace 1819
- birth of novelist George Eliot on the Arbury Hall estate 1819

ENJOYING TALMAN'S CHATSWORTH © CHATSWORTH ESTATES

LAUNCHING MAYFLOWER 2020 IN PLYMOUTH © VISIT BRITAIN IMAGES-MARK WHEELER

2020

Mayflower 2020

Expect celebrations of Mayflower 2020 on both sides of the Atlantic. The festival will celebrate the sailing of the Mayflower in 1620, carrying Pilgrims who came mostly from the East Midlands.
Start your Founding of America trip in 2018 with the tercentenary of the death of Sir Walter Raleigh. Start with our article on page 134.

PLUS

- birth of William Cecil, Lord Burghley, Elizabeth I's Chief Minister at Burghley House 1520
- birth of John Evelyn, diarist and designer of the gardens at Euston Hall 1620
- birth of Gilbert White, naturalist, at Gilbert White's House 1720
- opening of Britain first suspension bridge, The Union Chain Bridge 1820

11

HERITAGE OPEN DAYS

Heritage Open Days is England's biggest heritage festival when for one weekend in September, the doors to thousands of places are thrown open for free! From castles to cathedrals, stately homes to swimming baths, palaces to prisons, it's a chance for people of all ages to engage with the stories and heritage of their local area.

Every September, from Penzance to Berwick-upon-Tweed, pink bunting, balloons and banners appear across the country, signalling places that are free to explore. With over 5000 events to choose from, including special exhibitions, demonstrations, talks and tours, you are sure to find something of interest. It is a unique opportunity to visit places which are not normally open to visitors including offices and working industrial buildings so find out what is on offer in your locality.

To coincide with the 100th anniversary of the Universal Suffrage Act, Heritage Open Days in 2018 will focus on 'Extraordinary Women: Stories from the Second Sex', commemorating not just those who fought so hard to gain the vote, but the hundreds and thousands of other women who have changed our lives in both large and small ways over time.

ST JOHN'S GATEHOUSE, COLCHESTER © HERITAGE OPEN DAYS - RAHIL AHMAD

WIVENHOE HOUSE, ESSEX © HERITAGE OPEN DAYS - RAHIL AHMAD

Thanks to the generous funding from The National Trust and players of People's Postcode Lottery, Heritage Open Days continues to go from strength to strength, with more places and events than ever before. So what are you waiting for?
Visit www.heritageopendays.org.uk to find out what is going on near you!

Scotland, Wales and Northern Ireland also get a chance to enjoy a free heritage festival in September under the banner of European Heritage Days. The rules are slightly different. Participating heritage places are open for free over most weekends throughout September. In Scotland, the organisers are the Scottish Civic Trust who invite you through Doors Open Days at nearly 100 venues. In Wales, the co-ordinators are Cadw, the Welsh Government's historic environment service and in Northern Ireland the Department for Communities co-ordinates a Festival on the first weekend in September. Check www.visitheritage.co.uk for details.

MEET MRS HUDSON

Mrs Hudson is our favourite character and embodies all the things that are important about Hudson's. She is passionate about history and loves finding out about the past. She's sociable and busy and loves to share. She has a job that takes her all over the UK so she finds out about the best places to visit. As a child, her parents took her to visit heritage places – her Dad was a History don – and now she does the same with her own children. You might like to look out for her online and follow her on social media.

"...People are always asking me where is my favourite heritage place in the UK? What a question! They are all so different! It depends entirely on my mood. When I take my Dad, I might like a castle, because he can't resist old stories. When I go out with my Mum, she likes interiors and loves nothing better than to shop - Doddington is a favourite and so are Blenheim and Hatfield. Both of them are happiest of all in a garden, pottering about planning their own flowerbeds while I sneak off to buy a few choice seedlings. My girlfriends and I meet up regularly for coffee or lunch and a gossip; sometimes it's on the high street but it's much more fun to find an interesting place to meet. I wowed one recently at Burghley and last summer, Sherborne Castle was a real hit.

Of course, my favourite thing is spending time with my family. Celia is 15 and never still, she takes after my aunt, Dizzy, who is always off on some artsy project or other. Milne is 10, into science and, honestly, sometimes I think he's just on another planet. They both love an old-fashioned day out, so we all pile into the car and head off on a history adventure. It's funny how they like different things. Celia loves dressing up and is never happier than sending her gang of friends a selfie from somewhere cool. Milne just likes the space and spotting weird details (I think he's becoming a bit of a goth). Walpole-the-dog, is a bundle of energy and hates to be left behind. The trails at Holkham are a favourite but I totally wore him out last autumn in the hills above Blair Castle.

When Mr H is home, we like to capture a bit of the old romance. Sometimes dinner (The Alnwick Garden Treehouse is my favourite, but he was rather taken with the view at Leeds Castle) or sometimes a beer - have you tried the beer nights at Gibside? All the better if we can stop at an old pub or stay for the weekend in a really super hotel with a bit of history of its own. Signpost is a great source of suggestions for places to stay, places to eat, walks, cycle routes and many other activities around historical places. But mostly we just like to escape and soak up the glories of Britain..."

Mrs Hudson has found some hidden gems - rather lovely places that you might have overlooked - in her travels this year. Find them in our regional chapters.

HERITAGE, WHY BOTHER?

At Hudson's, we want you to appreciate the heritage of Britain as much as we do. We think there are lots of reasons why you might want to visit heritage places and why heritage is important. Here, in no particular order, are 10 of the best:

1. LOVE YOUR LOCALITY

Find out about where you live. Who used to live there too? Is there anything special about your bit of Britain? We are sure there is, and you will certainly be proud to know more about your local bit of heritage

WILBERFORCE HOUSE, HULL © VISIT BRITAIN IMAGES/PAWEL LIBERA

2. BE HEALTHY

We all need to take more exercise and get outdoors more. Historic places are often surrounded by acres of pristine parkland where the air is pure and you can stretch your legs.

BIRDWATCHING IN THE PARKLAND AT CROOME COURT, WORCESTERSHIRE © JOHN HUBBLE

3. BE CURIOUS

Give your brain a work out too. It's good to learn something new and there are plenty of opportunities to learn about the past or to learn a traditional skill. Give your family a great day out learning something new together.

BEAMISH MUSEUM, CO DURHAM

ALNWICK CASTLE, NORTHUMBERLAND

5. BE INVOLVED

Do your bit for your community and help out at your local heritage place. They are sure to need your skills and it is a great way to make friends and get involved.

4. BE A FAMILY

If heritage is important to you, pass it on. There are lots of age - appropriate things to do at heritage places and children who go with parents or grandparents tend to get into the habit and take their kids in turn. Keep it simple, just visit the playground, roll down a bank or find just one thing that is really cool.

NATIONAL TRUST GARDEN VOLUNTEERS AT TYNTESFIELD, SOMERSET

6. GO SHOPPING

If your high street is full of chain stores and the supermarket is where you seem to end up, take a trip to a heritage attraction shop. You'll be surprised. There may be local gifts, crafts and books. Find plants you can't get from elsewhere (and see how they grow). You may find a farm shop selling estate or farm produce and even kitchen garden vegetables. Sometimes you will find a whole shopping destination where you can also recharge with a cup of coffee.

IN THE GIFT SHOP AT HOLKHAM HALL, NORFOLK

SUMMER NIGHTS AT BURGHLEY HOUSE FILM FESTIVAL

7. HAVE FUN

Look out for one-off events; the range of things happening at heritage places is huge. You'll find everything from Father Christmas to fairy days, from chilli festivals to car rallies, from living history to horse trials, from rock concerts to art talks.

CLOWNING AROUND, OUTDOOR THEATRE, HOLKHAM HALL, NORFOLK

8.
TRY SOMETHING DELICIOUS

Restaurants and cafés at heritage places don't just sell scones. There are renowned eateries of all sorts often in wonderful settings, so go for lunch or dinner or have a superb afternoon tea as a treat. Look out for kiosks at larger attractions where you may get local ice-creams or distinctive coffee. Sometimes there is beer and pizza too.

AFTERNOON TEA AT BLENHEIM PALACE

9. MEET SOMEONE NEW

Don't think about heritage places as buildings, these are places where people lived and loved, cried and laughed and sometimes behaved in very peculiar ways. Learn a new story about someone from the past you haven't met before.

PORTRAITS AT WESTON PARK, SHROPSHIRE © VISIT BRITIAN IMAGES

"..the loveliest view in England…"
Lord Randolph Churchill

10. BE WELL

Wellbeing is a contemporary buzzword. Remember that beauty is often undervalued. Take time to go and find something beautiful, it might be a view or a tree, a painting or a tiny piece of porcelain. Give yourself a wellbeing boost with beauty.

CAPABILITY BROWN PARKLAND AT BLENHEIM PALACE

TREASURE HOUSES
OF ENGLAND

Explore ten of the most magnificent palaces, houses and castles in England

Treasure Houses of England represent ten of the most magnificent palaces, houses and castles in England today.
Each has its own unique charm and all combine together to give a fascinating insight into life in England over the centuries.

One of the most compelling features of the Treasure Houses of England is that they all offer the visitor a living history.
Most are still homes to the great families who have owned them for generations.
Others keep their heritage alive by re-creating scenes and events that have dominated and shaped England from
the 9th century to the present day.

Between them they house some of the most important art collections in the world with famous works from artists such
as Van Dyck and Gainsborough. The connoisseur of fine furniture, porcelain and china will find priceless examples of
Chippendale, Wedgwood and Meissen.

Each House is an architectural masterpiece surrounded by beautiful parklands and gardens.
Visit each of the Treasure Houses of England to fully appreciate their own individualities.

Find out more at www.treasurehouses.co.uk

Castle Howard

Harewood House

Chatsworth

Holkham Hall

Burghley House

Woburn Abbey

Blenheim Place

Hatfield House

Beaulieu

Leeds Castle

OUR WORLD HERITAGE SITES

© VISIT BRITAIN IMAGES - GUY RICHARDSON - SALTAIRE, WEST YORKSHIRE

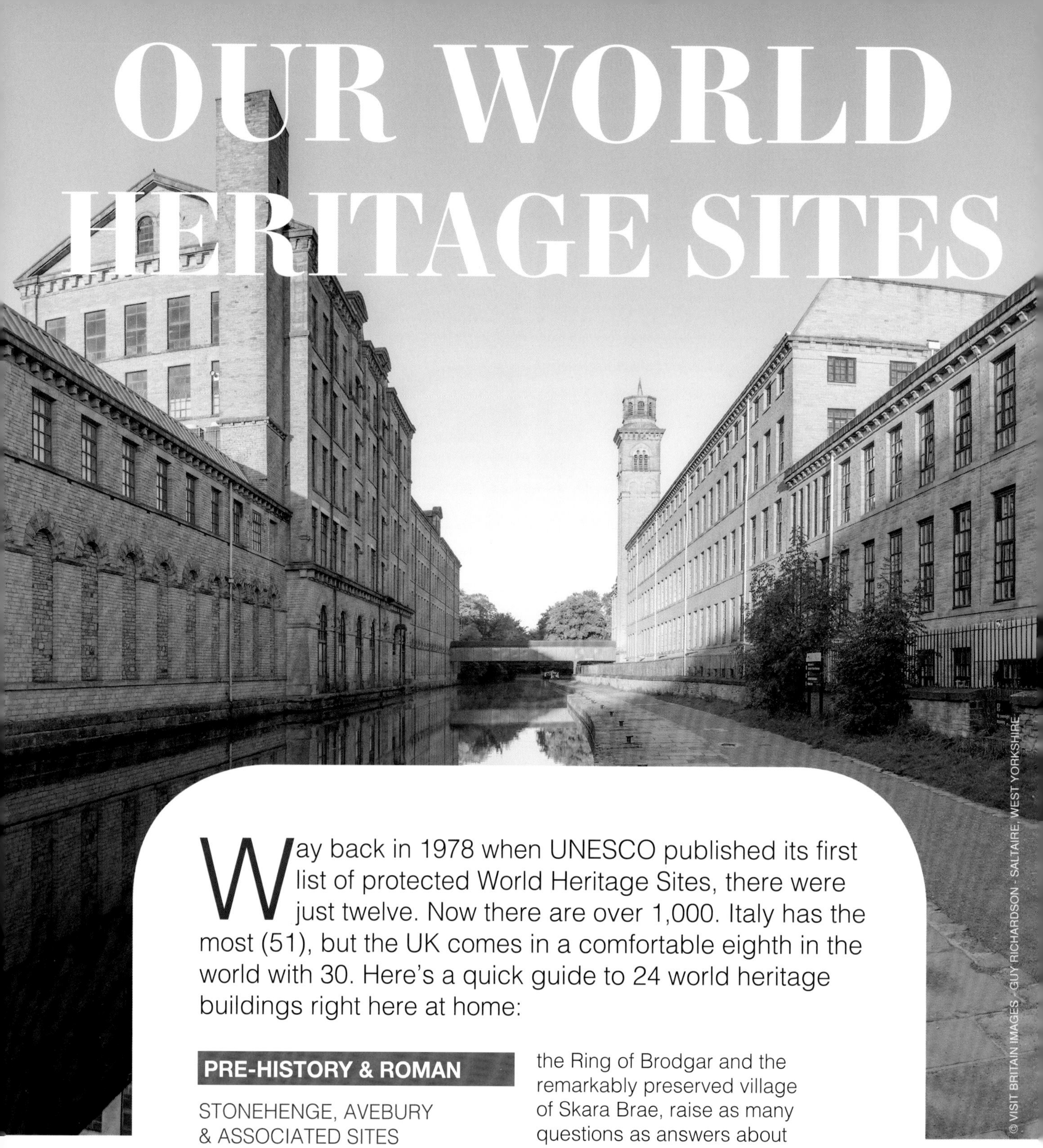

Way back in 1978 when UNESCO published its first list of protected World Heritage Sites, there were just twelve. Now there are over 1,000. Italy has the most (51), but the UK comes in a comfortable eighth in the world with 30. Here's a quick guide to 24 world heritage buildings right here at home:

PRE-HISTORY & ROMAN

STONEHENGE, AVEBURY & ASSOCIATED SITES

Stonehenge, the most sophisticated prehistoric stone circle in the world, is right next door to Avebury, the largest stone circle and Silbury Hill, Europe's largest prehistoric mound. These 5,000-year-old cultural centres retain their mystical, mysterious power today. Don't just drive past, stop and savour.

HEART OF NEOLITHIC ORKNEY

Four sites, the Maeshowe tomb, the Standing Stones at Stenness, the Ring of Brodgar and the remarkably preserved village of Skara Brae, raise as many questions as answers about our ancestors and are the most important Neolithic sites in Western Europe.

FRONTIERS OF THE ROMAN EMPIRE

Hadrian's Wall marks the northern edge of the Roman Empire that stretched continuously as far South as the Sahara and as far East as the Euphrates. Don't overlook the remains of the abandoned Antonine Wall, 20 years earlier and 100 miles further north.

MEDIEVAL

PALACE OF WESTMINSTER

Symbol of Parliament and the monarchy, home of gothic architecture from the 13th century and gothic revival from the 19th, Westminster has a special place in the Nation's heart. Westminster Abbey and the parish church of St Margaret are the burial places of Kings, Queens, statesmen and heroes. The Palace of Westminster is due for some TLC but should be clear of scaffolding till 2020.

CANTERBURY CATHEDRAL, ST AUGUSTINE'S ABBEY & ST MARTIN'S CHURCH

The home of Christianity in Britain, our greatest cathedral, our oldest church and the abbey home of our greatest Christian missionary combine to give visitors a feast of history and symbolism.

TOWER OF LONDON

William the Conqueror's massive fortress still dominates the Thames. Resonant with history, the Tower is at once palace, prison, barracks, home of the Crown Jewels and storehouse for some of the best stories of the past.

DURHAM CATHEDRAL & CASTLE

The 11th century cathedral is the finest Norman building in Britain, resting place of Christian scholar St Cuthbert and our first historian the Venerable Bede. Seen from afar, together with the handsome Norman castle (a venue for the Harry Potter films), this is one of the most exciting views in the country.

CASTLES & TOWN WALLS OF KING EDWARD IN GWYNEDD

Edward I's four magnificent castles of Conwy, Caernarfon, Harlech & Beaumaris represent the highpoint of castle design and are the finest examples of 13th and 14th century military architecture in Europe.

ENLIGHTENMENT

MARITIME GREENWICH

The complex of baroque buildings encapsulates the artistic and scientific dynamism of the 17th and 18th centuries in a period we know as the Enlightenment. At its heart is the Queen's House, the first Palladian building in Britain and the Prime Meridian which marks the centre of world time.

BLENHEIM PALACE

A gift to Britain's heroic commander John, Duke of Marlborough, Blenheim is the masterpiece of baroque architect Sir John Vanbrugh set in a park designed by the genius of Capability Brown.

CITY OF BATH

The Roman Baths at Aqua Sulis were probably Britain's first thermal spa. Back in high fashion again from 1770 until 1820, Bath was the most popular spa town in the UK and its creamy stone columns and terraces stand as witness to that elegant era.

ROYAL BOTANIC GARDENS, KEW

The historic landscape garden at Kew traces the development of garden design since 1759 as well as being a global centre of plant conservation, leading the battle against loss of diversity.

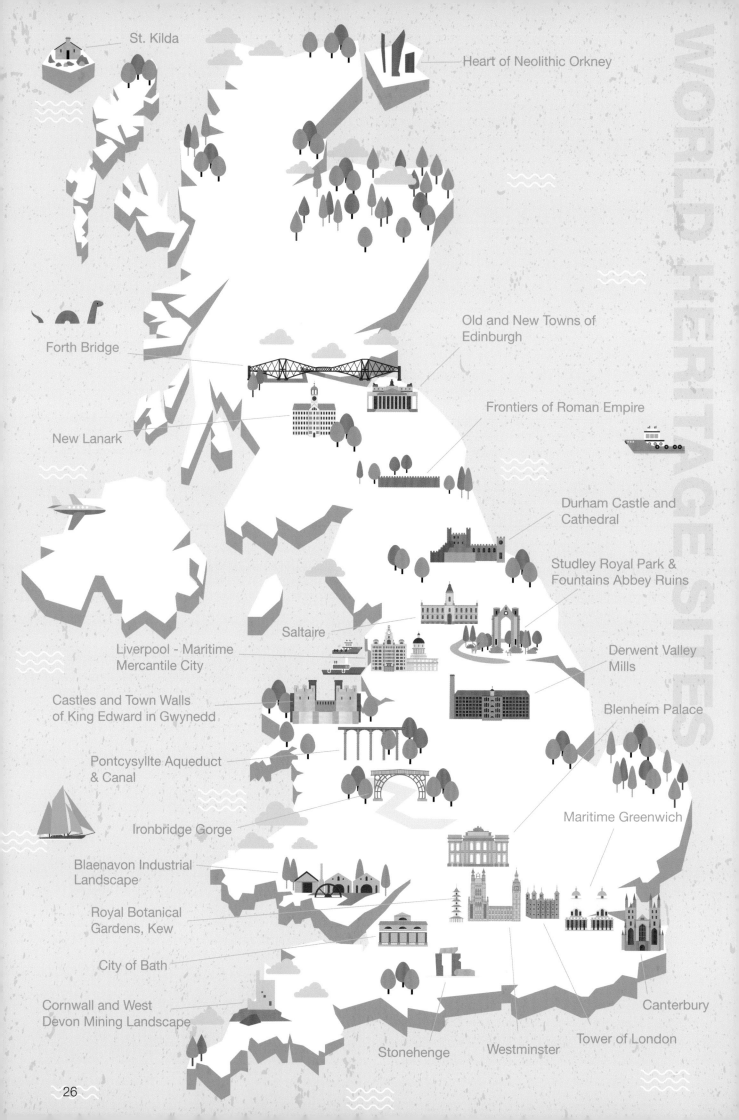

St. Kilda

Heart of Neolithic Orkney

Old and New Towns of Edinburgh

Forth Bridge

Frontiers of Roman Empire

New Lanark

Durham Castle and Cathedral

Studley Royal Park & Fountains Abbey Ruins

Saltaire

Liverpool - Maritime Mercantile City

Derwent Valley Mills

Castles and Town Walls of King Edward in Gwynedd

Blenheim Palace

Pontcysyllte Aqueduct & Canal

Maritime Greenwich

Ironbridge Gorge

Blaenavon Industrial Landscape

Royal Botanical Gardens, Kew

City of Bath

Canterbury

Cornwall and West Devon Mining Landscape

Stonehenge

Westminster

Tower of London

STUDLEY ROYAL & FOUNTAINS ABBEY

Founded in 1132, Fountains Abbey was one of the richest of the monastic houses which dominated medieval culture in Britain until Henry VIII dissolved the monasteries. The awesome ruins now form an integral part of the designed Georgian parkland at Studley Royal which links temples, lakes and follies with walks and vistas.

EDINBURGH OLD & NEW TOWNS

Medieval Edinburgh is a unique townscape of tall, crowded tenements and closes contrasting with the planned squares and gardens of the neoclassical Georgian New Town.

INDUSTRIAL

IRONBRIDGE

The birthplace of the Industrial Revolution from the smelting of coke in 1709 in Coalbrookdale symbolised by the first iron bridge The survival of mines, railways, foundries, factories, workshops and housing are testament to the rapid economic growth that followed.

CORNWALL & WEST DEVON MINING LANDSCAPE

This tranquil holiday area was once home to a pioneering copper and tin mining industry from which mining technologies spread worldwide.

CORNWALL & WEST DEVON MINING LANDSCAPE
© VISIT BRITAIN IMAGES - NATALIA BURIANOVA

PONTCYSYLLTE AQUEDUCT & CANAL

The elegant and powerful arches of the 18km aqueduct recall the inventive genius of architect and road builder Thomas Telford and are a monument to the mass transport of Britain's canal system.

LIVERPOOL – MARITIME MERCANTILE CITY

The premier port and shipbuilding centre of the expanding British Empire through the 18th and 19th centuries, the docks of Liverpool bore witness to the slave trade, mass migration to North America and the development of dock technology.

DERWENT VALLEY MILLS

A series of mills powered by the river Derwent trace the growth of Britain's global textile industry from the 1721 Silk Mill to the mills that used Richard Armitage's spinning jenny and became pioneers of the factory system of production and the social revolution that accompanied it.

NEW LANARK

A model industrial landscape based around cotton mills, the dream of industrialist Robert Owen seeking a Utopian society based on good housing and education.

SALTAIRE

The philanthropy of mill owner, Titus Salt, gave us the first planned industrial town, where factories and homes for workers provided a fitting environment for the industrial revolution.

BLAENAVON INDUSTRIAL LANDSCAPE

The industrial powerhouse of the South Wales Valleys was the leading producer of iron and coal in the 19th century. The town, mine, railway and ironworks contain the memories of a lost past.

FORTH BRIDGE

The much loved rust-red span of the Forth Bridge of 1890 has as much to tell us about the dominance of rail travel in the 19th century as about innovative bridge design and the celebration of industrial style.

ST. KILDA

Part unique landscape and part surviving built heritage, the remote Hebridean islands of St Kilda retain the memory of the now lost culture of the sea-bird-eating inhabitants who left in 1930.

TOWER OF LONDON © HISTORIC ROYAL PALACES

WHO ARE YOU?

Mark Pearsall is head of Family History Research at The National Archives. Hudson's asked him to shed some light on how to find out who you are and why you might want to.

National Archives

Family history is one of the UK's most popular pastimes. Genealogy is the study of lines of descent with the basic details that make up a family tree. Family history goes further, placing your ancestors into an historical context and how they fitted into their community. Adding flesh to the bones is the fascination and addiction of family history.

It's easy to begin research online and you can quickly find out lots of information about your ancestors. More and more records have been indexed and made searchable online, and many can be accessed digitally, but it can't all be done online. You need to work back from what you know. Start with your immediate family, drawing up a basic tree with dates of births, marriages and deaths. Question all the family members you can; ask for access to any documents and memorabilia, especially birth, marriage and death certificates, school reports, educational or employment certificates, letters, wills, photographs etc. Once you have a basic tree and dates, you can apply for other certificates for earlier generations and access online census returns to establishearlier relationships.

Civil registration of births, marriages and deaths began in England and Wales from 1 July 1837. Certificates are held by the General Register Office (GRO) for England and Wales, and whilst copies are not yet available online, the indexes are and can be accessed at The National Archives and many other county record offices and libraries. There are also a number of commercial family history sites where you can access the indexes. You can then apply online for certificates from the GRO at www.gro.gov.uk. Civil registration in Scotland began from 1 January 1855 and you can search and order certificates from the Scotland's People website www.scotlandspeople.gov.uk.

© NATIONAL TRUST IMAGES

> *" I refuse to admit that I am more than fifty-two, even if that does make my sons illegitimate. "*
>
> **Nancy Astor**

If you can identify grandparents or great-grandparents who were alive in 1911, you can work back through the census returns. There has been a census in the UK every ten years from 1801, with the exception of 1941. The earlier censuses were mainly statistical, but from 1841 the names of every individual are recorded, and from 1851 relationships, ages and birthplaces. The returns for England and Wales, the Channel Islands and the Isle of Man from 1841 to 1911 can be accessed from The National Archives website: www. nationalarchives.gov.uk, whilst Scotland's for the same period are available on the Scotland's People website:www.scotlandspeople.gov.uk. Records are closed for 100 years, so the 1921 census won't be opened until January 2022.

Sometimes the jump back to 1911 can be difficult, but it has been made easier by the release of the 1939 Register, which can be searched online for a fee, or free at The National Archives. The 1939 Register was created in September that year for the issue of identity cards and later ration books. The database can be used to search for individuals but the records of those born less than 100 years ago remain closed, unless evidence has been found that the person is no longer living.

Wills are some of the most informative and useful documents. All wills granted probate and letters of administration (for those dying intestate) in England and Wales from 1858 are held by the Principal Registry of the Family Division in London: www.gov.uk/search-will-probate. The indexes can be searched online and wills and grants of administration can be ordered online or by post. Before 1858 wills and letters of administration were granted in one of a number of church courts, usually depending on where the deceased left property. The National Archives holds the records of the senior court for England and Wales, the Prerogative Court of Canterbury, and the Borthwick Institute holds the records of the Prerogative Court of York. The records of other church courts and what are called 'peculiar' jurisdictions are held locally in diocesan and county record offices. Many indexes can be searched online and some documents have been digitised.

> *" If you cannot get rid of the family skeleton, you may as well make it dance. "*
>
> **George Bernard Shaw**

"I'm trying to prove we're not related to the kids."

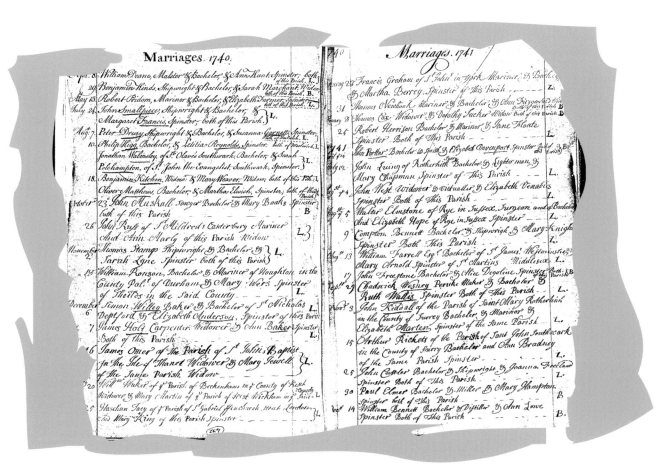

PARISH RECORD FROM ST PAUL'S DEPTFORD

Before 1837 the primary source for tracing ancestors are the parish registers, created by order of Thomas Cromwell in 1538. They record baptisms, marriages and burials and continue to the present day, so they should still be used in conjunction with civil registration records after 1837. Not all registers survive from 1538. Many early registers were lost, and during the civil wars and inter-regnum between 1642 and 1660 many parishes were without properly kept records. Other parish records, where they survive, should be consulted for additional information on your ancestors including vestry minutes, churchwardens' accounts, and the overseers of the poor accounts. To supplement parish records, manorial documents such as court rolls can supply information on tenants and life on the manor. The Manorial Documents Register held by The National Archives shows where surviving manorial documents are held. Go to www.nationalarchives.gov.uk/mdr to search the register.

66 *Why waste your money looking up your family tree? Just go into politics and your opponents will do it for you.* **99**

Mark Twain

Treat family traditions and stories with scepticism. Always look for documentary evidence. If your research is thorough and accurate you will discover the facts.
Be prepared for family skeletons. Illegitimacy was more common than people like to think, many of our ancestors were poor and some resorted to crime. Always be sensitive to the feelings of family members. Family history is addictive and once you begin tracing your ancestors it's hard to stop. By its nature, it is open-ended and is never finished but it is the discovery of the unknown that makes family history so fascinating. ■

JUST FOLLOW THAT SIGNPOST

www.signpost.co.uk

The publication of the first SIGNPOST hotel guide by W G McMinnies in 1935 was a watershed, reflecting a crucial change in the way we all take our holidays. The advice may have migrated online, but the desire for selected hotels is perennial.

1935 was a momentous year for car drivers in Britain. For the first time, you needed to pass a driving test, reduce your speed to 30mph in towns and follow cats-eyes on country roads. Elsewhere, the founding of the Ramblers' Association reflected a growing interest in the countryside and in Britain's untamed spaces. It was also the year that Signpost, the first independent consumer guide to hotels in Britain arrived.

Signpost in 1935 was expressly a guide for motorists, published in the heyday of the motoring holiday, when the opportunity to explore Britain independently was suddenly available to the aspirant middle classes. The advice is very personal, just as today, the hotels and bed & breakfasts that are included by Signpost have always been carefully selected and inspected, chosen because they are privately run and have an old-fashioned ambience married with modern standards of comfort and luxury. The 1935 definition still works today, they have 'a tremendous personal connection, intimate and hospitable'.

MOTORING AT CHATSWORTH © VISIT BRITAIN IMAGES - DANIEL BOSWORTH

34

The names of the hotels in the inter-war Signpost guides reflect an unashamed love affair with the motor car: MGs, north of Stratford; The Roundabout in Sussex; or Mile 3 outside Bristol. It is hard to imagine today being drawn to stop for a meal in the KCB Roadhouse & Petrol Filling Station but in 1935, the owner states with pride that it was 'the most beautiful filling station in the country'. Back then, there were only just over 1 million private cars on the roads compared with nearly 32 million today. Congestion, pollution and motorways have changed our relationship with holidays by car. The pleasure is now much more about the hotel at the end of the journey and the attractions of the place at which you have arrived rather than the journey itself.

The type of hotelier has changed dramatically. Back then, owners were usually 'ex-army men… or retired professional men, schoolmasters, lawyers and the like'. Today owners are more likely to be hard-working couples where each partner contributes equally to the enterprise (and gets equal recognition) though one owner in the original guide does jump from the pages, 'a young woman with definite ideas'.

Heritage was always important. Many inns append the prefix 'Ye Olde' and beams and Windsor chairs are everywhere in the black and white photographs. Now, many hotels are country houses enjoying a change of ownership and a new purpose. Signpost has been able to remain true to its original love of the heritage of Britain, choosing hotels that not only have a history of their own, but also make a perfect base for exploring some of the key heritage places in the country.

SOME OF THE EARLIEST VISITORS TO BLENHEIM PALACE IN THE 1940S©BLENHEIM PALACE

In 1935 W G McMinnies divided his guide into three chapters: Inns and Hotels; Country Clubs; and 'Roadhouses and Other Pleasant Places'. The first were traditional places to stop overnight, the second, places where there was enough to do to keep you busy (and a way around the licensing laws which favoured 'clubs') and the third offered food and entertainment only. Comfort was important and tired motorists expected to be revived with 'good beds… woolly blankets, soft sheets and a hot bottle' and perhaps 'tea and a paper in the morning'. Today's Signpost hotels are more likely to promise 'an outdoor hot tub' or 'Villeroy & Boch china, bathrobes and Molton Brown toiletries'. The Country Club chapter is a charming glimpse into the social habits of the 1930s. Guests were treated to indoor and outdoor tennis courts, squash and badminton courts, swimming baths, table tennis rooms, putting greens, riding and even aerodromes. Certainly they sound like 'jolly places' to spend time but there is little emphasis on the surrounding area. Today's Signpost hotels know that they are part of a local economy and recognise that their visitors are often drawn to the area by the range of heritage attractions to visit or the access to open countryside for walking and cycling.

Roadhouses too had a good line in swimming pools, particularly outdoor lidos. The growth in spa holidays in the past few decades is a continuation of that tradition, so that the inclusion of treatments and saunas are often as much a part of a weekend away as a three-course dinner. Other desirable characteristics of the popular Roadhouse in 1935 seem to have been 'splendid dancefloors and expensive radiograms'. Clearly Britain in the 1930s was full of budding Fred Astaires.

Good food was important in the 1930s as it is today, and Signpost was even then on the lookout for dining rooms which were supplied from their own farms or kitchen gardens. Overall, however, apart from some excitement about the new prevalence of 'grill rooms', far less space is devoted to discussing the relative excellence of the food on offer. At least a third of the recommendations for a Signpost hotel today will be spent considering the quality, originality and local sourcing of the hotel restaurant as well as a frequent reference to the chef by name.

The birth of the Signpost brand saw the arrival of the first consumer advice for hotel choice, driven by personal selection. Cars and travelling may have changed a bit since 1935 but for the independent traveller a Signpost to a hotel with heritage character that offers you a real chance to engage with history and countryside is right on trend for a break in the UK.

GILPIN HALL HOTEL, CUMBRIA

LOCH MELFORT HOTEL

Within ten years of Signpost's first edition historic houses opening to the public provided new enticement for motoring holidays.

MODERN COMFORTS AT CRUG GLAS HOTEL, PEMBROKESHIRE

THE PHEASANT INN, CUMBRIA

UK HERITAGE AWARDS

The UK Heritage Awards have been spotlighting the best heritage places to visit for the past six years. In 2018, more categories have been added to recognise more of the UK's heritage.

BERRINGTON HALL, HEREFORDSHIRE WWW.NATIONALTRUST.ORG.UK

A REPLICA DURHAM CATHEDRAL IN LEGO

HEDINGHAM CASTLE, ESSEX

THE NEW EXHIBITION CENTRE AT STONEHENGE
© ENGLISH HERITAGE

UK HERITAGE AWARDS 2018

The UK has more heritage than almost any country in the world. If you are looking for a good day out, nothing is more rewarding than taking a trip into history. Once a year, Hudson's gathers some of the innovators in the heritage industry together to celebrate what is new, inspiring and enjoyable. Our distinguished judges are experts in their field and their deliberations each year reveal the vibrancy and freshness of the heritage world. Thank you to our sponsors and welcome to Bidwells, new sponsor in 2018.

Join us here as we review some of our recent winners and be assured that your visit will be rewarded. Join our discussions online and go to www.visitheritage.co.uk to make your own suggestions.

Sponsor of the 2018 awards reception:
Bidwells, property & agribusiness consultants

BIDWELLS

SPECIAL AWARD FOR HERITAGE ACHIEVEMENT

Stonehenge, Wiltshire

Recognising English Heritage's achievement in the reinterpretation of Stonehenge which is creating a national monument we can finally all be proud to visit.

FAMILY DAY OUT

Holkham Hall, Norfolk

Continuously innovating to provide an exciting choice of experiences for all age groups both inside this great house and in the parkland and woods.

PLACES TO EAT

Sherborne Castle, Dorset

A well-run tearoom making the most of its lakeside setting with not just local produce but estate and home-made food using family recipes.

PLACES TO SHOP

JARROLD publishing

Holkham Hall, Norfolk

A modern attractive retail space with a vintage vibe which promotes local talent, estate produce and imaginative bespoke items that celebrate the history of the house and family.

PLACES TO STAY

Combermere Abbey, Shropshire

Overnight stays for bed & breakfast and events, which have breathed new life into a once threatened house, offering guests superb bedrooms, outstanding bathrooms and attention to detail.

LOOS

Hedingham Castle, Essex

A loo designed with a sense of humour that gives you an insight into the past, flexible enough for different visitor activities while preserving the integrity of this remarkable Norman keep.

NEW DISCOVERY

HUNTERS INCORPORATING MAY, MAY & MERRIMANS

Eltham Palace, London

In the Map Room, English Heritage not only discovered something of unique heritage significance but also shared it with the visiting public, allowing first class conservation in action.

INNOVATION

savills

Durham Cathedral

Raising funds by selling 300,000 lego bricks at £1 each, to build an accurate scale model of the cathedral has created a new visitor attraction in its own right.

WEDDING VENUE

Hedingham Castle

Cleverly adapting a unique Norman keep provides flexible options for wedding parties, while working closely with conservation bodies in an ancient building.

EVENT OR EXHIBITION

Berrington Hall, Herefordshire

A season of National Trust events, part of the 'Capability' Brown Festival, which stood out for entertainment, original interpretation and sheer fun.

HIDDEN GEM

Plumpton Rocks

Meandering paths, rock formations, lakeside walks and expansive views are frozen in time in a restored Georgian picturesque landscape garden.

SIGNPOST HOTELS

Best Hotel Dining: Roman Camp Hotel, Callander
Best Family Hotel: The Cottage Hotel, Hope Cove
Hotel of the Year: Alexandra Hotel, Lyme Regis

• Nominations for UK Heritage Awards can be made at any time at www.visitheritage.co.uk or email awards@specialistguides.com

LONDON

Westminster | City of London

GREATER LONDON

🌳 COUNTRYSIDE:

- Royal Parks
- Hampstead Heath
- River Thames

⧗ HERITAGE:

- Royal palaces
- Homes of the Famous
- Parliament & Democracy

🍴 FOOD:

- Cuisines of the world
- Fish & chips
- Chelsea Buns

THE TRIBUNAL OR SALOON AT CHISWICK HOUSE

DON'T MISS!

CHISWICK HOUSE

An exquisite entertainment pavilion designed by Richard Boyle, 1st Earl of Burlington, Chiswick is a perfect Palladian villa with rooms set around an octagonal painted saloon. William Kent designed both the interiors with their grand classical paintings and the formal gardens where radiating avenues terminate in statuary.

Highlights:

- The Triumph of the Arts, ceiling of the Red Velvet Room
- Portraits of the Stuart kings in the Tribunal
- RIBA award-winning Garden café
- Rare camellias in the Conservatory

THE KING'S STAIRS, KENSINGTON PALACE BY WILLIAM KENT © HISTORIC ROYAL PALACES

KENSINGTON PALACE

Built as a private home for William & Mary away from the bustle of St James' Palace, Kensington Palace still plays that role for today's royals. Here arose the scandal of the 'Warming Pan Baby', here Queen Victoria awoke to find herself Queen and here accumulated a huge floral tribute at the death of Diana, Princess of Wales.

Highlights:

- The Royal Dress collection
- Queen Mary's Bedroom
- Portrait of Peter the Wild Boy on the King's Staircase
- Tiny Explorers Toddler Sessions

SYON PARK

SYON PARK

A country house in London on the banks of the River Thames. A Tudor house embellished by architect Robert Adam in the 1760s, to create a dazzling suite of rooms for the Earls of Northumberland, further enhanced by the spoils of demolished Northumberland House in the Strand.

Highlights:

• Classical perfection in the Great Hall
• The pink & blue NE Turret Room
• Princess Victoria's bedroom
• The Great Conservatory

TOWER OF LONDON © HISTORIC ROYAL PALACES - VISIT BRITAIN

TOWER OF LONDON

At times a palace, a prison and a fortress but at the heart of English history for over 900 years, William the Conqueror's statement of power in stone is essential visiting for history lovers. When were you last there?

Highlights:

• The Line of Kings armour display
• Chatting with the Yeoman Warders
• Crown Jewels
• Ceremony of the Keys

MRS HUDSON'S HIDDEN GEM

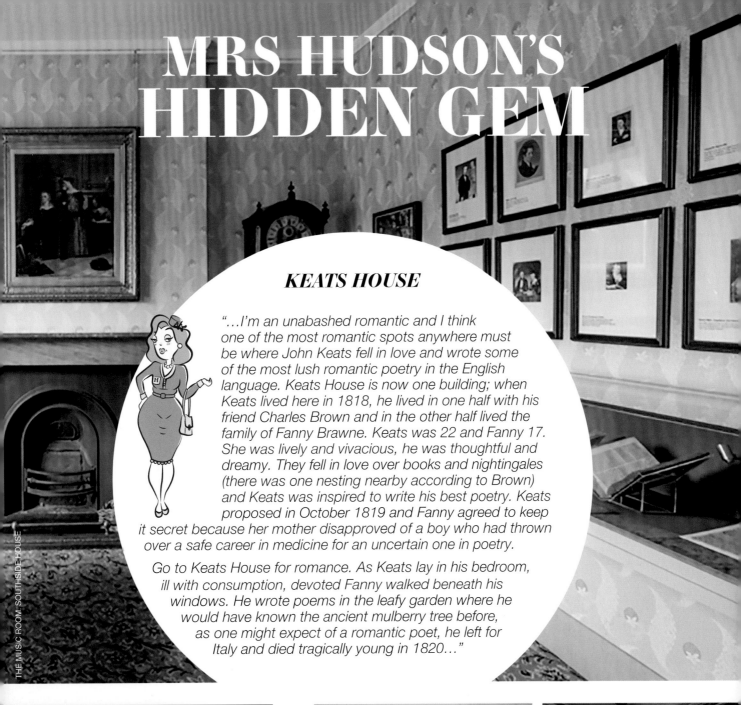

THE MUSIC ROOM, SOUTHSIDE HOUSE

KEATS HOUSE

"…I'm an unabashed romantic and I think one of the most romantic spots anywhere must be where John Keats fell in love and wrote some of the most lush romantic poetry in the English language. Keats House is now one building; when Keats lived here in 1818, he lived in one half with his friend Charles Brown and in the other half lived the family of Fanny Brawne. Keats was 22 and Fanny 17. She was lively and vivacious, he was thoughtful and dreamy. They fell in love over books and nightingales (there was one nesting nearby according to Brown) and Keats was inspired to write his best poetry. Keats proposed in October 1819 and Fanny agreed to keep it secret because her mother disapproved of a boy who had thrown over a safe career in medicine for an uncertain one in poetry.

Go to Keats House for romance. As Keats lay in his bedroom, ill with consumption, devoted Fanny walked beneath his windows. He wrote poems in the leafy garden where he would have known the ancient mulberry tree before, as one might expect of a romantic poet, he left for Italy and died tragically young in 1820…"

MARK THE YEAR

KENWOOD HOUSE © ENGLISH HERITAGE

200 YEARS
REPTON

Enjoy the gardens of Humphry Repton 200 years after his death.
- ✔ Kenwood
- ✔ London parks:
  - -Wanstead
  - -Wembley
  - -Trent
  - -Grovelands
  - -Highams

CHINESE CHIPPENDALE CABINET AT OSTERLEY HOUSE © NATIONAL TRUST IMAGES

THE STATE BEDROOM, OSTERLEY HOUSE © NATIONAL TRUST IMAGES

300 YEARS
CHIPPENDALE

Celebrate our greatest furniture maker 300 years after his birth.
- ✔ Osterley Park

100 YEARS
WOMEN & SUFFRAGE

ELIZABETH COUNTESS OF DYSART

EMILY WILDING DAVISON © EMILY INSPIRES

PRINCESS SOPHIA - DULEEP SINGH OUTSIDE HAMPTON COURT IN 1910

1.
ELIZABETH, COUNTESS OF DYSART (1626-1698)

Peer, leading Royalist, woman of taste at Ham House.

2.
EMILY DAVISON (1872-1913)

Militant suffragette at the Houses of Parliament.

3.
SOPHIA DULEEP SINGH (1876-1948)

Suffragette and grand-daughter of the Last Maharaja of the Punjab at Hampton Court Palace.

HERITAGE LONDON FOR KIDS

CRYSTAL PALACE PARK

CRYSTAL PALACE PARK
Full size Victorian Dinosaurs
Maze
Italian gardens

THE MAGIC GARDEN AT HAMPTON COURT
© HISTORIC ROYAL PALACES

ROYAL BOTANIC GARDENS, KEW
The Palm House
The Hive
Treetop Walkway
Childsized Badger Sett
Be an Explorer

SUMMER FUN AT KEW GARDENS
© ROYAL BOTANIC GARDENS

HAMPTON COURT PALACE
The Magic Garden
The Maze
The Great Vine
Ghost of Queen Catherine Howard

NATURAL HISTORY MUSEUM
Carved animals on the Alfred Waterhouse building
The Blue Whale
Dinosaurs
Ice skating (winter only)

WESTMINSTER HALL, HOUSES OF PARLIAMENT
© VISIT ENGLAND IMAGES

HOUSES OF PARLIAMENT
Guided & self-guided tours for families aimed at 7-12 year olds.

THE NEW BLUE WHALE DISPLAY AT THE NATURAL HISTORY MUSEUM
© TRUSTEES OF THE NHM

DID YOU KNOW ?

MARBLE HILL HOUSE © ENGLISH HERITAGE

1 MARBLE HILL HOUSE

Marble Hill House was built by George II's mistress Henrietta Howard, Countess of Suffolk with money given in compensation after she became deaf in her early 40s and the King threw her over for another.

2 BANQUETING HOUSE

Ironically, almost the last thing Charles I would have seen as he stepped out to have his head cut off was the Banqueting House ceiling that he had commissioned from Peter Paul Rubens to celebrate the triumph of monarchy in his father's reign.

3 CHELSEA PHYSIC GARDEN

The Pond Rock garden at the Chelsea Physic Garden, begun in 1771, is the oldest rockery in Europe. Its striking white rocks are rubble from the rebuilding of the Tower of London and the black ones, Icelandic lava brought by famous botanist, Sir Joseph Banks. The clamshell adds an exotic edge.

SARAH ANNE CHILD BY OZIAS HUMPHREY © NATIONAL TRUST IMAGES

4 FULHAM PALACE

At Fulham Palace the medieval Bishops had rights over all 'great fish' (whales) found in the River Thames. The last whale seen in the Thames was in 2006.

THE POND ROCK GARDEN AT CHELSEA PHYSIC GARDEN

5 OSTERLEY PARK

In 1782, Sarah Anne Child, the heiress to the Child banking fortune which included Osterley Park, eloped to Gretna Green with her sweetheart, John Fane, 10th Earl of Westmorland. Her furious father cut her out of his will and left his fortune to her second child, Lady Sarah Sophia Fane.

6 2 WILLOW ROAD

The modernist house built at 2 Willow Road, NW3 in 1939 was so resented by local residents that neighbour Ian Fleming named the arch villain of his James Bond novel after the architect, Erno Goldfinger.

47

3 INTERIORS WITH THE WOW FACTOR

LEIGHTON HOUSE, ARAB HALL ® WILL PRYCE

1.
THE ARAB HALL, LEIGHTON HOUSE MUSEUM

A Middle Eastern fantasy room, based on a 12th century Sicilian palazzo with a golden dome, intricate mosaics and walls lined with beautiful antique Islamic tiles; the creation of the painter Frederick, Lord Leighton.

2.
THE ENTRANCE HALL, ELTHAM PALACE

Winner, Best New Discovery, UK Heritage Awards 2016

Circular room panelled in blackbean veneer and marquetry, designed by Swedish architect Rolf Engstomer for cocktail parties, part of the Art Deco home of Stephen & Virginia Courtauld within the medieval palace.

SYON PARK

3. THE ANTEROOM, SYON PARK

A riotous cacophony of colour in startling contrast to the cool marble entrance hall. Robert Adam used composite scagliola for the floor and columns, employed Joseph Rose for plasterwork and John Cheere for the golden figures.

PLACES TO STAY

HISTORIC HOTELS IN LONDON

www.signpost.co.uk

SAN DOMENICO HOUSE HOTEL, SW3

"Pont Street Dutch" townhouses built in 1890 are home to a boutique hotel with the luxury of an Italian palazzo. Antique furnishings & European art in the calm of fashionable Chelsea.

CHASE LODGE HOTEL, RICHMOND

Chase Lodge is a small romantic, independent hotel, dating back 30 years. This tranquil building is just a stone's throw from Hampton Court Palace, the River Thames and Bushy Park with its 300 deer.

Shh....SHARE A

By Mark Francis, General Manager, Burgh House

Everyone knows about the great palaces of London but there is so much more to the city. Tourists pour in their millions to sites like the Tower of London and Windsor Castle but the history of London is not just about Kings and Princesses, it is about all aspects of our history, religion, science, the arts, literature, music and fashion. As a global centre of culture and trade, London has attracted famous figures from all over the world. Walking the streets, it is impossible to miss the blue plaques that mark the homes of the famous. How many times have you wanted to open the door and walk in?

London Shh stands for London's Smaller Historic Houses but also suggests a secret that should be shared. Tucked away down intriguing streets and alleys, off the beaten tourist track. You will be glad you took time to find some of the city's best kept secrets

SECRET

BURGH HOUSE

There is no thrill to match standing in the spot where history happened; perhaps the room where Handel wrote The Messiah or where Samuel Johnson wrote his famous Dictionary. If great literary moments are what you are after, you can visit the house where Keats wrote Ode to a Nightingale or where Charles Dickens wrote Oliver Twist, The Pickwick Papers and Nicholas Nickleby. Musical history was made in Brook Street not just by Frederick Handel but three centuries later by guitarist Jimi Hendrix. There are painters to discover, William Hogarth in his country house at Chiswick, Helen Allingham in the collection at Burgh House or the Campden Town artists at Fenton House in Hampstead. Influential thinkers came to London for its stimulating society, John Wesley's house has become the global centre of Methodism, Benjamin Franklin's famous search for knowledge brought him to London and the couch in Sigmund Freud's house has provided the archetype for all psychoanalysts. A less globally renowned inventor was Inky Stephens whose father's patent on an indelible ink brought wealth to Stephens House in Finchley. Discover the Arts and Crafts movement at William Morris Society and Emery Walker's House in Hammersmith and the Modernist movement at Erno Goldfinger's 2 Willow Place.

Dickens' front door, Freud's couch and Handel's composing room have each changed the world.

So step right in through the door and explore some of the capital's more intriguing historic houses. You are guaranteed variety, history and a few secrets to share. ■

www.londonshh.org

Syon Park

www.syonpark.co.uk

London home of the Duke of Northumberland with magnificent Robert Adam interiors, 40-acres of gardens, including the spectacular Great Conservatory.

Described by John Betjeman as the 'Grand Architectural Walk', Syon House and its 200-acre park is the London home of the Duke of Northumberland, whose family, the Percys, have lived here for 400 years. Originally the site of a late medieval monastery, excavated by Channel 4's Time Team, Syon Park has a fascinating history. Catherine Howard was imprisoned at Syon before her execution, Lady Jane Grey was offered the crown whilst staying at Syon, and the 9th Earl of Northumberland was imprisoned in the Tower of London for 15 years because of his association with the Gunpowder Plot. The present house has Tudor origins but contains some of Robert Adam's finest interiors, which were commissioned by the 1st Duke in the 1760s. The private apartments and State bedrooms are available to view.

The house can be hired for filming and photo shoots subject to availability. Within the 'Capability' Brown landscaped park are 40 acres of gardens which contain the spectacular Great Conservatory designed by Charles Fowler in the 1820s. The House and Great Conservatory are available for corporate and private hire. The Northumberland Room in Syon House is an excellent venue for conferences, meetings, lunches and dinners (max 60).

The State Apartments make a sumptuous setting for dinners, concerts, receptions, launches and wedding ceremonies (max 120). Marquees can be erected on the lawn adjacent to the house for balls and corporate events.

The Great Conservatory is available for summer parties, launches, filming, photoshoots and wedding receptions (max 150).

OWNER
The Duke of Northumberland

CONTACT
Contact: Estate Office
Tel: 020 8560 0882

Email: info@syonpark.co.uk
Events: events@syonpark.co.uk
Visitors Centre: visitorcentre@syonpark.co.uk

LOCATION
Syon House, Syon Park, Brentford,
Middlesex TW8 8JF
Map Ref: 19:B8
Between Brentford & Twickenham, off A4, A310 in SW London.

TRANSPORT ROUTES
Car I Bike I Bus I Train I Tube I Aeroplane

OPENING TIMES
Syon House: 14 Mar-28 Oct 2018 Weds, Thus, Suns and BHs 11am-5pm. (Last entry 4pm.)
Gardens only: 12 Mar-28 Oct 2018 Daily 10.30am-5pm. (Last entry at 4pm.)
House, Gardens and Great Conservatory: Closed from 30 Oct 2017-12 Mar 2018.

ADMISSION
House, Gardens & Conservatory
Adult: £13, Child: £6, Conc: £11.50,
Family (2+2): £30.

Booked groups (25+)
Adult: £11.50, Conc: £10.50, School Group: £4.

Gardens & Great Conservatory
Adult: £8, Child: £4.50, Conc: £6.50,
Family (2+2): £18, School Group: £3.

ADDITIONAL
Syon House Ventures reserves the right to alter opening times. Please phone or check website for up to date details and special events.

KEY FACTS

 No photography in the House.

 WC's.

 Free parking.

 WC's. House - Limited access. Gardens and Great Conservatory - fully accessible.

 London Syon Park Hilton Hotel at www.londonsyonpark.com

 By arrangement.

 By arrangement.

 Café in the Garden Centre.

 The Garden Kitchen Restaurant in the Garden Centre.

 Syon Park Visitor Centre, open daily 10.30am-5pm during the season.

 Garden Centre.

 Syon House & the Great Conservatory available for exclusive luncheons, meetings & corporate.

 Available for formal dinners, ceremonies, receptions & parties.

 See website for details.

Tower of London

www.hrp.org.uk/toweroflondon

The Tower of London is a 1,000-year-old castle that protects the Crown Jewels. It was a secure fortress, a royal palace and an infamous prison.

The Tower of London, founded by William the Conqueror in 1066-7, is one of the world's most famous fortresses, and one of Britain's most visited historic sites. Despite a grim reputation for being a place of torture and death, there are so many more stories to be told about the Tower and its intriguing cast of characters.

This powerful and enduring symbol of the Norman Conquest has been enjoyed as a royal palace, served as an armoury and for over 600 years even housed a menagerie! Don't miss the Crown Jewels in the famous Jewel House, unlocking the story behind the 23,578 gems in the priceless royal jewels. Marvel at the Imperial State Crown and the largest diamond ever found; and see the only treasure to escape destruction in 1649, after the Civil War. For centuries, this dazzling collection has featured in royal ceremonies, and it is still in use today.

Join Yeoman Warder Tours to be entertained by captivating talks of pain, passion, treachery and torture at the Tower. Visit Tower Green and see the memorial to the people who died within the Tower walls. Find out why the last execution at the Tower was in 1941 and see how instruments of torture were used to extract 'confessions' from prisoners. Explore the story of how five coins changed history in the Coins and Kings Exhibition, discover what life was like in the surprisingly luxurious Medieval Palace, and explore the stories of Henry II, Edward I and their courts at work.

See one of the Tower's most famous sights, the ravens. Legend has it Charles II believed that if the ravens were ever to leave the Tower, the fortress and the kingdom would fall. Step into 1,000 years of history every day at the Tower of London.

©ROYAL COLLECTION TRUST © 2017, HER MAJESTY QUEEN ELIZABETH II

KEY FACTS

 No photography in Jewel House.

 Toilet and disabled WC facilities available.

 Baby changing facilities available.

 Closed 24-26 Dec and 1 Jan.

 None for cars. Coach parking nearby.

 Dedicated facilities, tours and wheelchair hire are available. Please view the access guide.

 Tower audio guides are available (subject to availability).

 Yeoman Warder tours are free and leave front entrance every ½ hr.

 Offering everything you need for the perfect educational visit. To book 0844 482 7777.

 Apostrophe: by the river. New Armouries Café: Light bites. Raven Café: Gourmet sausages.

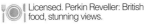 Licensed. Perkin Reveller: British food, stunning views.

 Shop for gifts & souvenirs inspired by this famous royal residence and its iconic Yeoman Warders.

 Visit www.hrp.org.uk/hireavenue or call 020 3166 6226.

 Please see the 'Explore' website page to see what's on.

OWNER
Historic Royal Palaces

CONTACT
Tel: 0844 482 7777
Email: visitorservices.tol@hrp.org.uk

Venue Hire & Corporate Hospitality:
020 3166 6226

LOCATION
London EC3N 4AB
Map Ref: 20:P7

Bus: 15, 42, 78, 100, RV1.
Underground: Tower Hill on Circle/District Line.
Docklands Light Railway: Tower Gateway Station.
Rail: Fenchurch St Station & London Bridge Station.
Boat: From Embankment Pier, Westminster or Greenwich to Tower Pier. London Eye to Tower of London Express.

OPENING TIMES
Summer:
Mar-Oct, Tue-Sat 9am-5.30pm.
Last admission 5pm.
Mon & Sun 10am-5.30pm.
Last admission 5pm.

Winter:
Nov-Feb, Tue-Sat 9am-4.30pm (last admission 4pm).
Mon & Sun 10am-4.30pm (last admission 4pm).
Closed 24-26 Dec and 1 Jan.

ADMISSION
Visit www.hrp.org.uk/toweroflondon or call 0844 482 7777 for more information.

CONFERENCE/FUNCTIONS
Conferences: Up to 150
Meetings: 6 to 200
Receptions: 10 to 300
Lunches: Up to 150
Dinners: 6 to 240

Kensington Palace
www.hrp.org.uk/kensingtonpalace

Once the childhood home of Queen Victoria, for over 300 years Kensington Palace has been home to Britain's young royal families. Share the experience of the public palace and private house in the heart of Kensington Gardens.

Follow in the footsteps of Georgian courtiers in the sumptuous King's State Apartments which show some breathtaking examples of the work of architect and painter William Kent.

Visit the Queen's State Apartments, the intimate, private rooms created for Queen Mary II, who ruled jointly with her husband, King William III, in the 17th Century.

Discover a collection of Diana Princess of Wales's most memorable outfits on display in her former home. Trace the evolution of her style into a fashion icon that used her image to communicate with the world.

CONTACT
Owner: Historic Royal Palaces
Tel: 0844 482 7777
Email: kensingtonpalace@hrp.org.uk
Venue Hire & Corporate Hospitality: 020 3166 6115

LOCATION
Kensington Gardens, London W8 4PX
Map Ref: 20:I8 - In Kensington Gardens.
Underground: Queensway on Central Line,
High Street Kensington on Circle & District Line.

OPENING TIMES
Nov-Feb: Daily, 10am-5pm (last admission 4pm).
Mar-Oct: Daily, 10am-6pm (last admission 5pm).
Closed 24-26 Dec.

ADMISSION
Kids under 16 go free.
Visit www.hrp.org.uk/kensingtonpalace or
call 0844 482 7777 for more information.

CONFERENCE/FUNCTIONS
Conferences: Up to 120 **Receptions:** Up to 300
Lunches: Up to 200 **Dinners:** 20 to 200

KEY FACTS

 Information centre.

 Toilet facilities available.

 Baby changing facilities available.

 Closed 24-26 Dec.

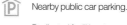 Nearby public car parking.

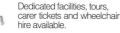 Dedicated facilities, tours, carer tickets and wheelchair hire available.

 Assistance dogs only.

 Please book, 0844 482 7777.

 Palace café: Light bites, hot drinks.

 The Orangery: a favourite destination for breakfast, lunch or afternoon tea.

 The shop is open throughout your visit, offering everything from souvenirs and gifts, to fine jewellery.

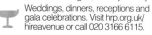 Weddings, dinners, receptions and gala celebrations. Visit hrp.org.uk/hireavenue or call 020 3166 6115.

Special events throughout the year. See website for details.

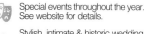 Stylish, intimate & historic wedding venue. For more details see the brochure online.

Osterley Park & House

www.nationaltrust.org.uk/osterley

©NATIONAL TRUST IMAGES / ANDREW BUTLER

A suburban palace caught between town and country, Osterley Park and House is one of the last surviving country estates in London. Past fields and grazing cattle, just around the lake the magnificent house awaits; presented as it would have been when it was redesigned by Robert Adam in the late 18th century for the Child family. A place for entertaining friends and clients, fashioned for show and entertaining, the lavish state apartments tell the story of a party palace. Recently returned family portraits and furniture now add a personal touch to grand rooms, and then downstairs, see the contrast of the domestic quarters. Elegant pleasure gardens and hundreds of acres of parkland are perfect for whiling away a peaceful afternoon.

©NATIONAL TRUST IMAGES / JAMES DOBSON

KEY FACTS

 No flash photography inside House. Visitor Information is available at the Garden Kiosk.

 Toilet and disabled WC's facilities available.

 Baby changing facilities available.

 Park, gardens & café open all year (closed 25 Dec).

 Limited for coaches, pre-booking essential. Parking is free for members and £7 for non-members.

 Full garden access & partial basement floor access. Mobility vehicles on request. House access via stairs.

 Cycling skills programme.

 Dogs welcome in wider estate on leads but not in the house or formal gardens.

 Audio tour guides are available from the main entrance to the house.

 Schools programme available when booked in advance.

 Seasonal menus, freshly baked cakes & cream teas. Family friendly. Kids' lunchboxes.

 NT gift shop with wide range of goods plus second-hand bookshop.

 Home grown plants in peat-free soil available from second-hand bookshop.

 Meeting rooms available.

 Please see the 'What's on' section on the website for all upcoming events.

 Filming opportunities available, please contact for details.

CONTACT
Owner: National Trust **Tel:** 020 8232 5050
Email: osterley@nationaltrust.org.uk
LOCATION
Jersey Road, Isleworth, Middlesex TW7 4RB
Map Ref: 19:C7 - A4 between Hammersmith and Hounslow. Main gates at Thornbury & Jersey Road junction. SatNav: TW7 4RD.

OPENING TIMES
All year, 10am-5pm (closes 4pm between 1 Jan-4 Feb & 5 Nov-31 Dec).
House: Open fully 24 Feb-4 Nov, 11am-5pm (last entry 1 hour before closing); from 1 Jan-23 Feb & 5 Nov-31 Dec, selected areas open 11am-4pm (last entry 1 hour before closing).
Shop: Weekends only in Jan, Feb & Nov & daily in Dec 11am-4pm; daily between 24 Feb-4 Nov 11am-5pm.
Park & Car Park: 7am-7pm all year.
Whole property (aside from park) closed 25 Dec.
ADMISSION
*****House & Garden -** Adult: £12.70, Child: £6.35, Family: £31.75, Groups (15+): £10.80.
*****Winter Admission -** Adult: £10.10, Child: £5.05, Family: £25.40, Groups (15+): £8.60.
*Includes voluntary 10% Gift Aid donation.

London

Houses of Parliament

www.parliament.uk/visit

Tours of the Houses of Parliament offer visitors a unique combination of 1,000 years of history, modern day politics and stunning art and architecture. See the famous green benches in the Commons Chamber, the gilded throne canopy in the Lords Chamber and the medieval hammer-beam roof in Westminster Hall. Add stylish afternoon tea with a view of the River Thames.

KEY FACTS

 Photography and mobile phone use in Parliament is limited to certain areas. Please ask for advice.

 Toilet facilities and disabled WC available.

 Family friendly with baby changing facilities available.

 When the Houses are sitting, visitors are welcome to watch debates from the public galleries.

 Tour route accessible. Alt route via a lift available if required.

 Assistance dogs only.

 Approx. 60-75 mins.

 Approx. 90 mins.

 Jubilee Café - selection of light meals & drinks.

 Jubilee Shop off Westminster Hall offers an attractive range of gifts, souvenirs & books.

 For seasonal activities and events please see the website.

CONTACT
Contact: Bookings Team **Tel:** 020 7219 4114
Email: visitparliament@parliament.uk

LOCATION
Westminster, London SW1A 0AA
Map Ref: 20:M8 - Central London, 1km S of Trafalgar Square.
Underground: Westminster.

OPENING TIMES
Tours every Sat throughout the year & most weekdays during parliamentary recesses including the summer, Christmas & Easter.

ADMISSION
Check website for tour dates & prices. Discounted group rates for groups of 10 plus if booked in advance.

Keats House

www.keatshouse.org.uk

Discover the beauty of poetry and place in the former home of the Romantic poet John Keats. Displays of original manuscripts, artefacts and paintings tell the story of how the young poet found inspiration, friendship and love in this stunning Regency villa. Listen to Keats's famous odes, see the engagement ring he gave to his true love Fanny Brawne, or explore our beautiful garden. The House comes alive with regular events, from poetry performances to family fun days.

KEY FACTS

 Prams can be left in the covered veranda area outside.

 An accessible toilet is available.

 Toilets are located at the back of the building and include baby changing facilities.

 Open all year round.

 Disabled parking space.

 Ground floor. Tactile & subtitled AV exhibits. Accessible toilet.

 1.30pm and 3pm - check before visiting.

 Learning programme.

 Books, souvenirs, vintage items and gifts.

 Available for private hire.

 Poetry performances, talks, walks and special events. 3rd Sunday of every month is Family Day.

CONTACT
Owner: City of London Corporation
Tel: 020 7332 3868 **Email:** keatshouse@cityoflondon.gov.uk

LOCATION
10 Keats Grove, Hampstead, London NW3 2RR
Map Ref: 20:K3
Hampstead Heath (London Overground):
Hampstead or Belsize Park (Northern Line).

OPENING TIMES
Wed-Sun: 11am-5pm. Also Bank Holiday Mons.

ADMISSION
Adult: £6.50
Seniors (over 65): £5.50
Concessions (students, jobseekers, disabled): £4.50
Child (17 and under): Free

Banqueting House

hrp.org.uk/banquetinghouse

This revolutionary structure was the first in England to be built in a Palladian style. It was designed by Inigo Jones for James I, and work finished in 1622. Intended for the splendour and exuberance of court masques, the Banqueting House is probably most famous for one real life drama: the execution of Charles I which took place here in 1649. One of Charles's last sights as he walked to his death was the magnificent ceiling painted by Peter Paul Rubens in 1630-4.

CONTACT
Owner: Historic Royal Palaces
Contact: Banqueting House Visitor Services
Tel: 0844 482 7777
Email: banquetinghouse@ hrp.org.uk

LOCATION
Whitehall, London SW1A 2ER
Map Ref: 20:M8
Located on Whitehall in central London, a short walk from Westminster, Charing Cross & Embankment stations.

OPENING TIMES
Mon-Sun 10am-5pm.
Closed 24, 25, 26 Dec & 1 Jan.
Before visiting, please confirm we are open.

ADMISSION
See website for prices.

KEY FACTS

 Due to limited lift access, it's advised that visitors with mobility needs contact before visiting.

 Special sessions and workshops designed for pupils of all ages.

 The shop offers everything from souvenirs and gifts, to fine jewellery.

 Weddings, receptions, dinners, award ceremonies.

Please see the 'Explore' page online for all upcoming events.

Kew Palace

www.hrp.org.uk/kewpalace

Kew Palace was built as a private house in 1631 but became a royal residence between 1729 and 1818. More like a home than a palace, the privacy and intimacy of this smallest of English royal palaces made it the favourite country retreat for King George III and his family in the late 18th Century. Don't miss the Royal Kitchens; the most perfectly preserved Georgian royal kitchens in existence. At weekends Queen Charlotte's Cottage is also open to visitors.

London

CONTACT
Owner: Historic Royal Palaces
Tel: 0844 482 7777
Email: kewpalace@hrp.org.uk

LOCATION
Kew, Richmond, Surrey TW9 3AB
Map Ref: 19:C7
A307. Junction A307 & A205 (1m Chiswick roundabout M4).

OPENING TIMES
Apr-Sep 10.30am-5.30pm.
Last entry 5pm.

ADMISSION
Free of charge. Admission tickets to Kew Gardens must be purchased to gain access to Kew Palace. (For gardens prices, see website).

KEY FACTS

 Toilet facilities available.

 Baby changing facilities available.

 Parking available.

 WC's.

Weddings, receptions, dinners, meetings.

Dr Johnson's House

www.drjohnsonshouse.org

A charming 300-year-old townhouse nestled amongst a maze of courts and alleys in the historic City of London. Samuel Johnson, the writer and wit, lived and worked here during the 18th Century, compiling his great 'Dictionary' in the Garret. Today, the House is open to the public with a collection relating to Johnson and his circle of friends, restored interiors, and a wealth of original features.

CONTACT
Owner: Dr Johnson's House Trust
Contact: The Curator
Tel: 020 7353 3745
Email: curator@ drjohnsonshouse.org

LOCATION
17 Gough Square, London EC4A 3DE **Map Ref:** 20:N7 North of Fleet Street.

OPENING TIMES
11am-5pm Oct-Apr.
11am-5.30pm May-Sep.

ADMISSION
Adult: £6, Conc: £5, Child: £2.50, Family: £12.50.
Members of the National Trust are entitled to a 50% discount on admission.

KEY FACTS

 Disabled bays only in Gough Square & neighbouring streets.

 Many unavoidable steps. A DVD, audio guide and large-print interpretation can be provided.

 Pre-booked groups for 10+. Audio tours: £2. Available in 3 languages.

 Small shop selling books, gifts and souvenirs.

 Available for private hire on evenings and Sundays.

 Runs a varied programme of events & exhibitions, from staged performances to Curator's talks.

Westminster Cathedral

westminstercathedral.org.uk

The Roman Catholic Cathedral of the Archbishop of Westminster. Spectacular building in the Byzantine style, designed by J F Bentley, opened in 1903, famous for its mosaics, marble and music. Tower viewing gallery has spectacular views across London. Exhibition of vestments, rare ecclesiastical objects and sacred relics.

CONTACT
Owner: Diocese of Westminster
Contact: Revd Canon Christopher Tuckwell
Tel: 020 7798 9055

LOCATION
Victoria St, London, SW1P 1QW
Map Ref: 20:L9 - Off Victoria Street, near Victoria Station.
Sat Nav: SW1P 1LT

OPENING TIMES
All year: 7am-7pm.

ADMISSION - Free.
Tower lift/viewing gallery
Adult: £6, Conc: £3, Family (2+4): £12.
Exhibition - Adult: £5, Conc: £2.50, Family: £11.
Joint Tower & Exhibition
Adult: £9, Conc: £4.50, Family: £18.50.

KEY FACTS

 A TripAdvisor 2014 Winner with Certificate of Excellence.

 Tel. for times at Easter & Christmas.

 Booking required.

 Worksheets & tours.

 Café.

 Range of products which relates to or echoes the art and architecture of the Cathedral.

 Tel. 020 7798 9028 for Tower/Exhibition opening times.

18 FOLGATE STREET
Spitalfields, East London E1 6BX
Tel: 020 7247 4013 **Email:** info@dennisevershouse.co.uk

18 STAFFORD TERRACE
London W8 7BH
Tel: 020 7602 3316 **Email:** museums@rbkc.gov.uk

2 WILLOW ROAD ✄
2 Willow Road, Hampstead, London NW3 1TH
Tel: 020 7435 6166 **Email:** 2willowroad@nationaltrust.org.uk

APSLEY HOUSE ⊞
Hyde Park Corner, London W1J 7NT
Tel: 020 7499 5676 **Email:** customers@english-heritage.org.uk

BENJAMIN FRANKLIN HOUSE
36 Craven Street, London WC2N 5NF
Tel: 020 7925 1405 **Email:** info@benjaminfranklinhouse.org

BOSTON MANOR HOUSE
Boston Manor Road, Brentford TW8 9JX
Tel: 0845 456 2800 **Email:** victoria.northwood@cip.org.uk

BUCKINGHAM PALACE
Brentford SW1A 1AA
Tel: 020 7766 7300 **Email:** bookinginfo@royalcollection.org.uk

BURGH HOUSE & HAMPSTEAD MUSEUM
New End Square, Hampstead, London NW3 1LT
Tel: 020 7431 0144 **Email:** info@burghhouse.org.uk

CARLYLE'S HOUSE ✄
24 Cheyne Row, Chelsea, London SW3 5HL
Tel: 020 7352 7087 **Email:** carlyleshouse@nationaltrust.org.uk

THE CHARTERHOUSE
Charterhouse Square, London EC1M 6AN
Tel: 020 3818 8873 **Email:** tours@thecharterhouse.org

CHELSEA PHYSIC GARDEN
66 Royal Hospital Road, London SW3 4HS
Tel: 020 7352 5646 **Email:** enquiries@chelseaphysicgarden.co.uk

CHISWICK HOUSE & GARDENS ⊞
Chiswick House, Burlington Lane, London W4 2RP
Tel: 020 3141 3350 **Email:** mail@chgt.org.uk

ELTHAM PALACE & GARDENS ⊞
Eltham Palace, Court Yard, Eltham, London SE9 5QE
Tel: 020 8294 2548 **Email:** customers@english-heritage.org.uk

EMERY WALKER'S HOUSE 📖ⒻF
7 Hammersmith Terrace, London W6 9TS
Tel: 020 8741 4104 **Email:** admin@emerywalker.org.uk

FENTON HOUSE ✄
Hampstead Grove, London NW3 6SP
Tel: 020 7435 3471 **Email:** fentonhouse@nationaltrust.org.uk

FORTY HALL
Forty Hill, Enfield, Middlesex EN2 9HA
Tel: 020 8363 8196 **Email:** forty.hall@enfield.gov.uk

FREUD MUSEUM
20 Maresfield Gardens, London NW3 5SX
Tel: 020 7435 2002 **Email:** info@freud.org.uk

FULHAM PALACE & MUSEUM
Bishop's Avenue, Fulham, London SW6 6EA
Tel: 020 7736 3233 **Email:** admin@fulhampalace.org

HAM HOUSE & GARDEN
Ham Street, Richmond-upon-Thames, Surrey TW10 7RS
Tel: 020 8940 1950 **Email:** hamhouse@nationaltrust.org.uk

HANDEL & HENDRIX
25 Brook Street, London W1K 4HB
Tel: 020 7495 1685 **Email:** mail@handelhendrix.org

HOGARTH'S HOUSE
Hogarth Lane, Great West Road, London W4 2QN
Tel: 020 8994 6757 **Email:** john.collins@carillionservices.co.uk

KENWOOD HOUSE
Hampstead Lane, London NW3 7JR
Tel: 020 8348 1286 **Email:** kenwood.house@english-heritage.org.uk

LEIGHTON HOUSE MUSEUM
12 Holland Park Road, London W14 8LZ
Tel: 020 7602 3316 **Email:** museums@rbkc.gov.uk

MARBLE HILL HOUSE ⊞
Richmond Road, Twickenham TW1 2NL
Tel: 020 8892 5115 **Email:** customers@english-heritage.org.uk

OLD ROYAL NAVAL COLLEGE & QUEEN'S HOUSE
King William Walk, Greenwich, London SE10 9NN
Tel: 020 8269 4747 **Email:** boxoffice@ornc.org

RANGER'S HOUSE ⊞
Chesterfield Walk, Blackheath, London SE10 8QX
Tel: 020 8853 0035 **Email:** customers@english-heritage.org.uk

RED HOUSE ✄
Red House Lane, Bexleyheath DA6 8JF
Tel: 0208 303 6359

SOMERSET HOUSE
Strand, London WC2R 1LA
Tel: 020 7845 4600 **E-mail:** info@somersethouse.org.uk

SOUTHSIDE HOUSE 📖ⒻF
3 Woodhayes Road, Wimbledon, London SW19 4RJ
Tel: 020 8946 7643 **E-mail:** info@southsidehouse.com

SPENCER HOUSE
27 St James's Place, London SW1A 1NR
Tel: 020 7514 1958 **E-mail:** tours@spencerhouse.co.uk

STRAWBERRY HILL
268 Waldegrave Road, Twickenham TW1 4ST
Tel: 020 8744 1241 **E-mail:** enquiry@strawberryhillhouse.org.uk

WILLIAM MORRIS GALLERY
Lloyd Park, Forest Road, Walthamstow, London E17 4PP
Tel: 020 8527 9782

SOUTH EAST

OXFORDSHIRE • BERKSHIRE • BUCKINGHAMSHIRE • HAMPSHIRE
ISLE OF WIGHT • SURREY • SUSSEX • KENT

KINGSGATE BAY, KENT © VISIT BRITAIN/ROD EDWARDS

Oxford

• *Aylesbury*

OXFORD SHIRE

BUCKS

• *Abingdon*

SURREY

Sevenoaks •

HAMPSHIRE

• *Guildford*

KENT

Winchester

• *Dover*

Tunbridge Wells •

Southampton

Midhurst •

SUSSEX

Portsmouth

Petersfield

Chichester

Brighton and Hove

Brockenhurst •

• *Lewes*

Bognor Regis •

• *Arundel*

Bournemouth

ISLE OF WIGHT

⚘ COUNTRYSIDE:

- Chalk downs
- New Forest
- The Solent

⧖ HERITAGE:

- Mansions & manor houses
- Plant collector gardens
- Naval heritage

✕ FOOD:

- Apples & cherries
- Banoffee pie
- Fine English wine

DON'T MISS: SOUTH

- OXFORDSHIRE
- BERKSHIRE
- BUCKINGHAMSHIRE
- HAMPSHIRE
- ISLE OF WIGHT

BLENHEIM PALACE

The World Heritage Site of Blenheim is a bravura monument to the victories of the 1st Duke of Marlborough, designed in flamboyant Baroque style by Sir John Vanbrugh. Exceptional art collection, gardens, and parkland and celebrated as the birthplace of Sir Winston Churchill.

Highlights:

- The Great Hall
- Grinling Gibbons carving
- The Marlborough Tapestries
- Long Library

THE LONG LIBRARY - BLENHEIM PALACE

BROUGHTON CASTLE

Moated 16th century house famous for its Civil War history, where the plans for opposition to Charles I were hatched. Elizabethan state rooms visited by James I with fine panelling, fireplaces and plasterwork.

Highlights:

- Civil War armour in Great Hall
- King's Chamber
- Council Chamber
- Herbaceous borders

ENTRANCE HALL - BUSCOT PARK

GREAT HALL - BROUGHTON CASTLE

BUSCOT PARK

A pleasing Palladian exterior hides an interior full of extraordinary treasures, collected by wealthy railway investor Lord Faringdon in the early 20th century, combining a world class art gallery and a family home. Paintings from the Italian Renaissance to the present day, sculpture and fine furnishings with extensive gardens.

Highlights:

- Egyptian revival furniture by Thomas Hope
- Works by Rubens, Rembrandt & other old masters
- The Legend of the Briar Rose by Edward Burne-Jones
- Normanton State Bed

BEAULIEU

Still a 'beau-lieu' - beautiful place - in the New Forest, Beaulieu has so much to offer for a heritage visit. Whether cars, houses, abbeys, sci-fi (there's a monorail), wartime spies or gardens are your thing, Beaulieu has it all in bucket-loads.

Highlights:

- Victorian kitchens
- Cars of the Big & Small Screen
- Skytrain & Veteran Bus rides
- Walks along the Beaulieu River

OLD KITCHENS - PALACE HOUSE, BEAULIEU

THE ENTRANCE COURT - CHENIES MANOR HOUSE

LANCING COLLEGE CHAPEL LOOKING TO SIMON DYKES BOWER'S ROSE WINDOW

CHENIES MANOR HOUSE

Brick manor house with decorative Tudor chimneys, the surviving wing of a palace regularly visited by Henry VIII and Elizabeth I, with extensive flower gardens developed since the 1950s.

Highlights:

- Queen Elizabeth's Room
- The Long Room
- Tulips in the Sunken Garden
- The Physic Garden

LANCING COLLEGE CHAPEL

The largest school chapel in the world built in 1868 and a building that attracts superlatives. The height of the soaring clerestory and the Rose Window (largest in England) give it a distinctly French feel but at heart, it is English gothic executed with true Victorian audacity.

Highlights:

- The 90 ft high nave
- Rose Window
- Trevor Huddleston window

'He ... raises his eyes to the horiz[...]
and listens'
Virginia Woolf

'From reading White's
wondering why every [...]
an ornithologist'
Charles Darwin

'Watching Narrowly'

GILBERT WHITE'S HOUSE & THE OATES COLLECTION

"…I've always thought that Gilbert White, country parson & famous Georgian naturalist, was really just a small boy who never grew up. I mean, isn't it small children who like collecting earthworms, counting birds and spotting snails? This means that visiting Gilbert White's home in Selbourne brings out the small child hidden inside all of us. White spent his life just pottering about at Selborne, watching his garden carefully, and then wrote a book that quietly invented the science of natural history.

With no trace of irony, Gilbert White's house is also home to the Oates Collection, celebrating the life of Captain Oates of Scott's doomed 1910 Antarctic expedition. Oates was already a hero of the Boer War long before he walked out of Scott's tent ("I may be some time") and sacrificed himself for his team-mates. Setting a hero whose life was characterised by travel, military exploits and extraordinary bravery right next door to White, a hero who stayed at home pretty well all his life shows you either model works. Not a bad life lesson for children! Mine loved the interactive exhibits too, and remember to turn over a few leaves and look for snails in the 18th century landscaped grounds…"

DON'T MISS: SOUTH EAST

- EAST SUSSEX
- WEST SUSSEX
- SURREY
- KENT

ARUNDEL CASTLE

Iconic Norman castle, home of one of Britain's great families, the Dukes of Norfolk for 850 years. Heavily restored both for a visit by Queen Victoria in 1845 and again after she left, the interiors are Victorian enhanced by the surviving works of art from the 17th century collection of the Collector Earl of Arundel.

Highlights:

- The Collector Earl's Garden
- Armoury
- The 12th century Fitzalan Chapel
- Mary Queen of Scots' rosary

OBERON'S PALACE IN THE COLLECTOR EARL'S GARDEN AT ARUNDEL CASTLE

KNOLE

Exceptional medieval and Jacobean house with its original deer park. Newly restored staterooms are now opening, revealing unrivalled English renaissance interiors. Knole is thought to be a rare calendar house with 7 courts, 12 entrances, 52 staircases and 365 rooms.

Highlights:

- Great Staircase
- Oldest playable organ in Britain
- Reynolds Room
- 3 state beds

FRONT MEADOW. GREAT DIXTER

WEST FRONT GATEHOUSE, KNOLE © NATIONAL TRUST IMAGES - ROBERT MORRIS

GREAT DIXTER

Family home of legendary garden writer, Christopher Lloyd, created from two medieval houses by the architect, Sir Edwin Lutyens. The surrounding garden hosts gardening courses and preserves the dynamic experimental gardening style characteristic of Christopher Lloyd, now under the guiding hand of head gardener, Fergus Garrett.

Highlights:

- The medieval Great Hall
- The Long Border
- The Exotic Garden
- The Barn Garden

GOODWOOD

A large Regency villa that started as a hunting lodge and has had sport at its heart ever since, from the 1st Duke of Richmond's love of the chase through cricket and racing to today's annual Festival of Speed. The art collection includes canvasses by Canaletto, Stubbs, van Dyck, Romney and Ramsay.

Highlights:

- The Egyptian Dining Room
- Paintings by George Stubbs
- William Kent mantelpiece from Richmond House
- Gobelins tapestries

HAMPTON COURT PALACE

The most interesting royal palace in Britain, incorporating Henry VIII's Tudor palace with William III's, with a bit of interference from Charles II and the Georges. Interiors are a rich concoction of period style, paintings and furnishings with fun for all.

Highlights:

- Tudor Kitchens
- Queen's Stair
- The Great Maze
- Mantegna's The Triumphs of Caesar

GOODWOOD HOUSE

THE CHAPEL ROYAL, HAMPTON COURT PALACE © HISTORIC ROYAL PALACES

PENSHURST PLACE

Still a medieval house at heart with a magnificent run of Tudor state rooms, this was the home of Renaissance man Sir Philip Sidney, poet, soldier, courtier and mega-celebrity of the Elizabethan era. Records for the garden trace it back to 1346, the oldest in England.

Highlights:

- Great Hall
- Queen Elizabeth dancing with The Earl of Leicester
- Tapestries and embroidery
- Toy Museum

LONG GALLERY, PENSHURST PLACE

HEVER CASTLE

Childhood home of Anne Boleyn. The exquisite moated castle was painstakingly restored by William Waldorf Astor in the 1900s and filled with mementoes and portraits of Anne and her contemporaries set off by Tudor furnishings and Edwardian craftsmanship, all in extensive Italian gardens.

Highlights:

- Anne Boleyn's Book of Hours
- Tudor portraits
- Four poster in King Henry VIII's Room
- The oldest working portcullis in Britain

HEVER CASTLE

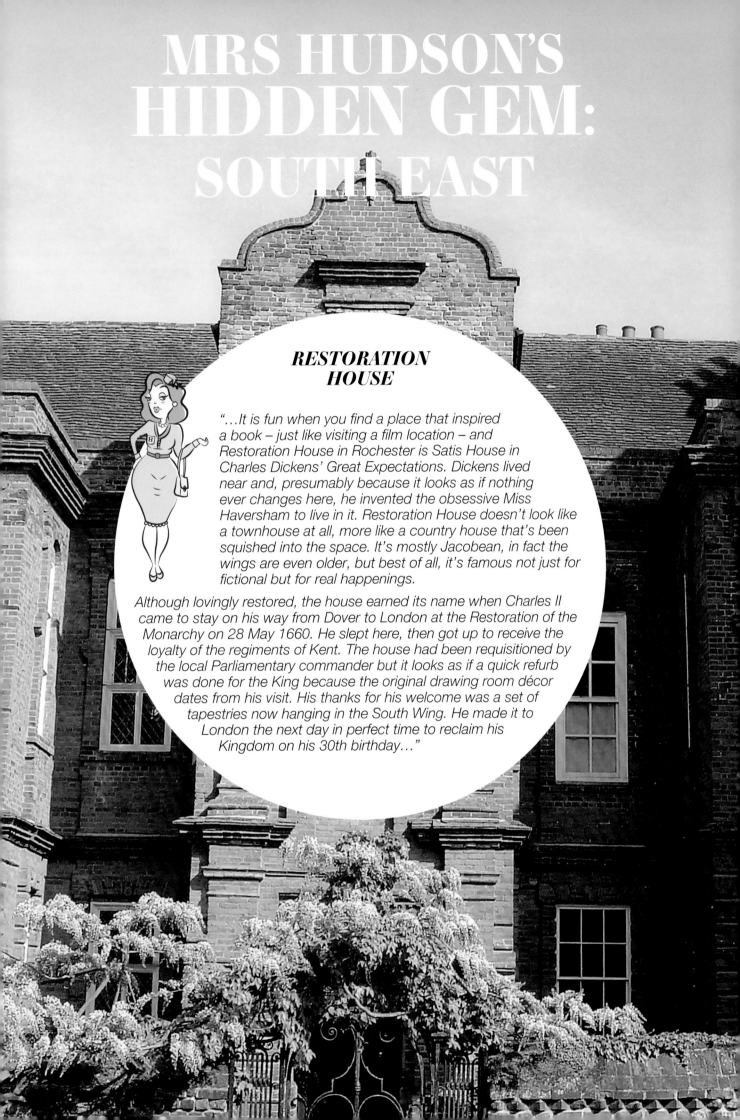

MRS HUDSON'S HIDDEN GEM: SOUTH EAST

RESTORATION HOUSE

"…It is fun when you find a place that inspired a book – just like visiting a film location – and Restoration House in Rochester is Satis House in Charles Dickens' Great Expectations. Dickens lived near and, presumably because it looks as if nothing ever changes here, he invented the obsessive Miss Haversham to live in it. Restoration House doesn't look like a townhouse at all, more like a country house that's been squished into the space. It's mostly Jacobean, in fact the wings are even older, but best of all, it's famous not just for fictional but for real happenings.

Although lovingly restored, the house earned its name when Charles II came to stay on his way from Dover to London at the Restoration of the Monarchy on 28 May 1660. He slept here, then got up to receive the loyalty of the regiments of Kent. The house had been requisitioned by the local Parliamentary commander but it looks as if a quick refurb was done for the King because the original drawing room décor dates from his visit. His thanks for his welcome was a set of tapestries now hanging in the South Wing. He made it to London the next day in perfect time to reclaim his Kingdom on his 30th birthday…"

MARK THE YEAR

300 YEARS
CHIPPENDALE

Celebrate our greatest furniture maker 300 years after his birth.
- ✔ Firle Place
- ✔ Petworth Park

ONE OF TWO CHIPPENDALE 'PANSHANGER' CABINETS AT FIRLE PLACE (RIGHT)

200 YEARS
REPTON

Enjoy the gardens of Humphry Repton 200 years after his death.
- ✔ Ashridge Estate
- ✔ Bayham Abbey
- ✔ Hatchlands
- ✔ Royal Pavilion
- ✔ Uppark
- ✔ West Wycombe Park
- ✔ Stanmer Park
- ✔ Cobham Hall

REPTON NORTH ENTRANCE TO UPPARK © NATIONAL TRUST IMAGES - ANDREW BUTLER

100 YEARS
WORLD WAR 1

In 1918 Lord Astor turned his Italian garden into a War Memorial Garden for the 42 men of the 24,000 injured troops from the hospital at Cliveden who died here.

The estate at Basildon Park was transformed into a working farm from 1915 to 1918 run by 60 women of the Women's Land Army farming livestock, cheese making, charcoal burning and brick making. The house was a convalescent home for 50 Guards officers.

MODERN DAY VOLUNTEERS IN THE GARDENS AT BASILDON PARK © NATIONAL TRUST IMAGES

DID YOU KNOW?

THE QUEEN'S APARTMENTS, LEEDS CASTLE

1 LEEDS CASTLE

Margaret, Baroness Badlesmere was the first female prisoner in the Tower of London. Her offence? When her husband was away in revolt against Edward II, she refused the Queen entry to Leeds Castle, launched an attack on her entourage and held out against the ensuing ferocious 5 day siege.

2 CARISBROOKE CASTLE

Charles I's midnight escape from imprisonment in Carisbrooke Castle in 1648 failed because he got wedged in the bars of the window and couldn't climb out to reach the waiting boat. He was executed 10 months later.

3 GOODWOOD HOUSE

By 1719 the gambling debts of the 2nd Duke of Richmond of Goodwood House were so big he was married off to a 13 year old heiress, Lady Sarah Cadogan. He promptly left on Grand Tour for 3 years. Back in London, he asked to be introduced to a pretty girl at the theatre only to find that she was his wife. They had 12 children.

THE PAINTED ROOM, ST MARY'S, BRAMBER

GATEHOUSE. CARISBROOKE CASTLE © ENGLISH HERITAGE

4 PARHAM PARK

Parham Park got unwittingly caught up with notorious smugglers The Hawkhurst Gang. In 1747, the smugglers stole 1.5 tonnes of tea and the body of one of their victims was dumped in the pond at Parham. The natural daughter of Parham's owner, Sir Cecil Bishopp, was married to one of the gang, Thomas 'Slotch' Lillywhite.

5 HAMMERWOOD PARK

The Capitol & The White House in Washington share an architect with Hammerwood Park. Benjamin Latrobe built this Greek revival house around 1792 before leaving to become America's first architect.

6 ST MARY'S BRAMBER

The Edwardian owner of St Mary's Bramber, the Hon Algernon Bourke, founder of White's Club, and his wife Gwendoline were lampooned by Oscar Wilde as the main characters in The Importance of Being Earnest.

73

100 YEARS
WOMEN & SUFFRAGE

ELEANOR OF CASTILE AT LINCOLN CATHEDRAL

QUEEN ANNE BOLEYN FROM A PORTRAIT AT HEVER CASTLE

1. ELEANOR OF CASTILE (1241-90)
Edward I's Queen, first to have an independent income at Leeds Castle.

2. ANNE BOLEYN (1501-36)
Henry VIII's Queen, protestant reformer at Hever Castle.

3. SARAH, DUCHESS OF MARLBOROUGH (1660-1744)
Political campaigner, intimate friend of Queen Anne at Blenheim Palace.

SARAH, DUCHESS OF MARLBOROUGH ATT. GODFREY KNELLER

4. NANCY ASTOR (1879-1964)
Politician, 1st woman in Parliament
at Cliveden.

5. ELIZABETH MONTAGU (1909-85)
Wartime spy, dialogue director & advertising executive
at Beaulieu.

6. VANESSA BELL
Painter, member of the Bloomsbury Group
at Charleston.

4 TOP GARDENS

1.
ROUSHAM

The first true landscape garden in England, created by William Kent around 1740. Walks, woods, pools, rills, statues and follies.

2.
BORDE HILL GARDENS

Created by Robert Stephenson Clarke from the 1890s in a series of garden rooms. Rose Gardens, Azalea Ring, Paradise Walk, Garden of Allah, Italian Gardens, Old Potting Sheds.

3.
GREAT DIXTER

Garden designed by Edwin Lutyens, created by garden writer Christopher Lloyd. Long Border, yew topiary, Sunk Garden, Blue Garden, meadow gardens, vegetable garden.

4.
NYMANS

Arts & Crafts garden established by Leonard & Maud Messel from 1915. Wall Garden; camellias, rhododendrons & heathers; Wild garden and woodlands.

NYMANS © NATIONAL TRUST IMAGES - JOHN MILLER

ROUSHAM

THE LONG BORDER, GREAT DIXTER

ROSE GARDENS, BORDE HILL

POWDER MILLS HOTEL, EAST SUSSEX

A former gunpowder works converted into a country house for its successful owner on land originally leased from Battle Abbey. The best gunpowder in Europe was once made here at the centre of an iron and arms industry whose heyday was in Roman and Tudor times.

4 CANON CLOSE, WEST SUSSEX

A former Archdeanery is through an arch to a quiet close behind the Cathedral. The flint and brick building has fine views of the Norman and Gothic cathedral and is central in a county town that dates back to the Romans.

THE FEATHERS, OXFORDSHIRE

Linked 17th century townhouses, in a main street in historic Woodstock, hide a varied past as a drapers, a butchers, a sanatorium and a row of cottages. Smart art-studded interiors now surround the Restaurant and gin bar.

WHITE HORSE HOTEL & BRASSERIE, HAMPSHIRE

The White Horse, a Grade II listed building, is one of only three late medieval structures in Hampshire designed as an Inn. From the bygone days of the stagecoach, for over 400 years, the White Horse has extended hospitality to guests.

DEANS PLACE HOTEL, EAST SUSSEX

Originally a vast farming estate, Deans Place became a private Hotel at the beginning of the 20th century. Since then the estate has evolved into a highly regarded Alfriston Hotel, set on the banks of the Cuckmere River at the foot of the South Downs National Park.

DRAKE'S HOTEL, EAST SUSSEX

On the seafront with fabulous views of the iconic Palace Pier, Drakes retains its pole position as the most luxurious and romantic boutique hotel in Brighton. Having opened its doors over 12 years ago, the hotel has lost none of its edginess and city chic. They're not into flashy displays at this double-fronted listed Georgian townhouse.

REPTON & THE PICTURESQUE

Humphry Repton is the last towering figure of the 18th century landscape gardening movement. He is generally considered a worthy successor to the great Capability Brown and certainly, at the outset of his career, he followed in the Brown tradition, creating open landscape settings for country houses that featured views, lakes and carefully sited clumps of trees.

Repton was a late starter and only began his career in 1788 when at the age of 36 he decided to try to fill the gap left by the death of Capability Brown five years before. To this point, he had been variously textile merchant, journalist, dramatist and political agent with little success. Unlike Brown, he was not a contractor but a designer who left the work of realising his vision to his clients. His genius was not just in the vision of a picturesque landscape but as a business man in his approach to his clients. To win a commission and help his clients visualise his designs, he created watercolour renditions of the current and future landscape and overlaid one upon the other. Today we know them as Red Books from the characteristic colour of the bindings while their charm and the quality of his painting makes them treasures in their own right.

STONELEIGH ABBEY GARDENS

Repton's first paid commission in 1788 was for the park of Mayor of Norwich, Jeremiah Ives, at Catton in Norfolk and he was to go on to create 400 designs all over Britain. Many are only partly completed but many remain to demonstrate his skill, and we have Repton to thank for several of our London parks and gardens. He incorporated garden buildings as essential elements of his designs, working in particularly with architect John Nash, to whom he lost the commission to build the Royal Pavilion Brighton. Like Brown, he created clear vistas across carefully organised landscapes divided by ha-has but unlike Brown, his planting often cut through the perimeter of the park to pick up on a distant eyecatcher, for example, a church tower. This embrace of the wider landscape was very much in line with the growing influence of the picturesque movement which celebrated beauty and the sublime in landscape. As his career progressed, Repton went further, recognising that the house needed detail in its immediate environs to relate it to the landscape rather than allowing lawns to run up to the walls. He reintroduced elements of formal gardens, terraces, gravel walks and flower beds. He developed a style of ornamental planting in themes, particularly in the extensive themed gardens at Woburn, where he was commissioned by the 5th Duke of Bedford. In many ways, he is the link between the informal English landscape gardening of the 18th century and the formal gardenesque movement of the early 19th century.

"as a landscape designer I have never been superseded by a more successful rival. My own profession, like myself, was becoming extinct."
Humphry Repton

Repton died in March 1818, having spent several years partially confined to a wheelchair following a carriage accident. It was he who invented the term 'landscape gardener' to describe his profession and his legacy is a series of unrivalled gardens and a continuing influence on garden design. Contrary to his own belief, his profession is far from extinct. ◾

REPTON'S BUSINESS CARD, ENGRAVED BY THOMAS MEDLAND

THE CONE HOUSE, WOBURN ABBEY, BEDFORDSHIRE © BEDFORD ESTATES

SHERINGHAM PARK FROM REPTON'S RED BOOK AND AS IT LOOKS TODAY © NATIONAL TRUST IMAGES - ROD EDWARDS

Dorney Court

www.dorneycourt.co.uk

"One of the finest Tudor Manor Houses in England" - Country Life. Grade I Listed and noted for its outstanding architectural and historical importance. Home of the Palmers for 400 years, passing from father to son over 14 generations. Highlights include the magnificent Great Hall, oak and lacquer furniture and artwork which combine to tell the story of the House. The stunning Coach House Barn with its landscaped courtyard provides a beautiful space for events.

KEY FACTS

 Film & photo shoots. Weddings. Events. No stiletto heels.

 Loo's equipped with disabled facilities are located at the House and at the Kitchen Garden.

 Accepts Euros.

 By special appointment. Min numbers apply: 20+

 Plenty of free parking available.

 Welcomes disabled visitors and those with special needs. Video tour of upstairs rooms.

 Obligatory. A range of flexible options for visiting Dorney Court.

 Schools welcome; offer a guided tour aimed at the curriculum with a focus on the Tudors.

 The Tea Room offers a range of light snacks, homemade goodies, soft drinks & delicious cream teas.

 Licensed. The Palmer Arms delivers extremely good hearty food in a classic pub setting.

 Small gift shop offering a range stationery, postcards & mementos of a wonderful day.

 Garden centre (www.dckg.co.uk).

 Flexible venue for conferences, meetings and launches.

 For events & activity days please see the 'Events' section of the website.

Perfect wedding reception venue with its fairy tale gabled roofs, landscaped gardens and 12C Church.

Perfectly suited for filming & photographic shoots; unquestionably unique with stunning backdrops.

CONTACT
Owner/Contact: Mr James Palmer
Tel: 01628 604638
Email: info@dorneycourt.co.uk
Twitter: @dorneycourt

LOCATION
Nr. Windsor, Berkshire SL4 6QP
Map Ref: 3:G2
5 mins off M4/J7, 10 mins from Windsor, 2m W of Eton.

OPENING TIMES
May Bank Holidays (6 & 7 May; 27 & 28 May) and all Aug - open afternoons 1.30pm-5pm.

ADMISSION
Adult: £9, Child (10 yrs+): £5.50, OAPs: £8.50.
Groups: 10+ £8.50pp when open to public.
Private group rates at other times.

Dorney Court

Hughenden

nationaltrust.org.uk/ hughenden

NATIONAL TRUST IMAGES / MATTHEW ANTROBUS

Amid rolling Chilterns countryside, discover the hideaway and colourful private life of Benjamin Disraeli, the most unlikely Victorian Prime Minister. Follow in his footsteps, stroll through his German Forest, relax in his elegant garden and imagine dining with Queen Victoria in the atmospheric manor. Uncover the Second World War story of Operation Hillside, for which unconventional artists painted maps for bombing missions - including the famous Dambusters raid.

CONTACT
Owner: National Trust
Contact: The Estate Office
Tel: 01494 755573
Info Line: 01494 755565
Email: hughenden@ nationaltrust.org.uk

LOCATION
High Wycombe, Buckinghamshire HP14 4LA **Map Ref:** 3:F1 - 1½ m North of High Wycombe on the West side of the A4128.

OPEN
1 Jan-31 Dec, daily.

ADMISSION (2018)
House & Garden - Adult: £12.65, Child: £6.35, Family: £31.65.
Garden only - Adult £6.35, Child £3.20, Family £15.90.
Groups - Adult: £10.50, Child £5.25. (Free for NT Members)

KEY FACTS

 Prices includes voluntary 10% donation but visitors can choose to pay the standard prices.

 Closed 24 & 25 Dec. Please see the property website for detailed opening times.

 Parking is available.

 Partial. WCs.

 Stableyard café & Dizzy's tea room, serving hot & cold food, snacks and drinks.

 Gift shop, with a range of local products and plant stall and a second hand book shop.

Wotton House

The Capability Brown Pleasure Grounds at Wotton, currently undergoing restoration, are related to the Stowe gardens, both belonging to the Grenville family when Brown laid out the Wotton grounds between 1750 and 1767. A series of man-made features on the 3 mile circuit include bridges, temples and statues.
NB Only the Pleasure Grounds are open to the public, not the House.

CONTACT
Owner/Contact:
David Gladstone
Tel: 01844 238363
Email:
david.gladstone@which.net

LOCATION
Wotton Underwood, Aylesbury, Buckinghamshire HP18 0SB
Map Ref: 7:B11
Either A41 turn off Kingswood, or M40/J7 via Thame.

OPEN
4 Apr-5 Sep, Weds only, 2-5pm. Also 2 Apr, 28 May, 30 Jun, 4 Aug and 1 Sep.

ADMISSION
Adult: £6, Child: Free, Conc: £3. Groups: max 25.

KEY FACTS

 Limited parking for coaches.

 Accessible.

 Dogs welcome on leads.

 Guided tours obligatory.

Wotton House

Beaulieu

🏛 Ⓕ www.beaulieu.co.uk

PALACE HOUSE

Beaulieu, at the heart of the New Forest, features a range of heritage attractions.

Palace House

Once the gatehouse of the medieval Beaulieu Abbey, Palace House has been the Montagu family home since 1538. Explore this gothic styled Victorian country home as costumed guides give you a flavour of life 'below stairs' and share with you the fascinating history of the house and the generations who have lived there. New for 2017, visit the restored Victorian Kitchen which has been put back to its original layout with a working range. Plus, enter through a false bookshelf door to the library which formed part of the late Lord Montagu's private apartments. Discover the remarkable story of two women in the Montagu family in 'The Lady and The Rebel' exhibition. Palace House is home to the first dedicated Soviet Russian art gallery in the UK, displaying a selection of paintings and sculptures from the Art Russe foundation.

Beaulieu Abbey & Exhibition

Founded on land gifted by King John to Cistercian monks in 1204, Beaulieu Abbey was largely destroyed during the Reformation. The conserved ruins demonstrate the scale of what was once a vast complex. One of the surviving buildings houses an exhibition on the history of the Abbey and the monks that lived and worked here.

The National Motor Museum

Over 250 vehicles tell the story of motoring in Britain from its pioneering origins to the present day. From the earliest motor carriages to classic family saloons, displays include historic sporting motors, modern rally cars, F1 racers, a rustic 1930's country garage and Wheels – a fascinating pod ride through motoring history.

Grounds & Gardens

Explore the informal Wilderness Garden, fragrant Victorian Flower Garden and the Victorian Kitchen Garden. Enjoy the Mill Pond walk through parkland woods and look out for the Rufus Memorial Cairn – to commemorate the death of King William Rufus who, evidence suggests, was killed by an arrow whilst hunting at Beaulieu in 1100.

OWNER
Lord Montagu

CONTACT
Visitor Enquiries
Tel: 01590 612345
Email: visit@beaulieu.co.uk

LOCATION
Beaulieu, Hampshire SO42 7ZN

Map Ref: 3:C6

M27 to J2, A326, B3054 follow brown signs.
Take the local bus service within the New Forest.
There is a Station at Brockenhurst 7m away.

TRANSPORT ROUTES
Car I Bus I Train

OPENING TIMES
Summer Whitsun-Sep Daily, 10am-6pm.
Winter Oct-Whitsun Daily, 10am-5pm

Please check website for exact dates.

ADMISSION
All year Individual and group rates upon application.
Group Discount: 15+

REGULAR EVENTS
Beaulieu hosts a range of family-friendly and motoring themed events throughout the year. Visit www.beaulieuevents.co.uk for details.

All ticket enquiries to our Special Events Booking Office. Tel 01590 612888.

KEY FACTS

 Allow 4-5 hours for visits. Helicopter landing point.

 Attendants on duty.

 WC's. There are three sets of disabled toilets across the site.

 Professional staff available to assist.

 Baby changing facilities available.

 Part of the Brabazon Restaurant-sandwiches to cooked meals and tea & cold drinks.

 Closed 25 Dec.

 Seats 250.

 Unlimited. Free admission for coach drivers plus voucher.

 Palace House Kitchen Shop & Main Reception Shop.

 WC. Wheelchairs in Visitor Reception by prior booking.

 Beaulieu offers a versatile & unique venue with a difference. Conferences, meetings or receptions.

 Cycle route going through the estate.

 Please see website.

In grounds, on leads only.

Please see www.beaulieu.co.uk/corporate-and-weddings.

HAMPSHIRE

South East

Avington Park

www.avingtonpark.co.uk

From the wrought iron gates and long avenue of limes, approach well-tended lawns, bordering the river Itchen and the elegant Palladian facade. William Cobbett wrote of Avington Park that it was 'one of the prettiest places in the County' and indeed it is true today. Dating back to the 11th Century, and enlarged in 1670, the house enjoys magnificent painted and gilded state rooms overlooking lawns and parkland. Over the years Charles II and George IV stayed at various times. St Mary's, a fine Georgian church, may also be visited.

KEY FACTS

 The rooms on show are the Main Hall, Library, Conservatory, Ballroom & Drawing Room.

 Toilet facilities available.

 Baby changing facilities available.

 Parking available within the grounds.

 Partial (ground floor only) and WC.

 In grounds, on leads. Guide dogs only in house.

 Guided tours.

 Tea bar open during public openings.

 Exclusive use for conferences, films, photoshoot's, private parties, seminars & corporate events.

 Open-air theatre, four performances in summer.

 Exclusive use for weddings.

CONTACT
Owner/Contact: Mrs S L Bullen
Tel: 01962 779260
Email: enquiries@avingtonpark.co.uk

LOCATION
Winchester, Hampshire, SO21 1DB
Map Ref: 3:D4 **OS Ref:** SU532323
4m NE of Winchester ½m S of B3047 in Itchen Abbas.

OPENING TIMES
May-Sep: Suns & BH Mons & Mons in Aug, 2.30-5.30pm. Last tour 4.30pm. Group visits welcome by appointment all year round. Please contact for details.

ADMISSION
Adult: £12, Child: £6.

Stratfield Saye House

www.stratfield-saye.co.uk

After the Duke of Wellington's victory against Napoleon at the Battle of Waterloo in 1815, the Duke chose Stratfield Saye as his country estate. The house contains many of the 1st Duke's possessions and is still occupied by his descendants being a family home rather than a museum.

KEY FACTS

 Toilet facilities available.

 Parking is available.

 WC. Please contact for further details and see access statement on the website.

 Camping and caravanning in the country park.

 Access to Stratfield Saye House is by guided tour only.

 Tailored school visit packages, please contact for further details.

 Sourcing the best local ingredients for the farm shop & cafe; simple and delicious.

 Farm shop selling cosmetics, home and garden goods.

 For possible Corporate bookings or packages in the country park please contact.

 Please see list of events in the country park section of the website.

CONTACT
Owner: The Duke of Wellington
Contact: Estate Office
Tel: 01256 882694

LOCATION
Stratfield Saye, Hampshire RG7 2BZ
Map Ref: 3:E2 - Equidistant from Reading (M4/J11) & Basingstoke (M3/J6) 1½m W of the A33.

OPENING TIMES
Thu 29 Mar-Mon 2 Apr. Fri 3-Tue 28 Aug.

ADMISSION
Weekdays - Adult: £11, Child: £4, Over 60s/Student: £10.
Weekends - Adult: £13, Child: £5, Over 60s/Student: £12.
Groups: By arrangement only.

Gilbert White & The Oates Collections

gilbertwhiteshouse.org.uk

Explore the lives of three explorers of the natural world. Home of the naturalist Gilbert White, and surrounded by 25 acres of garden and parkland. The Oates Collections celebrates the lives of 19th Century explorer Frank Oates, and Lawrence Oates who travelled on the ill-fated Terra Nova Expedition.

KEY FACTS

 In village, 2 min walk.

 Suitable. Assistance provided.

 Dogs welcome in grounds only.

 Wonderful café in restored 18th Century stables.

 Books, local produce and gifts.

 Buy plants from garden.

Provides the perfect British country venue; informal yet distinctive spaces to hire for your wedding.

CONTACT
Tel: 01420 511275
Email: info@gilbertwhiteshouse.org.uk

LOCATION
High St, Selborne, Alton GU34 3JH
Map Ref: 3:E4 Selborne is on B3006 from Alton to A3.

OPEN
1 Jan-19 Feb, Fri-Sun, 10.30am-4.30pm. 20 Feb-31 Mar, Tue-Sun, 10.30am 4.30pm. 1 Apr-31 Oct, Tue-Sun, 10.30am-5pm. 1 Nov-24 Dec, 10.30am-4.30pm. Jul & Aug 7 days a week 10.30-5pm.

ADMISSION
Adult: £9.50, Conc: £8.50, U16: £4, U5: Free. Family Ticket (2A+3C): £24. Pre-booked group of 10+: £7.50. **Garden Only:** £7.50.

Houghton Lodge Gardens

www.houghtonlodge.co.uk

The best surviving example in the United Kingdom of an 18th Century Cottage Orné, overlooking the River Test. Peaceful formal and informal gardens with fine trees. Chalk cob walls enclose traditional kitchen garden with espaliers, themed herb garden, wild flowers and orchid house. 14 acres of picturesque countryside, meadow walks, charming alpacas, topiary peacock garden and snorting dragon!

CONTACT
Owner: Daniel Busk
Contact: Sophie Busk
Tel: 01264 810502
Email: sophie@houghtonlodge.co.uk

LOCATION
Stockbridge, Hampshire SO20 6LQ **Map Ref:** 3:C4 1½m S of Stockbridge (A30) on minor rd to Houghton village.

OPEN
Daily from 1 Apr-30 Sep, 11am-5pm except weekends & Bank Holidays when open 10am-5pm. House tours & garden tours are available to pre-booked groups

ADMISSION
Adult: £6.50, Child: £3, Under 3 yrs: Free.
Coach Tours & Groups: Welcome on any day by appointment only.

KEY FACTS

 Hard standing for 2 coaches.

 On short leads.

 Tea House offers light refreshments.

 Please see the 'News' section for all upcoming events.

 Exclusive Wedding Venue in Hampshire for both wedding receptions and ceremonies.

Stratfield Saye House

Penshurst
Place & Gardens

www.penshurstplace.com

THE ITALIAN GARDEN IN SPRING ©DARRYL CURCHER PHOTOGRAPHY

THE BARONS HALL ©JIGSAW DESIGN & PUBLISHING

One of England's greatest family-owned historic houses with a history spanning nearly seven centuries.

In some ways time has stood still at Penshurst; the great House is still very much a medieval building with improvements and additions made over the centuries but without any substantial rebuilding. Its highlight is undoubtedly the medieval Baron's Hall, built in 1341, with its impressive 60ft-high chestnut-beamed roof. A marvellous mix of paintings, tapestries and furniture from the 15th, 16th and 17th Centuries can be seen throughout the House, including the helm carried in the state funeral procession to St Paul's Cathedral for the Elizabethan courtier and poet, Sir Philip Sidney, in 1587. This is now the family crest.

Gardens

The Gardens, first laid out in the 14th Century, have been developed over generations of the Sidney family, who first came to Penshurst in 1552 after the estate was gifted to them by King Edward VI. A major restoration and replanting programme undertaken by the 1st Viscount De L'Isle has been continued by his son the 2nd Viscount De L'Isle, to ensure they retain their historic splendour. The 1st Viscount De L'Isle is commemorated with an Arboretum, planted in 1991.

The Gardens are divided by a mile of yew hedges into 'rooms', each planted to give a succession of colour as the seasons change, with the completion of a major redevelopment project on the Blue and Yellow Border, and an ongoing regeneration of the Lanning Roper Border.

There is also an Adventure Playground, Woodland Trail, Toy Museum and Garden Restaurant, with the Porcupine Pantry café and a Gift Shop open all year. A variety of events in the park and grounds take place throughout the year

THE HERALDIC GARDEN ©SAM BOND

OWNER
Viscount De L'Isle MBE

CONTACT
Tel: 01892 870307
Email: contactus@penshurstplace.com

LOCATION
Penshurst, Nr Tonbridge, Kent TN11 8DG
Map Ref: 19:H12
From M25 Junction 5 follow A21 to Tonbridge, leaving at Hildenborough exit; then follow brown tourist signs. From M20/M26 Junction 2a follow A25 (Sevenoaks) A21 for Hildenborough, then follow brown tourist signs.

TRANSPORT ROUTES
Car | Bus | Train

OPENING TIMES
Open daily from 10-18 Feb, 10.30am-6pm.
House open weekends only 12noon-4pm.
Open Weekends only from 24 Feb-25 Mar, 10.30am-6pm or dusk if earlier.
House 12noon-4pm.
Open daily from 30 Mar-28 Oct, 10.30am-6pm.
House 12noon-4pm.
Gift Shop & Porcupine Pantry open all year.
Winter opening available to Groups by appt only.

ADMISSION
For individual & group prices, see website.

Season tickets are available for both individual visitors and families.

REGULAR EVENTS
Weald of Kent Craft & Design Show:
1st May Bank Holiday weekend (Sat-Mon) and 2nd weekend in Sep (Fri-Sun).
Maize Maze: Open during school Summer Holidays.

Most events are included within the cost of a standard garden entry ticket. See website for more details.

KEY FACTS

 Maps and guidebooks are available. No photography in house.

 Accessible toilets situated outside the Garden Restaurant and main entrance.

 Seasonal opening times. See website for further details.

 Ample free parking for cars and coaches.

 Partial. See website for further details.

 Sustrans cycle route to Tonbridge can be found across the wider estate parkland.

 Guided tours available by appointment only.

 See website for our educational information.

 Porcupine Pantry outside the paid perimeter. Open all year.

 Licensed Garden Restaurant within the paid perimeter.

 Gift Shop outside the paid perimeter. Open all year.

 Small Plant Centre outside the paid perimeter.

 Availability for a variety of corporate uses including conferences and Christmas parties.

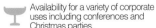 See www.penshurstplace.com/whats-on

 Licensed ceremony and reception venue.

 The Princess Bride, The Other Boleyn Girl. Wolf Hall, The Hollow Crown.

Chiddingstone Castle
www.chiddingstonecastle.org.uk

Situated in a beautiful Tudor village in the heart of the idyllic Kentish Weald, Chiddingstone Castle is a unique Historic House and Museum. Set in 35 acres of informal gardens, the building originates from the 1550s when High Street House, as it was known, was a family home. Several transformations have since taken place and the present building dates back to 1805. Rescued from creeping dereliction in 1955 by the gifted antiquary Denys Eyre Bower, the Castle became home to his remarkable collections which are exhibited throughout the building – Japanese, Ancient Egyptian, Buddhist, Stuart and Jacobite. Further exhibition rooms display the history of the Castle and the local area.

Delicious light lunches, cakes and traditional cream teas can be enjoyed in the cosy Tea Room or in the delightful sheltered courtyard.

CONTACT
Owner: The Denys Eyre Bower Bequest, Registered Charitable Trust
Tel: 01892 870347
Email: events@chiddingstonecastle.org.uk

LOCATION
Chiddingstone Castle, Nr Edenbridge, Kent TN8 7AD
Map Ref: 9:G12 - 10m from Tonbridge, Tunbridge Wells and Sevenoaks. 4m Edenbridge. Accessible from A21 and M25/J5. London 35m.
TRANSPORT ROUTES
Car I Bike I Bus I Train I Air

OPENING TIMES
Apr-end Oct, 11am-5pm, Sun, Mon, Tue, Wed & BH
Last entry to house 4.15pm.
(Check the website for any unforeseen alterations)

ADMISSION
Adults: £9.50
Children (5-13): £4.50 (Under 5s: Free)
Family (2+2): £25
Grounds & Tea Rooms: Free

KEY FACTS

 Museum, scenic gardens and lake, picnics, fishing available.

 Toilet and disabled toilet facilities available.

 Price: £2. All visitors to the Castle & Gardens to use the Castle car park.

 Partially, please see the access section of the website for further details.

 In grounds and Tea Room courtyard on leads.

 By arrangement.

 Welcoming visits from schools who wish to use the collections in connection with classroom work.

 Cream teas a speciality.

 Well stocked gift shop.

 Plant sales available at the gift shop.

 Available for private and corporate functions.

 We have a series of special event days. Visit the website What's On page for more information.

 Licensed for Civil Ceremonies. Wedding receptions.

 If you are looking for an outstanding media location in the Kent countryside, look no further!

Leeds Castle

www.leeds-castle.com

Set in 500 acres of beautiful Kent parkland, there's something to discover every day at "the loveliest castle in the world". During its near 900 year history, Leeds Castle has been a Norman stronghold, the private property of six of England's medieval Queens and a palace used by Henry VIII. In the 1930s the Castle was a playground for the rich and famous, as Lady Baillie, the last private owner, entertained high society down from London for the weekends. During your visit discover the glorious gardens and grounds, spiralling yew maze, free-flying falconry displays, leisurely punting trips and the unique Dog Collar Museum. Children will enjoy riding on Elsie the Castle Land Train, taking a trip on the ferry boat and the adventure playgrounds.

KEY FACTS

 Toilet and disabled toilet facilities available.

 Baby changing facilities available.

 Accepts Euros.

 Closed on the first weekend of November for fireworks and Christmas Day.

Free parking. Hard standing spaces reserved for visitors with disabilities.

 Please ask for assistance and information. Wheelchairs are available on loan free of charge.

 B&B, Holiday Cottages & Glamping.

 An audio tour can be collected from the Castle Shop at a reduced rate for visitors with disabilities.

 Restaurant available for lunch and evening dinner bookings.

 Banquets, meetings, seminars, presentations and conferences.

 For the latest events please see the 'What's On' section of the website.

CONTACT
Owner: Leeds Castle Foundation
Tel: 01622 765400
Fax: 01622 735616
Email: enquiries@leeds-castle.co.uk

LOCATION
Maidstone, Kent ME17 1PL
Map Ref: 4:L3
From London to A20/M20/J8, 40m, 1 hr. 7m E of Maidstone, ¼m S of A20.

OPENING TIMES
Summer: 1 Apr-30 Sep Daily, 10.30am-4.30pm (last adm).
Winter: 1 Oct-31 Mar Daily, 10.30am-3pm (last adm).

ADMISSION
Annual Tickets (prices valid until 31 Mar 2018).
Adults: £24.90
Senior Citizen: £21.90
Student: £21.90
Visitor with disabilities: £21.90
Child (4-15yrs): £16.90
Infants (under 4yrs): Free

Restoration House

www.restorationhouse.co.uk

Fabled city mansion deriving its name from the stay of Charles II on the eve of The Restoration. This complex ancient house has beautiful interiors with exceptional early paintwork related to decorative scheme 'run up' for Charles' visit. The house also inspired Dickens to create 'Miss Havisham' here. "Interiors of rare historical resonance and poetry", Country Life. Fine English furniture and strong collection of English portraits (Mytens, Kneller, Dahl, Reynolds and several Gainsboroughs). Charming interlinked walled gardens and ongoing restoration of monumental Renaissance water garden A private gem. "There is no finer pre-civil war town house in England than this" - Simon Jenkins, The Times. "Deserves a medal" - Jools Holland.

Make sure to visit the Renaissance garden, including access to oculus domed gazebo, dramatic tiered terracing with presiding Matthew Darbyshire Farnese Hercules and other compelling antique statues.

CONTACT
Owner: R Tucker & J Wilmot
Contact: Robert Tucker **Tel:** 01634 848520
Email: robert.tucker@restorationhouse.co.uk

LOCATION
17-19 Crow Lane, Rochester, Kent ME1 1RF
Map Ref: 4:K2
In Historic centre of Rochester, off High Street, opposite the Vines Park. 5 minutes' walk from Rochester Station with high-speed to St Pancras and regular services to Victoria and Charing Cross.

OPENING TIMES
31 May-28 Sep, Thu-Fri, 10am-5pm.
Plus Sat 2 Jun, 12-5pm. Photographer's hour Fridays 10-11am during opening times.
Tea Shop: Open same days as house.

ADMISSION
Adult: £8.50 (includes 36 page illustrated guidebook)
Concession: £7.50
Child: £4.25
Groups: +8 - Tours: £10.00pp

KEY FACTS

 No stilettos. No photography in house except Fri morns 10-11am.

 Antique privies with lavender strewn floors.

 To Tea Shop and half of garden.

 By appointment £11 per person, minimum 8 people.

 Charity run Tea Shop. Open when house is open.

Belmont House & Gardens

www.belmont-house.org

Belmont is an elegant 18th Century house, home to six generations of the Harris family. It contains many mementoes of the family's history and travels; including, fine paintings, furniture, Indian silverware and perhaps the finest private clock collection in the country. The gardens contain a Pinetum complete with grotto, a walled ornamental garden, specimen trees and a large kitchen garden with Victorian greenhouses, all set in parkland.

KEY FACTS

 No photography in house.

 Disabled toilet facilities available.

 Gardens. See opening times.

 Limited for coaches.

 Partial. WC's. Please see the access statement for further details.

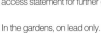 In the gardens, on lead only.

 Spend a relaxing week or two on the Belmont Estate in one of our delightful holiday cottages.

 The interior of the House can only be viewed by guided tour.

 Tea Room open from 1pm on Sat & Sun for cream teas & cakes. Self-service Mon-Fri.

 In the kitchen garden.

 For corporate event please contact.

 Spring Fair, NGS Days, Outdoor Theatre, Bushcraft, Woodfest, Xmas Events & Meet the Head Gardener Tours.

CONTACT
Owner: Harris (Belmont) Charity
Tel: 01795 890202
Email: administrator@belmont-house.org

LOCATION
Belmont Park, Throwley, Faversham, Kent ME13 0HH
Map Ref: 4:M3 - M2 Jct 6 - 4½m SSW of Faversham, off A251

OPENING TIMES
Open Apr-Sep. Please visit our website for opening hours, tour times & special events. Gardens open daily, 10am-6pm or dusk if earlier. Groups Tue & Thu by appointment. Pre-booked specialist clock tours 1.30pm last Sat of the month.

ADMISSION
House & Garden - Adult: £10 (Garden: £5), Child: £5 - Under 12's FREE (Garden 12-16yrs: £2.50), Concs: £8 (Garden: £4)
Groups: £8pp. **Clock Tour:** £20

©NATIONAL TRUST IMAGES/DAVID SELLMAN

Chartwell

www.nationaltrust.org.uk/chartwell

Chartwell was a home and a place that truly inspired Sir Winston Churchill. The house has been open to visitors for more than 50 years and is still much as it was when the family lived here, with pictures, books and personal mementoes. The studio contains a large collection of Churchill's paintings and offers an insight into Churchill the painter. The garden reflects Churchill's love of the landscape and nature including the lakes he created. The woodland estate offers family walks, swings, see-saws, trails, den-building, a Canadian camp and opportunities to blow away the cobwebs and stretch your legs.

KEY FACTS

 Entry to the house is by timed ticket, available on the day from the visitor welcome centre.

 Toilets located behind the shop and in the garden. Accessible toilet next to the visitor centre.

 Baby changing facilities available adjacent to the visitor welcome centre.

 The garden, shop and café are open daily from 10am - 5pm (closed 24 & 25 Dec).

 Car park open all year, roughly 250 yards from the main house. £3 all day parking for non-members.

 There are steps and steep slopes leading to the house. Volunteer driven mobility bus available.

 Dogs on short leads are permitted within the grounds with water bowls outside the café.

 Private tours available, contact the property for more details.

 Reinforce your classroom work with our creative learning sessions.

 Landemare café serves a selection of hot and cold meals, cakes scones and beverages.

 Gift shop offers Churchill memorabilia and items for the house and garden.

 Selling the same varieties of roses that can be found in the garden.

 Conference & function facilities. The Mulberry Room can accommodate up to 80 people.

Please see the 'What's On' section of the website to see all upcoming events.

CONTACT
Owner: National Trust
Contact: Marketing & Development Manager
Tel: 01732 868381 **Email:** chartwell@nationaltrust.org.uk

LOCATION
Mapleton Road, Westerham, Kent TN16 1PS
Map Ref: 19:F11 - 2m S of Westerham, forking left off B2026.

OPENING TIMES
House: 24 Feb-28 Oct, Daily, 10am-5pm last entry 4.10pm.
Garden, Shop, Café, Exhibition & Studio:
Daily, 10am-5pm. Times vary please call for further details.
Studio: Closed in Jan, by tour only in Feb.
Exhibition: Closes for short periods to change the display.

ADMISSION
House, Garden & Studio:
Adult: £16, Child: £8, Family: £40 (Gift Aid prices).
Garden, Exhibition, Studio & Winter season only:
Adult: £8, Child: £4, Family: £20 (Gift Aid prices).
Groups: 15+ Adult: £13, Child: £6.50
All visitors require a timed ticket to visit the house.

South East

Quebec House

nationaltrust.org.uk/quebec-house

This year we celebrate the centenary year of the National Trust owning Quebec House. In 1918 Quebec House was the first house and collection that was bequeathed to the National Trust. The childhood home of General James Wolfe, Quebec House retains much of its original charm and family feel. Interactive collections and objects belonging to Wolfe are used to explore Georgian family life and Wolfe's most celebrated victory at the Battle of Quebec in 1759. It gives a glimpse into family life in the 1730's and you can have a go at some of the pastimes Wolfe and his family would have enjoyed, such as quill pen writing and we have Georgian style clothes that families can try on.

In the exhibition on the first floor of the coach house re-live the dramatic battle to win Quebec that tragically ended in General Wolfe's death.

CONTACT
Owner: National Trust
Contact: Marketing & Development Manager
Tel: 01959 567430
Email: quebechouse@nationaltrust.org.uk

LOCATION
Quebec Square, Westerham, Kent, TN16 1TD **Map Ref:** 4:M3

OPENING TIMES
House open Weds-Suns, private tours at 12pm and 12.30pm, free flow around the house from 1-5pm.
Coach house, refreshment area and exhibition open from 11am-5pm, last entry 4.30pm.

ADMISSION
Adult: £6.20
Child: £3.10
Family: £15.50
Groups: +15 - Adult: £5.20, Child: £2.60.

KEY FACTS

 Translated hand held guides in French & German on the history of Quebec House & General Wolfe.

 Accessible toilets on the ground floor.

 Parking approximately 80 yards away in the main town car park, free parking for 3 hours.

 Gravel paths, a ramp at the front of the house. One step on the ground floor and staircase.

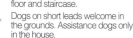 Dogs on short leads welcome in the grounds. Assistance dogs only in the house.

 Guided tours at 12pm & 12:30pm (book on arrival). On Suns Mrs Wolfe's recipes are re-created.

 Groups of children for educational visits by arrangement.

 Tea room selling light refreshments, outside chairs and tables.

 The shop is in the coach house, second hand books area in the tea room.

 See the 'What's on' section of the website for all upcoming events.

Long Gallery, Penshurst Place

Leeds Castle

Blenheim
Palace

✦ ⊞ 🏛 Ⓕ www.blenheimpalace.com

Spend an inspiring day exploring a National Treasure.

Receive a warm welcome into the home of the 12th Duke and Duchess of Marlborough and the birthplace of Sir Winston Churchill.

Wonder at this masterpiece of 18th Century Baroque architecture, which houses some of the finest antique collections in Europe. Take a tour of the State Rooms and admire the portraits, tapestries and exquisite furniture while learning about the 300-year history of this National Treasure.

Explore this World Heritage Site amongst over 2000 acres of 'Capability' Brown landscaped Parkland. Take a stroll and admire some of the finest views in England. Discover the array of Formal Gardens, including the Rose Garden, Water Terraces and Secret Garden. A short miniature train ride away from the Palace is the Pleasure Gardens, which boast a Giant Hedge Maze, Butterfly House, Lavender Garden and Adventure Playground.

Blenheim Palace hosts a wealth of events, exhibitions and tours throughout the year. From firm favourites to new experiences, there is something for everyone to enjoy. Relax in one of the on-site cafés and restaurants, serving everything from informal coffee and cake to luxury afternoon teas, fine dining and more. Spend some time in the award-winning East Courtyard shop and find locally produced crafts and gifts with many ranges that are exclusive to Blenheim Palace. Blenheim Palace is Britain's Greatest Palace, and offers visitors an experience to be treasured.

OWNER
The 12th Duke and Duchess of Marlborough

CONTACT
Contact: Visitor Information
Tel: 01993 810530
Email: customerservice@blenheimpalace.com

LOCATION
Blenheim Palace, Woodstock,
Oxfordshire OX20 1PP
Map Ref: 7:A11
By car: From London, M40, 144 (1.5 hours),
8 miles North West of Oxford. London 63 miles,
Birmingham 54 miles.
By bus: No.S3 from Oxford.
By coach: From London Victoria to Oxford.
By rail: Oxford Parkway Station.

OPENING TIMES
Open daily all year round with the exception of Christmas Day. Please check the website for up to date opening times as timings may change seasonally. Last admission to all areas is 45 minutes before closure.
Palace: 10.30am-5.30pm
Park: 9am-6pm or dusk if earlier
Formal Gardens & Pleasure Gardens: 10.30am-6pm

ADMISSION
Palace, Park & Gardens
Adult: £26, Concessions: £23,
Child: £14.50, Family: £62.50.
Park & Gardens
Adult: £16, Concessions: £13,
Child: £7.40, Family: £43.
Prices are subject to change.
Annual Pass Offer: Buy one day get 12 months free!
Discounts available on group bookings
(15+ visitors): contact Group Sales on 01993 815600 or email groups@blenheimpalace.com.

Contact the Events Team for hospitality enquiries: 01993 813874 or email sales@blenheimpalace.com

KEY FACTS

 Commercial photography or filming is not permitted without prior permission.

 Guided tours available from Mon-Sat year-round.

 Toilet facilities available.

 Talks and tours for school groups are available.

 Baby changing facilities available.

 Three cafés serving snacks, light meals and drinks are available on site.

 Open daily except Christmas Day.

 The Orangery Restaurant serves Afternoon Tea and delicious seasonal lunches.

 Free parking for cars and coaches.

 Two shops selling a range of gifts and souvenirs.

 Toilet facilities & lift access to the Palace. Blue Badge Holder parking & carers go free.

 Plants are available seasonally at our shops.

 The opportunity to cycle around the Parkland is available once per year on our Family Cycling Day.

 Weddings, corporate hospitality and private events are available.

 Dogs on leads may enter the Park only. Assistance dogs welcome.

 Please see the 'What's On' section of the website to discover our year-round event calendar.

 Options available in our local area.

 Wedding ceremonies available.

English audio tours available. International audio tours will be made available during 2018.

Popular filming location and also available for photoshoots.

Broughton Castle

🏛 Ⓕ **www.broughtoncastle.com**

"About the most beautiful castle in all England...for sheer loveliness of the combination of water, woods and picturesque buildings."
Sir Charles Oman (1898).

Broughton Castle is essentially a family home lived in by Lord and Lady Saye & Sele and their family. The original medieval Manor House, of which much remains today, was built in about 1300 by Sir John de Broughton. It stands on an island site surrounded by a 3 acre moat. The Castle was greatly enlarged between 1550 and 1600, at which time it was embellished with magnificent plaster ceilings, splendid panelling and fine fireplaces. In the 17th Century William, 8th Lord Saye & Sele, played a leading role in national affairs. He opposed Charles I's efforts to rule without Parliament and Broughton became a secret meeting place for the King's opponents. During the Civil War William raised a regiment and he and his four sons all fought at the nearby Battle of Edgehill. After the battle the Castle was besieged and captured. Arms and armour from the Civil War and other periods are displayed in the Great Hall. Visitors may also see the gatehouse, gardens and park together with the nearby 14th Century Church of St Mary, in which there are many family tombs, memorials and hatchments.

Gardens

The garden area consists of mixed herbaceous and shrub borders containing many old roses. In addition, there is a formal walled garden with beds of roses surrounded by box hedging and lined by more mixed borders.

OWNER
Lord Saye & Sele

CONTACT
Contact: Manager, Mrs James
Tel: 01295 276070
Email: info@broughtoncastle.com

LOCATION
Broughton, Nr Banbury, Oxfordshire OX15 5EB
Map Ref: 7:A10

Broughton Castle is 2½m SW of Banbury Cross on the B4035, Shipston-on-Stour - Banbury Road. Easily accessible from Stratford-on-Avon, Warwick, Oxford, Burford and the Cotswolds. M40/J11.

Rail: From London/Birmingham to Banbury.

TRANSPORT ROUTES
Car | Bus | Train

OPENING TIMES
Apr-Sep inclusive, 2-5pm Weds, Suns & Bank Holiday Mons.

Open all year for groups - by appointment only.

ADMISSION
Adult: £9
Child (5-15yrs): £5
Concession: £8
Garden only: £5

Groups
Adult: £9
Child (5-15yrs): £6
Garden only: £6
(There is a minimum charge for groups - please contact the manager for details).

KEY FACTS

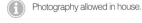 Photography allowed in house.

 Available for booked groups.

 Toilets open from 2pm, when the castle is open. Disabled toilets in car park with other toilets.

 Available by prior arrangement. Primary and secondary school groups are welcome.

 Open all year on any day, at any time, for group bookings - by appointment only.

 Teas on open days. Groups may book morning coffee, light lunches and afternoon teas.

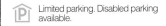 Limited parking. Disabled parking available.

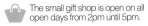 The small gift shop is open on all open days from 2pm until 5pm.

 Partial, please see the 'Disabled Access' section of the website for further details.

 Available for corporate events, small conferences and promotional events.

 Guide dogs only in house. On leads in grounds.

 Selected for a wide range of film shoots, including feature films, TV dramas and TV commercials etc.

Buscot Park

www.buscotpark.com

©NATIONAL TRUST/PAUL WATSON

Buscot Park is the home of the Henderson Family and the present Lord and Lady Faringdon, with their eldest son James and his wife Lucinda. They look after the property on behalf of the National Trust as well as the family collection of pictures, furniture, ceramics and objects d'art, known as the Faringdon Collection, which is displayed in the House. Built between 1780 and 1783 for a local landowner, Edward Lovedon Townsend, the estate was purchased in 1889 by Lord Faringdon's great-grandfather, Alexander Henderson, a financier of exceptional skill and ability, who in 1916 was created the 1st Lord Faringdon. He greatly enlarged the House, commissioned Harold Peto to design the famous Italianate water garden, and laid the foundations of the Faringdon Collection. Among his many purchases were Rembrandt's portrait of Pieter Six, Rossetti's portrait of Pandora, and Burne-Jones's famous series, The Legend of the Briar Rose. His grandson and heir, Gavin Henderson, added considerably to the Collection, acquiring important furniture designed by Robert Adam and Thomas Hope, and was instrumental in returning the House to its late 18th Century appearance. The family, together with their fellow Trustees, continue to add to the Collection, to freshen its display, and to enliven the gardens and grounds for the continuing enjoyment of visitors.

THE PETO WATER GARDEN

CONTACT
Owner: The National Trust
(Administered on their behalf by Lord Faringdon)
Contact: The Estate Office **Tel:** 01367 240786
Info Line: 01367 240932 **Email:** estbuscot@aol.com

LOCATION
Faringdon, Oxfordshire SN7 8BU **Map Ref:** 6:P12
Between Faringdon & Lechlade on A417.

OPENING TIMES
House, Grounds & Tea Rooms: 30 Mar-28 Sep,
Wed-Fri & BH's & weekends as listed below, 2-6pm
(last entry to House 5pm, Tea Room last orders 5.30pm).
Apr: 1/2/4/5/6/7/8/11/12/13/18/19/20/21/22/25/26/27
May: 2/3/4/5/6/7/9/10/11/12/13/18/19/20/21/22/25/2
6/27/28/30/31 **Jun:** 1/6/7/8/9/10/13/14/15/20/21/22/
23/24/27/28/29 **Jul:** 4/5/6/11/12/13/14/15/18/19/20/
25/26/27/28/29 **Aug:** 1/2/3/8/9/10/11/12/15/16/17/2
2/23/24/25/26/27/29/30/31 **Sep:** 5/6/7/8/9/12/13/14/
19/20/21/22/23/26/27/28
Grounds Only: 3 Apr-25 Sep, Mon-Tue, 2pm-6pm.

ADMISSION
House & Grounds - Adult: £10, Over 65s: £8,
Child (5-15): £5, Under 5: Free.
Grounds only - Adult: £7, Over 65s: £5,
Child (5-15): £3.50, National Trust members: Free.
Groups - Advance booking only.

KEY FACTS

 No photography in house.

 Toilet and disabled WC's facilities available.

 Ample car parking, 2 coach spaces.

 Partial. Ramps & motorised PMVs. Please contact prior to visit for more information. Steps to House.

 Not permitted - Guide dogs only. They may be exercised in the Paddock Field (the overflow car park).

 Open the same days as the House, offering cream teas, cakes & slices, cheese scones, hot & cold drinks.

 Small shop selling peppermint products, local cider, honey, guide books & a selection of postcards.

 A selection of plants and surplus kitchen garden produce available when in season.

Stonor Park

www.stonor.com

Stonor Park has been home to the Stonor family for over 850 years. The warm brick façade and Georgian windows conceal medieval buildings dating back to the 12th Century. Inside are many original architectural features including the 14th Century Catholic chapel and 12th Century medieval hall which today is the Pantry serving delicious snacks and light lunches. Visitors can view family portraits, old master paintings, artefacts and collections from around the world. Including a small exhibition celebrating the life and work of St Edmund Campion who sought refuge at Stonor during the reformation.

Nestled in a Chiltern valley with stunning views of the fallow deer park full of wild life including buzzards and red kites. Visitors can walk through to the 17th Century gardens with ancient terraces and lily ponds with fountains. The latest edition to Stonor is Wonder Woods, a stunning adventure play park for our younger visitors.

KEY FACTS

 No photography in house.

 WC's.

 The Visitor Centre is fully equipped with bathrooms and baby changing facilities.

 Parking 100 yards away.

 Partial access.

 Beautiful Stonor Valley is criss-crossed with walking and cycling routes.

 On leads in park at all times. Assistance dogs only in House & Gardens.

 Open all year for private guided tours - by appointment only.

 Please contact the Manager for further details.

 Stonor Pantry serves a selection of hot & cold lunches and homemade cakes and scones.

 Gift shop with local crafts and honey from the estate.

 Please contact the Manager for further details.

 Please see the 'What's On' section of the website for upcoming events.

 A frequent location in feature films, television productions, commercials & product launches.

CONTACT
Owner: The Lord & Lady Camoys
Manager: Neil Scott
Tel: 01491 638587 **Email:** enquiries@stonor.com

LOCATION
Stonor Park, Henley-On-Thames, Oxfordshire RG9 6HF
Map Ref: 3:E1 - 1 hr from London, M4/J8/9. A4130 to Henley-On-Thames. A4130/B480 to Stonor. On B480 NW of Henley. M40/J6. B4009 to Watlington. B480 to Stonor.

TRANSPORT ROUTES Car I Bus I Train I Air

OPENING TIMES
House, Gardens and Chapel: Apr-Sep.
Nov-Dec for Christmas viewings.
Stonor Wonder Woods - Adventure Play Park: Apr-Oct.
Private Groups: Open all year - by appointment only.
For up to date open days & times visit the website.

ADMISSION
For up to date admission prices visit the website.

Kingston Bagpuize House

www.kbhevents.uk

This lovely family home built in circa 1660 was remodelled in the early 1700's for the Blandy family. With English and French furniture in the elegant panelled rooms the entrance hall is dominated by its handsome cantilevered staircase. The surrounding mature parkland and gardens contain an interesting collection of cultivated plants giving year round interest including snowdrops and magnolia in spring, flowering trees and shrubs in summer and autumn colour. The 18th Century panelled pavilion overlooking the gardens is reached from the raised terrace walk. A venue for civil marriages, wedding receptions and small conferences. Available for filming and featured as Lord Merton's home in Downton Abbey series 5,6 and the 2016 Christmas finale.

CONTACT
Owner: Mrs Francis Grant **Contact:** Virginia Grant
Tel: 01865 820259 **Email:** info@kbhevents.uk

LOCATION
Kingston Bagpuize, Abingdon, Oxfordshire OX13 5AX
Map Ref: 7:A12 - Kingston Bagpuize village, off A415 1/2 mile south of the A415/A420 intersection. Abingdon 5m, Oxford 9m.

OPENING TIMES (2018)
Gardens only (snowdrops): 4, 11, 18 & 25 Feb.
House & Gardens: Mar 11, 12, 25 & 26, Apr 8, 9, 15, 16, 29 & 30, May 13, 14, 27 & 28, Jun 10, 11, 24 & 25, Jul 8-10 & 22-24, Aug 5-7 & 19-21, Sep 2, 3, 16 &17. All days 2-5pm (last entry to house 4pm). Free flow visit to ground floor.

ADMISSION
House & Garden
Adult: £9, Child/Student (11-21): £5.50.
Garden - Adult: £6, Child/Student (11-21): £4.
NB: please visit website to confirm open dates & times before travelling. Group Rates 20+ by written appointment weekdays all year.

KEY FACTS

 Restricted photography in house on open days.

 Toilet and disabled WC facilities available.

 Baby changing facilities available.

 Open days: Feb -Sep. Pre-booked group visits all year.

 Free parking is available.

 Disabled access in the garden, but restricted to house.

 For pre-booked group visits 20+. Self guided tours with notes on open days.

 By arrangement.

 Afternoon teas available. Morning coffee for pre-booked groups.

 Pre-booked lunches available for 20+.

 Cards & pottery in the tearoom.

 Rare Plant Fair Sun 27 May www.rareplantfair.co.uk.

 Please see 'Corporate' section of the website.

 Please see the 'Visiting' section of the website for events.

 Available on an exclusive basis, for civil ceremonies & wedding receptions. See website.

 Featured in Downton Abbey 2015/16.

Rousham House

www.rousham.org

©HARPUR GARDEN IMAGES

Rousham represents the first stage of English landscape design and remains almost as William Kent (1685-1748) left it. One of the few gardens of this date to have escaped alteration. Includes Venus' Vale, Townsend's Building, seven-arched Praeneste, the Temple of the Mill and a sham ruin known as the 'Eyecatcher'. The house was built in 1635 by Sir Robert Dormer. Don't miss the walled garden with it's herbaceous borders, small parterre, pigeon house and espalier apple trees. A fine herd of Longhorn cattle are to be seen in the park. Excellent location for fashion, advertising, photography etc.

©HARPUR GARDEN IMAGES

KEY FACTS

 Open access to the house and garden can be arranged for events.

 Open all year.

 Parking available.

 Partial.

Local accommodation: The Holt Hotel, Hopcrofts Holt (about 1 ½ miles, special rates for visitors.)

 Please see website. Available for photographic shoots.

 Car rallies, The Bentley, MG & Aston Martin owners clubs have all held rallies at Rousham.

 Ideal Oxfordshire venue for wedding receptions, offering a site to pitch a marquee.

 The gardens, park & exterior are available as a location for television and feature films.

CONTACT
Owner/Contact: Charles Cottrell-Dormer Esq
Tel: 01869 347110
Mobile: 07860 360407
Email: ccd@rousham.org

LOCATION
Nr Steeple Aston, Bicester, Oxfordshire OX25 4QX
Map Ref: 7:A10
E of A4260, 12 miles North of Oxford, South of B4030, 7 miles West of Bicester.

OPENING TIMES
Garden: All year, daily, 10am-4.30pm (last admission).
House: May-Sep, Pre-booked groups.

ADMISSION
House & Garden: £12
Garden: £6
No children under 15 years.

REGULAR EVENTS
Events are held in the park, immediately next to the house. Please see website for more information.

Hampton
Court Palace

www.hrp.org.uk/hamptoncourtpalace

Immerse yourself in the greatest and most authentic Tudor experience in the world.

Explore the home of Henry VIII, his wives and children, experiencing their public dramas and private lives in the unique world of the Tudor court. Learn how Henry's marriages changed the course of history, in the same rooms where his family affairs became international crises. Discover atmospheric corridors, where Tudor ghosts are said to still wander. Marvel at the grandeur of the magnificent Great Hall, see the stunning vaulted ceiling of the Chapel Royal and explore the enormous kitchens, the most extensive surviving 16th Century kitchens in Europe today.

Then experience a second palace – a Baroque masterpiece by Sir Christopher Wren built for William II and Mary II – its spectacular views and ornamental gardens providing a fascinating glimpse of Stuart and Georgian privilege.

Equally stunning inside and out; the palace is surrounded by formal gardens and sits in 60 acres of parkland gardens, including the 18th Century Privy Garden and world famous maze.

Don't miss the Magic Garden, our interactive play garden for families. Populated by mysterious mythical beasts, with battlements to storm, towers to besiege, and even a secret grotto to discover, the Magic Garden is a unique way for your family to explore the palace's past.

OWNER
Historic Royal Palaces

CONTACT
Tel: 0844 482 7777
Email: hamptoncourt@hrp.org.uk

Venue Hire & Corporate Hospitality:
020 3166 6507 / www.hrp.org.uk/hireavenue

LOCATION
Surrey KT8 9AU

Map Ref: 19:B9

Car: From M25/J15 or M25/J12 or M25/J10.
Rail: 30 mins from Waterloo, zone 6 travelcard.
Boat: From Richmond, Kingston or Runnymede.

OPENING TIMES
Mar-Oct: Daily, 10am-6pm
(last admission 5pm).
Nov-Feb: Daily, 10am-4.30pm
(last admission 3.30pm).

Closed: 24-26 Dec.

The Magic Garden is closed during the winter.

Please check our website before visiting for full details.

ADMISSION
Visit www.hrp.org.uk for admission prices, or call 0844 482 7777.

CONFERENCE/FUNCTIONS
Conferences: Up to 250
Receptions: Up to 400
Lunches: Up to 220
Dinners: Up to 270
Marquees: Up to 3000

KEY FACTS

Information Centre.

 Toilet and disabled WC's facilities available.

 Baby changing facilities available off Base Court & in the Tiltyard Café.

 Closed 24-26 Dec.

 Ample for cars, coach parking nearby.

 Dedicated facilities, tours, carer tickets & wheelchair hire available. Accessibility guide available.

 Assistant dogs only.

 Audio tours available.

Private guided tours are available (subject to availability).

Rates on request 0844 482 7777.

The Privy Kitchen Café: Traditional food. Fountain Court Café: Afternoon teas, restaurant setting.

 Licensed. The Tiltyard: self-service restaurant, children's meals.

Shop offer everything from souvenirs & gifts, to fine jewellery.

Weddings, dinners, receptions.

Special events all year round, visit website for details.

 One of the most stunning wedding venues in Surrey. Download the wedding brochure for more details.

Loseley Park

www.loseleypark.co.uk

Loseley Park, built in 1562 by Sir William More, is a fine example of Elizabethan architecture. The rooms contain fascinating works of art, furniture from the 17th Century and many unique features. The Walled Garden is compared favourably to gardens of national renown.

KEY FACTS

 No photographs that are taken at Loseley may be sold commercially except with written permission.

 Toilet facilities available.

 Baby changing facilities available.

 For weddings, private and corporate functions.

 Plentiful parking and free of charge to visitors. 150 cars, 6 coaches.

 Ground floor of house accessible to non-motorized wheelchairs only. Full Access Statement available.

 Obligatory: 45 mins. Pre-booked Garden tours available.

 Please contact for further details on educational visits.

 Wisteria Tea Room serves lunches and teas. Fully licensed.

 Plant sales available.

 The outstanding range of facilities cater for an array or functions.

 Please see the 'What's On' section of the website for all upcoming events.

 The perfect venue for Civil Ceremonies and wedding receptions. Please see website for full details.

 For filming location enquires please contact.

CONTACT
Owner: Alexander More-Molyneux
Contact: Joanna Phillips
Tel: 01483 304440 / 01483 405112
Wisteria Tea Room bookings: 01483 457103
Email: enquiries@loseleypark.co.uk

LOCATION
Guildford, Surrey GU3 1HS **Map Ref:** 3:G3 - 30m SW of London, leave A3 S of Guildford on to B3000. Signposted.

OPENING TIMES
House: May-Jul Mon-Thu 12pm-4pm. Sun & BHs: 1pm-5pm
Gardens & Grounds: May-Jul: Sun-Thu: 11am-5pm & BHs

ADMISSION
House & Gardens
Adult: £10-£15, Child (5-16yrs): £0-£5, Under 5yrs: Free, Concs: £5-£10, Family (2+3): £25-£30.
Gardens & Grounds only
Adult: £5-£10, Child (5-16yrs): £0-£5, Concs: £5-£10.
Groups: 10+ Please contact for group bookings.
Prices are a guide only; please refer to the website.

The Magic Garden, Hampton Court Palace

Painshill Park Trust Ltd.

www.painshill.co.uk

Painshill is a beautiful 18th Century landscape garden. The 158 acre wonderland has something for everyone. Discover magical follies, including the restored the Crystal Grotto (limited opening times), historic plantings, the John Bartram Heritage Collection of North American trees and shrubs (Plant Heritage) and spectacular vistas. Visitor entrance is off Between Streets, Cobham.

CONTACT
Owner: Painshill **Contact:** Anuj Misra
Tel: 01932 868113 **Fax:** 01932 868001
Email: anujmisra@painshill.co.uk

LOCATION
Portsmouth Road, Cobham, Surrey KT11 1JE
Map Ref: 19:B9 - M25/J10/A3 to London. West of Cobham on A245. Signposted. Closest Sat Nav Ref: KT11 1AA.

OPENING TIMES
All Year (Closed 25-26 Dec).
Mar-Oct 10am-6pm.
Nov-Feb 10am-4pm.

ADMISSION
Adult: £8, Concs: £7, Child (5-16 yrs): £4.50,
Family (2 Adults & 4 Children): £27.
U5's & Disabled Carer: Free.
Group rates available.

KEY FACTS

Landscape garden with various follies, lake, vineyard, Walled Garden, wildlife, fruits & vegetables.

Ladies, Men's, disabled & baby changing facilities available.

Open everyday except Christmas Day & Boxing Day.

Free parking facilities available.

WC's. Accessible route. Free pre-booked wheelchair loan. Pre-booked guided buggy tours.

Dogs are welcome on a short lead.

 Painshill offers a variety of guided tours to meet your interests and requirements.

Running various camps & activities for children like den building, bush craft, pond dipping.

Tearoom serves both hot & cold food using fresh vegetables from the Walled Garden.

Purchase gifts, games, Painshill wine & honey, special gift memberships & hampers at the shop.

Offering a great venue for conferences, meetings, corporate parties and also catering services.

Please visit the 'What's on' section of the website for all upcoming events throughout the year.

Great Fosters
www.greatfosters.co.uk

Set in 50 acres of stunning gardens and parkland Great Fosters is a fine example of Elizabethan architecture and is now a luxury hotel with two restaurants, The Estate Grill and The Tudor Room. Open to non-residents for lunch, dinner and afternoon tea, its past is evident in the mullioned windows, chimneys and brick finials, whilst the gardens include a Saxon moat, Japanese bridge, amphitheatre, lake and knot garden designed by WH Romaine-Walker and Gilbert Jenkins.

CONTACT
Owner: The Sutcliffe family
Contact: Amanda Dougans
Tel: 01784 433822
Email: reception@greatfosters.co.uk

LOCATION
Stroude Road, Egham, Surrey TW20 9UR
Map Ref: 3:G2
M25 J/13, follow signs to Egham and then brown historic signs for Great Fosters.

OPENING TIMES
All year.

ADMISSION
No Charge.

KEY FACTS

 200 parking spaces for cars at the hotel.

 WC's.

 43 suites & bedrooms are individually decorated in 3 separate places to stay.

 Meeting the demand for professional, modern conference facilities within the most inviting of settings.

 Hosts wedding receptions & the hotel is licensed to hold civil ceremonies.

Loseley Park

Arundel Castle & Gardens

www.arundelcastle.org

Ancient Castle, Stately Home, Gardens & The Collector Earl's Garden.

A thousand years of history is waiting to be discovered at Arundel Castle in West Sussex. Dating from the 11th Century, the Castle is both ancient fortification and stately home of the Dukes of Norfolk and Earls of Arundel.

Set high on a hill, this magnificent Castle commands stunning views across the River Arun and out to sea. Climb the Keep, explore the battlements, wander in the grounds and recently restored Victorian gardens and relax in the garden of the 14th Century Fitzalan Chapel.

In the 17th Century during the English Civil War the Castle suffered extensive damage. The process of structural restoration began in earnest in the 18th Century and continued up until 1900. The Castle was one of the first private residences to have electricity and central heating and had its own fire engine.

Inside the Castle over 20 sumptuously furnished rooms may be visited including the breathtaking Barons' Hall with 16th Century furniture; the Armoury with its fine collection of armour and weaponry, and the magnificent Gothic library entirely fitted out in carved Honduras mahogany. There are works of art by Van Dyck, Gainsborough, Canaletto and Mytens;

tapestries; clocks; and personal possessions of Mary Queen of Scots including the gold rosary that she carried to her execution.

There are special event days throughout the season, including, Shakespeare in The Collector Earl's Garden, Arundel International Jousting & Medieval Tournament, and medieval re-enactments.

Do not miss the magnificent Collector Earl's Garden based on early 17th Century classical designs.

OWNER
Arundel Castle Trustees Ltd

CONTACT
Stephen Manion, Castle Manager
Tel: 01903 882173
Email: visits@arundelcastle.org

LOCATION
Arundel Castle, Arundel, West Sussex BN18 9AB

Map Ref: 3:G6

Central Arundel, N of A27. Brighton 40 mins, Worthing 15 mins, Chichester 15 mins. From London A3 or A24, 1½ hrs. M25 motorway, 30m.

Bus: Bus stop 100 yds. **Rail:** Station 1½m.

Air: Gatwick 25m.

OPENING TIMES
Fri 30 Mar-Sun 28 Oct. Tues to Suns, Good Fri & Easter Mon. May BH Mons, and Mons in Aug.

Fitzalan Chapel, Gardens & Grounds, Gift Shop:
10am-5pm.

Castle Keep, Restaurant & Coffee Shop:
10am-4.30pm.

Main Castle Rooms:
12 noon-5pm.
Last entry 4pm.

ADMISSION
Please contact us or see website for up-to-date admissions rates. Group rates available.

KEY FACTS

 No photography or video recording inside the Castle.

 By prior arrangement. Tour time 1½-2 hrs. Tours available in various languages - please enquire.

 Lavatories / WC are located adjacent to The Collector Earl's Garden and on the ground floor of the Castle.

 Norman Motte & Keep, Armoury & Victorian bedrooms. Special rates for school children (5-16yrs) & teachers.

 Ample car & coach parking in town car park. Free admission & refreshment voucher for coach driver.

 Licensed coffee shop offer refreshments including hot & cold drinks, light lunches, cakes and pastries.

 WC's, ramps and lifts. Please see website.

 Licensed counter service restaurant.

 On special event days admission prices may vary.

 Discover the distinctive & exclusive gift range in the Castle Shop and old Castle kitchens.

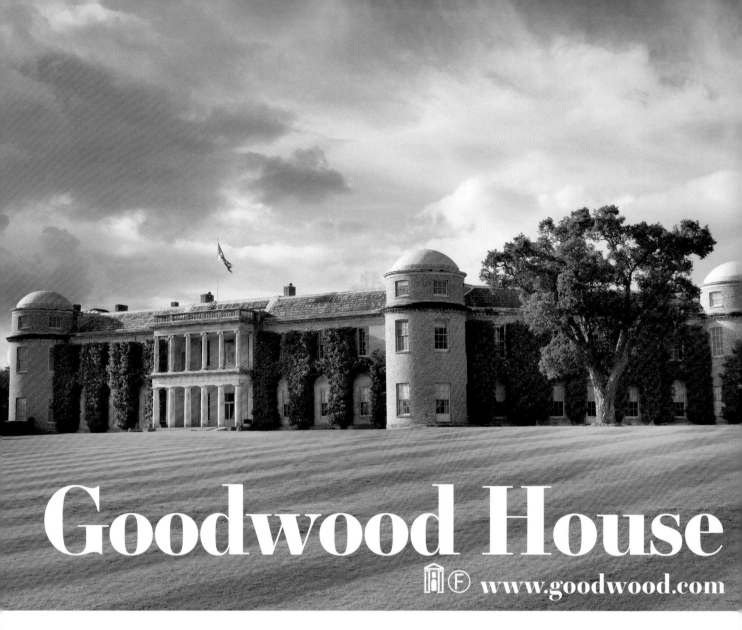

Goodwood House

www.goodwood.com

Goodwood House, ancestral home of the Dukes of Richmond and Gordon with a magnificent art collection

Goodwood is one of England's finest sporting estates. At its heart lies Goodwood House, the ancestral home of the Dukes of Richmond and Gordon, direct descendants of King Charles II. Today, it is lived in by the 11th Duke and Duchess of Richmond with their children. Their home is open to the public on at least 60 days a year.

The art collection includes a magnificent group of British paintings from the 17th and 18th Centuries, such as the celebrated views of London by Canaletto and superb sporting scenes at Goodwood by George Stubbs. The rooms are filled with fine English and French furniture, Gobelins tapestries and Sèvres porcelain. Special works of art are regularly rotated and displayed and the books can be viewed by written application to the Curator (there is a special charge for these viewings).

Goodwood is renowned for its entertaining, enjoying a reputation for excellence. Goodwood's own organic farm provides food for the table in the various restaurants on the estate. With internationally renowned horseracing and motor sport events, the finest downland golf course in the UK, its own aerodrome and hotel, Goodwood offers an extraordinarily rich sporting experience.

OWNER
The Goodwood Estate Co. Ltd
(The Duke and Duchess of Richmond & Gordon)

CONTACT
Tour & Tea bookings:
01243 755055 / customer.sales@goodwood.com
Events (including weddings/corporate events):
01243 520195 / events@goodwood.com
Curatorial enquiries: 01243 755012
curators.assistant@goodwood.com
curator@goodwood.com

LOCATION
Goodwood House, Goodwood, Chichester, West Sussex PO18 0PX **Map Ref:** 3:F6
3½m NE of Chichester. A3 from London then A286 or A285. M27/A27 from Portsmouth or Brighton.
Rail: Chichester 3½m Arundel 9m. Air: Heathrow 1½ hrs Gatwick ¾hr.

OPENING TIMES
House: 4 Mar-29 Oct
Sun & Mons, 1-5pm (last admission 4pm).
5-30 Aug, Sun-Thurs, 1-5pm (last admission 4pm).
Please note these dates are provisional. Please always call the Customer Sales team to check closed dates on 01243 755055 and book tickets in advance.
Closed: For some special events & around Members Meeting, the Festival of Speed & Revival Meeting.

ADMISSION
Please book tickets via our Customer Sales team on 01243 755055.
Adult: £9.50, Child: £5, Child (under 12): Free.
Goodwood House Tour and Tea:
£25 (must be booked 48 hrs in advance).
Groups (must be over 20 guests):
£20 per person. Please call the Curators assistant to book groups far in advance. Group bookings are only available on Sun & Mon mornings.

SPECIAL EVENTS
76th Members' Meeting, Festival of Speed, Qatar Goodwood Festival and Goodwood Revival Meeting.

KEY FACTS

 No photography. Informed guides.

 Groups and schools tours of the state apartments offers a unique and historic insight.

 Toilet facilities and one disabled toilet in the house.

 Aero Club Café & Afternoon Tea at Goodwood House.

 Baby changing facilities available.

 Farmer, Butcher, Chef & The Goodwood Bar and Grill, both at the hotel.

 Coaches drop guests off at the front of the House then park in the main Ballroom car park (for cars also).

 Purchase postcards and guide books from the front desk (subject to availability).

 The House and tearoom are fully accessible for wheelchair users. Ramp access at Front Entrance.

 Event bookings or enquiries 01243 520195/events@goodwood.com - please call or email.

 Goodwood Hotel -To book call the Reservations Team on 01243 775537.

 76th Members' Meeting, Festival of Speed, Qatar Goodwood Festival and Goodwood Revival Meeting.

 A guided tour will be of the State Apartments and Old House, by one of our knowledgeable guides.

 Civil wedding licence. Call the wedding line or email EstateSalesTeam@goodwood.com

Lancing
College Chapel

www.lancingcollege.co.uk

THE GLORIOUS GOTHIC ARCHITECTURE OF LANCING COLLEGE CHAPEL

INTERIOR OF LANCING COLLEGE CHAPEL LOOKING EAST

'I know of no more spectacular post-Reformation ecclesiastical building in the kingdom.' Evelyn Waugh, former pupil.

Lancing College Chapel is the place of worship for the community of Lancing College, the central minster of the Woodard Schools and a well-loved Sussex landmark. The Chapel stands prominently on the South Downs. The exterior, with its pinnacles and flying buttresses, is a testament to Victorian structural bravado. Designed by Herbert Carpenter in the 13th Century French gothic style, it is the fourth tallest ecclesiastical building in England.

The foundations were laid in 1868 and the atmospheric crypt came into use in 1875. The upper chapel was dedicated in 1911 but the west wall and rose window were added in the 1970s. There is now a plan to complete the building with a west porch. A beautiful war memorial cloister was built in the 1920s.

The interior is breathtaking. Soaring columns branch out into fan vaulting, perfectly proportioned arches and vast clerestory windows. There are stained glass windows by Comper and Dykes Bower, and one commemorating former pupil Fr Trevor Huddleston, made by Mel Howse in 2007. Behind the high altar are superb tapestries woven on the William Morris looms in the 1920s. The oak stall canopies are by Gilbert Scott.

THE SPLENDID ROSE WINDOW AND WALKER ORGAN

There are two organs (Walker 1914 and Frobenius 1986) with intricately carved oak cases.

The Chapel has a fascinating history which is still unfolding and it is a treasure house of ecclesiastical art. Lancing College Chapel welcomes visitors both as an important heritage landmark and as a place of quiet reflection and prayer.

OWNER
Lancing College Chapel Trust

CONTACT
The Verger
Tel: 01273 465949
Email: verger@lancing.org.uk

Reception, Lancing College
Enquiries Tel: 01273 452213.

LOCATION
Lancing, West Sussex BN15 0RW
Map Ref: 3:H6

Car: North of the A27 between Shoreham-by-Sea & Lancing at the Coombes Rd/Shoreham Airport traffic lights. Filter right if coming from the East. Turn off Coombes Rd at sign for Lancing College and proceed to the top of Lancing College drive, then follow signs to the Main Car Park.
Rail: Train to Shoreham-by-Sea or Lancing on the London-Littlehampton & Portsmouth line & take a taxi.
Bus: The nearest bus routes are Brighton & Hove Buses 2A, Compass Buses, 106 & Coastliner 700.

OPENING TIMES
10am-4pm Mon-Sat.
12 noon-4pm on Sun.
Every day of the year except for Easter Sunday, Christmas Day, Boxing Day and New Year's Day.

ADMISSION
Free. Donations are requested for the Friends of Lancing Chapel. Visitors are asked to sign in for security purposes as they enter the Chapel. The other College buildings are not open to the public.

SPECIAL EVENTS
Visitors can reserve seats for Public Carol Services by applying in writing to Lancing College Chapel, Lancing, West Sussex, BN15 0RW with a stamped, self-addressed envelope. Visitors wishing to attend other services should contact the Verger.

KEY FACTS

 Guide books, information leaflets and a DVD.

 Guide dogs only in chapel. Dogs on leads welcome in college grounds.

 Toilet facilities available.

 Guided tours & brief talks can be booked with the Verger. Groups should be booked in advance.

 Open all year except Easter Sunday, Christmas Day, Boxing Day and New Year's Day.

 School & other educational groups are welcome & may request guided tours & other information.

 Please follow signs to the main car park.

 Stall with guide books and postcards at entrance to the chapel.

 The upper chapel (but not the crypt) is easily accessible for those with mobility issues.

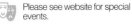 Please see website for special events.

Parham House & Gardens

www.parhaminsussex.co.uk

©PARHAM PARK LIMITED, PHOTOGRAPHY E ZESCHIN

One of the top twenty in Simon Jenkins's book 'England's Thousand Best Houses'. Idyllically set in the heart of an ancient deer park, below the South Downs, the Elizabethan House contains an important collection of needlework, paintings and furniture. The magnificent Long Gallery is the third longest in England. The spectacular gardens include a four-acre Walled Garden with stunning herbaceous borders, plus Pleasure Grounds. Parham has always been a well-loved family home, and only three families have lived here since its foundation stone was laid in 1577. Its tranquillity and timeless beauty have changed little over the years. It is now owned by a charitable trust, and lived in by Lady Emma Barnard, her husband James and their family.

©PARHAM PARK LIMITED, PHOTOGRAPHY E ZESCHIN

CONTACT
Owner: Parham Park Ltd
Contact: Estate Office **Tel:** 01903 742021
Email: enquiries@parhaminsussex.co.uk
Facebook: /ParhamHouseAndGardens
Twitter: @parhaminsussex
Instagram: /parham_house_gardens

LOCATION
Parham Park, Pulborough, West Sussex RH20 4HS
Map Ref: 3:G5 - Midway between Pulborough & Storrington on A283. SatNav: RH20 4HR.

OPENING TIMES
1 Apr-28 Oct 2018 on Weds, Thurs, Fri, Sun and BHs. Only open on Sun in Oct. Gardens are open from 12 noon and the House from 2pm. Please visit website for further information and events.

ADMISSION (all prices are inclusive of Gift Aid)
House & Gardens - Adult: £12.10, Concs: £11, Child: £6.60 (Under 5s: Free), Family: £35.20.
Gardens only - Adult: £9.90, Concs: £8.80, Child: £5.50 (Under 5s: Free), Family: £28.60.
Season Ticket - SGL: £24, DBL: £42, Family: £66.
This information was correct when going to print but is subject to change.

KEY FACTS

 Toilet facilities available.

 Ample free parking. Designated parking for coaches and disabled visitors is within 50 metres.

 Disabled access in the gardens & ground floor of the house. Full accessibility statement on website.

 In gardens only, on leads.

 Lettings - If you are interested in discussing rental opportunities with Parham Park, please contact.

 House & Garden tours are available by arrangement, led by Parham guides & the gardening team.

 Please enquire.

 Open on house & garden open days only.

 Licensed.

 Gifts including Parham's own jams and preserves.

 Plants grown by our own garden team.

 Exclusive packages by arrangement on Mon and Tues during the open season.

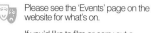

 Please see the 'Events' page on the website for what's on.

If you'd like to film or carry out a photoshoot at Parham please contact.

Petworth

www.nationaltrust.org.uk/petworth

©NATIONAL TRUST IMAGES/JOHN MILLER

Home to an extraordinary collection of art, this magnificent 17th Century mansion stands as a monument to the evolving taste of one family over 900 years. Rooted in the powerful northern Percy dynasty, their journeys through the Tudor Reformation, the Gunpowder Plot, the Napoleonic Wars and up to the present day are reflected in an astonishing array of treasures that survive at Petworth today. The palatial state rooms offer an infinity of paintings and sculptures, including major works by van Dyck, Turner,

Flaxman and Blake. Separate Servants' Quarters offer a glimpse of life 'below stairs', featuring domestic rooms and Historic Kitchen with a 1000 piece copper batterie de cuisine while the 700 acre Capability Brown landscaped deer park offers panoramic views. 2018 is the year we celebrate the remarkable women of Petworth whose taste and influence quietly helped to shape the development of Petworth's famous collection and its wider cultural reputation.

©NATIONAL TRUST IMAGES/ANDREAS VON EINSIEDEL

CONTACT
Owner: National Trust
Contact: The Administration Office
Tel: 01798 342207
Email: petworth@nationaltrust.org.uk

LOCATION
Petworth, Church Street, West Sussex GU28 0AE
Map Ref: 3:G5 - Both mansion & park car parks located on A283; Follow signs from centre of Petworth (A272/283). Sat-Nav: GU28 9LR

OPENING TIMES
Mansion:
1 Jan-28 Feb, 11am-4pm
1 Mar-4 Nov, 11am-5pm
5 Nov-31 Dec, 11am-4pm
Pleasure Grounds, Café & Gift Shop:
1 Jan-28 Feb, 10am-4pm
1 Mar-4 Nov, 10am-5pm
5 Nov-31 Dec, 10am-4pm

ADMISSION
Adult: £15, Child (5-17yrs): £7.50, Family: £37.50, Groups: £12 (pre-booked).

KEY FACTS

 Photography without flash is permitted in the mansion and servants' quarters.

 Adapted mobility toilets in car park and servants' quarters.

 Baby changing facilities available and pushchairs admitted.

 Closes 24 and 25 Dec.

 Parking 700 meters from mansion. Parking charge for non- members (£4), NT Members parking free.

 Mobility vehicle runs between car park and mansion. Wheelchairs to borrow.

 Dogs allowed in Petworth deer park only, with the exception of guide dogs (full access).

 Guided tours available, please check website for details.

 Educational visits by arrangement.

 Café and coffee shop, serving seasonal food and beverages.

 Two shops selling range of gifts.

 Plant sales.

 For special events, please see website.

 Mr Turner.

117

St Mary's House & Gardens

www.stmarysbramber.co.uk

©ANTHONY CAPO-BIANCO

Enchanting medieval house and family home, winner of Hudsons Heritage 'Best Restoration' award in 2011. Features in Simon Jenkins' book 'England's Thousand Best Houses'. Fine panelled interiors, including unique Elizabethan 'Painted Room'. Magnificent Victorian Music Room. Interesting family memorabilia and other fascinating collections.

Charming cottage-style tea room.

Five acres of grounds. Formal gardens with amusing topiary, and exceptional example of prehistoric tree Ginkgo biloba. 'Secret' Garden, with Victorian fruit-wall and rare pineapple pits, Rural Museum, Jubilee Rose Garden, Terracotta Garden, King's Garden, unusual circular Poetry Garden, woodland walk and Landscape Water Garden with island and waterfall.

A haven of tranquillity and beauty.

CONTACT
Owner: Mr Peter Thorogood MBE & Mr Roger Linton MBE
Tel: 01903 816205
Email: info@stmarysbramber.co.uk

LOCATION
Bramber, West Sussex BN44 3WE

Map Ref: 3:H6
Bramber village off A283. From London 56m via M23/A23 or A24. Buses from Brighton, Shoreham and Worthing.

OPENING TIMES
May-end Sep: Suns, Thus & BH Mons, 2-6pm.
Extra Weds in Aug, 2-6pm. Last entry 5pm.
Groups at other days and times by arrangement.

ADMISSION
House & Gardens
Adult: £10, Conc: £9, Child: £5, Groups 20+: £10.
Garden only
Adult: £6, Child: £3, Groups 20+: £6.

KEY FACTS

 No photography in house. Printed room guides for visitors on open days.

 In main house and the tea rooms. Disabled toilets available.

 Car park for visitors. 20 cars or 2 coaches.

 Partial. Welcoming visitors with disabilities; please see access statement on the website.

 Obligatory for groups (max 55). Visit time 2½-3 hrs.

 Contact to organise a school visit for an educational experience.

 A wide selection of refreshments are available in the cottage-style Orchard Tea Rooms.

 Well-stocked gift shop selling souvenirs, collectables, books and music.

 Plant sales available in restored 19th Century glasshouse.

 Surrounded by formal and topiary gardens with fountains, makes this perfect for private functions.

 For events and concerts, please see website and make sure to sign up to the mailing list for updates.

Elegant Victorian Music Room is licensed for up to 90 ppl. Exclusive use of reception rooms & gardens.

South East

Clinton Lodge Garden

www.clintonlodgegardens.co.uk

A formal but romantic garden, around a Caroline and Georgian house, reflecting the gardening fashions throughout its history, particularly since the time of Sir Henry Clinton, one of Wellington's generals at Waterloo. Tree lined lawn and parkland, double blue and white herbaceous borders between yew and box hedges, a cloister walk swathed in white roses, clematis and geraniums, a 17th Century Herb Garden, enclosed by pleached limes, where hedges of box envelop herbs, seats are of turf, paths of camomile. A Pear Tree Walk bursts with alliums or lilies, a Potager of flowers for cutting, tall old roses surround a magnificent water feature by William Pye, a newly built stone classical Pavilion and much more. Private groups by appointment - Lunches can be arranged for groups of 10-30.

CONTACT
Owner/ Contact: Lady Collum
Tel: 01825 722952
Fax: 01825 723967
Email: garden@clintonlodge.com

LOCATION
Fletching, Uckfield, East Sussex TN22 3ST **Map Ref:** 4:I5
In centre of village behind tall yew and holly hedge.

ADMISSION
Private Visits: £12-£14. Homemade teas available.
Lunch by arrangement for groups of 10-30. No Sundays.

NGS
Entrance: £6, Child: Free.
Sun 29 Apr, Mon 11 & 25 Jun & Mon 30 Jul 2-5.30pm.

KEY FACTS

 For more information please see website.

 WC not suitable for disabled access.

 Limited. Off road parking on NGS open days.

 Partial. Please contact for further details.

 By arrangement.

 Vinery: Homemade cakes and tea.

 Vinery: Postcards and preserves.

 NGS days only.

Firle Place

www.firle.com

The family's 500 year old history at Firle Place commenced when Sir John Gage (1479-1556) completed his manor house c.1543, in the lee of the chalk folds of the Sussex South Downs. The house was remodelled in the 18th Century, providing its present Georgian façade, including the rare Serlian window on the entrance front. The celebrated works of art now housed at Firle, comprising Old Master paintings, furniture and Sèvres porcelain, reflect the taste of successive generations of collectors and familial relationships, significant additions arriving in the mid-1950s from the Cowper collection at Panshanger House, Hertfordshire and the Grenfell collection from Taplow Court, Berkshire.

CONTACT
Owner: The Rt Hon Viscount Gage
Tel: 01273 858567
Email: enquiries@firle.com

LOCATION
Firle, Nr Lewes, East Sussex BN8 6LP **Map Ref:** 4:J6
4m SE of Lewes on A27 Brighton/Eastbourne Road.

OPENING TIMES
Jun-Sep. Please see website for 2018 opening days & times.
Tea Room opens, without charge on House opening days only.

ADMISSION
Please see the website or contact for 2018 admission prices.
Private group tours can be arranged by prior appointment.
Call 01273 858307 or see website for details.

KEY FACTS

 No photography in house.

 Wheelchair access will be to the ground floor and Tea Room only, and can be provided if required.

 In grounds on leads.

 The Firle Estate is home to a wide range of accommodation for parties of any size.

 Exclusive out-of-hours guided tours: 25+ people £8.50pp. -25 people £9pp (minimum £215).

 Licensed Tearoom, serving tea, coffee, light lunches & cakes. Open 12.30pm-4.30 pm (on open days).

 Shop.

 Available for private hire.

 Please see website for special events.

 For details on weddings at Firle, please contact Bryony at weddings@firle.com or 07788 446621.

Hammerwood Park

www.hammerwoodpark.co.uk

The best kept secret in Sussex, with house and park preserved "untouched by a corporate plan". Built by White House architect Latrobe in Greek Revival style in 1792 as a temple to Bacchus, left derelict by Led Zeppelin, painstakingly restored by the Pinnegar family over the last 30 years and brought to life with guided tours, concerts (some including ex-Finchcocks' instruments) and filming.

KEY FACTS

 Helipad (see Pooley's - prior permission required).

 Toilet facilities available.

 Accepts Euros.

 Small groups by appointment all year round.

 Parking spaces are available.

 Bed & Breakfast.

 In grounds only.

 Obligatory.

 Educational visits by arrangement.

 Tea is served in the Elgin Room.

 Conferences.

 Please see the 'Concerts' section of the website to see brochure.

CONTACT
Owner: David and Anne-Noelle Pinnegar
Tel: 01342 850594 **Email:** antespam@gmail.com

LOCATION
East Grinstead, Sussex RH19 3QE
Map Ref: 4:J4 - 3.5 m E of East Grinstead on A264 to Tunbridge Wells, 1m W of Holtye.

OPENING TIMES
1 Jun-end Sep: Wed, Sat & BH Mon, 2-5pm. Guided tour starts 2.05pm. Private groups: Easter-Jun. Coaches strictly by appointment. Small groups any time throughout the year by appointment.

ADMISSION
House & Park
Adult: £8.50, Child: £2.
Private viewing by arrangement.

Stansted Park

www.stanstedpark.co.uk

Stansted House and its Chapel stand in 1800 acres of parkland and ancient forest within the South Downs National Park. The state rooms are furnished as though the 10th Earl was still at home giving the visitor a real sense of a bygone era. The extensive servants' quarters below stairs are filled with historic artefacts that are brought to life by the very knowledgeable and friendly stewards who will guide you through the vibrant history of Stansted Park.

KEY FACTS

 Toilet and baby changing facilities are available.

 The grounds are open all year.

 The Garden Centre car park is the main car park with designated disabled next to the Tea Room.

 Suitable. WC's. Please download the access statement on the website for further details.

 By arrangement. Guided tours max group size 50 and free-flow group visits.

 By arrangement. A wonderful educational resource for school visits.

 The Pavilion Tearoom, serving breakfast, light lunches, afternoon tea, cakes and beverages.

 Visit the Farm Shop where you can purchase locally sourced food and drink.

 Visit the garden centre focused on plants and gardening, offering great value and top quality plants.

 Private and corporate hire with the 'wow' factor.

Please see the 'What's on' section of the website for full events and activities.

Offering a beautiful venue for your ceremony.

CONTACT
Owner: Stansted Park Foundation **Contact:** Estate Office
Tel: 023 9241 2265 **Email:** enquiry@stanstedpark.co.uk

LOCATION
Rowlands Castle, Hampshire PO9 6DX
Map Ref: 3:F5 - Follow brown heritage signs from A3(M) J2 Emsworth or A27 Havant.

OPENING TIMES
House & Chapel: Easter Sun-end Sep; Sun, Mon, Tue & Wed 1pm-5pm (last adm. 4pm).
Tea Room, Farm Shop & Garden Centre: Open every day.
Maze: Weekends and school holidays 11am-4pm (Feb-Oct).
Light Railway: Weekends & Weds. Please call 023 9241 3324.

ADMISSION
Adult: £10, Child (5-15yrs): £5, Concs: £8, Family (2+3): £25, Groups/educational visits: By arrangement.

Arundel Cathedral

www.arundelcathedral.org

French Gothic Cathedral, church of the RC Diocese of Arundel and Brighton built by Henry, 15th Duke of Norfolk and opened 1873.

Mass Times
Tue, Wed, Fri, Sat: 10am
Mon & Thu: 8.30am at Convent of Poor Clares
Sat: 6.15pm Vigil Mass at Convent of Poor Clares
Sun: 9.30am & 11.15am

CONTACT
Owner: Diocese of Arundel & Brighton
Contact:
Rev. Canon T. Madeley
Tel: 01903 882297
Email: aruncath1@aol.com

LOCATION
London Road, Arundel, West Sussex BN18 9AY
Map Ref: 3:G6 - Above junction of A27 and A284.

OPEN
Summer: 9am-6pm.
Winter: 9am-dusk.

ADMISSION
Free

KEY FACTS

 Open all year round.

 Accessible.

 By arrangement.

 Shop open in summer, Mon-Fri, 10am-4pm & after services, on special occasions & on request.

 For all upcoming Cathedral events please see the website.

Borde Hill Garden

www.bordehill.co.uk

Botanical heritage and stunning landscapes make Borde Hill the perfect day out for horticulture enthusiasts, country lovers, and families. The Elizabethan House nestles in the centre of the formal garden which is set as outdoor 'rooms', including the Azalea, Rhododendron, Rose and Italian gardens.

CONTACT
Contact: Manager
Tel: 01444 450326
Email: info@bordehill.co.uk

LOCATION
Borde Hill Lane, Haywards Heath, West Sussex RH16 1XP
Map Ref: 4:15 - 1½ miles North of Haywards Heath, 20 mins North of Brighton.

OPEN
20 Mar-1 Oct & 20-31 Oct, 10am-5pm, Jul-Aug daily, 10am-6pm
ADMISSION
Adult: £9.50, Concs: £9, Child: £6.35.

KEY FACTS

 Free parking.

 WC's. Maps.

 Dog friendly. Dogs welcome on leads.

 Garden, park and woodland. House tours for pre booked groups.

 Homemade food at the café.

 Award-winning restaurant.

 Gift shop, tea garden & gallery.

 Themed events.

Parham ©Elizabeth Zeschin

Cowdray Heritage Trust

www.cowdray.co.uk

Cowdray is one of the most important survivals of a Tudor nobleman's house. Set within the stunning landscape of Cowdray Park, the house was partially destroyed by fire in 1793. Explore the Tudor Kitchen, Buck Hall, Chapel, Gatehouse, Vaulted Storeroom and Cellars, Visitor Centre and Shop.

CONTACT
The Manager
Tel: 01730 812423
Visitor Centre:
01730 810781
(during opening hours only)
Email:
heritage@cowdray.co.uk

LOCATION
River Ground Stables, Midhurst, West Sussex GU29 9AL
Map Ref: 3:F5 - On the outskirts of Midhurst on A272.

OPEN / ADMISSION
Please check our website for opening times and admissions. Groups all year round by arrangement.

KEY FACTS

 In Midhurst by bus stand, a short walk along causeway.

 Full level access, WC's, limited disabled parking.

 Dogs on leads welcome.

 Free audio guides. Children's tour available.

 Nearby Cowdray Farm Shop & Café opens daily & serves breakfast, sandwiches, snacks & meals.

 Gift shop on site.

 Please see the 'Events' section of the website to see full events brochure.

ASHDOWN HOUSE
Lambourn, Newbury, Berkshire RG17 8RE
Tel: 01494 755569 **Email:** ashdown@nationaltrust.org.uk

BASILDON PARK
Lower Basildon, Reading, Berkshire RG8 9NR
Tel: 0118 984 3040 **Email:** basildonpark@nationaltrust.org.uk

ENGLEFIELD HOUSE GARDENS
The Estate Office, Englefield Road, Theale Berkshire RG7 5DU
Tel: 0118 930 2221

THE SAVILL GARDEN
Wick Lane, Englefield Green, Surrey TW20 0UU
Tel: 01784 485400 **Email:** enquiries@windsorgreatpark.co.uk

SHAW HOUSE
Church Road, Shaw, Newbury, Berkshire RG14 2DR
Tel: 01635 279279 **Email:** shawhouse@westberks.gov.uk

WASING PARK
Aldermaston, Reading, RG7 4NB
Tel: 0118 971 4140 **Email:** info@wasing.co.uk

WINDSOR CASTLE
Windsor, Berkshire SL4 1NJ
Tel: 020 7766 7304 **Email:** bookinginfo@royalcollection.org.uk

ASCOTT
Wing, Leighton Buzzard, Buckinghamshire LU7 0PR
Tel: 01296 688242 **Email:** info@ascottestate.co.uk

BLETCHLEY PARK
The Mansion, Bletchley Park, Milton Keynes MK3 6EB
Tel: 01908 640404 **Email:** info@bletchleypark.org.uk

CHENIES MANOR HOUSE
Chenies, Buckinghamshire WD3 6ER
Tel: 01494 762888 **Email:** macleodmatthews@btinternet.com

CLAYDON HOUSE & GARDENS
Claydon House, Middle Claydon, Buckinghamshire MK18 2EY
Tel: 01296 730349 **Email:** claydon@nationaltrust.org.uk

CLIVEDEN
Taplow, Maidenhead SL6 0JA
Tel: 01628 605069 **Email:** cliveden@nationaltrust.org.uk

Nether Winchendon House

Nether Winchendon, Nr Thame, Buckinghamshire HP18 0DY
Medieval Manor Strawberry Hill Gothick. Home last Royal Governor
Massachussetts. Continuous family occupation since 1559. **Map Ref:** 7:C11
Tel: 01844 290101 **Email:** contactus@netherwinchendonhouse.com
Website: www.nwhouse.co.uk **Open:** 2018 Guided Tours (excluding Fri &
Sats): 3 Apr-30 Apr, 7 May-9 May, 28 May-31 May & 27 Aug. 2.45pm, 3.45pm
& 4.45pm. **Admission:** £10 (Conc. mid-week only, for HHA & Arts Fund)

STOWE HOUSE
Stowe House, Stowe, Buckingham MK18 5EH
Tel: 01280 818002 **Email:** Houseinfo@stowe.co.uk

STOWE LANDSCAPE GARDENS
New Inn Farm, Buckingham MK18 5EQ
Tel: 01280 817156 **Email:** stowe@nationaltrust.org.uk

WADDESDON MANOR
Waddesdon, Nr Aylesbury, Buckinghamshire HP18 0JH
Tel: 01296 820414 **Email:** enquiries@waddesdon.org.uk

WEST WYCOMBE PARK
West Wycombe, High Wycombe, Buckinghamshire HP14 3AJ
Tel: 01494 513569 **Email:** westwycombe@nationaltrust.org.uk

BREAMORE HOUSE & MUSEUM
Breamore, Fordingbridge, Hampshire SP6 2DF
Tel: 01725 512858 **Email:** breamore@btinternet.com

Broadlands

Romsey, Hampshire SO51 9ZD
Broadlands is the historic home of the Mountbatten family.
Map Ref: 3:C5
Tel: 01794 505080
Website: www.broadlandsestates.co.uk
Open: Jun-Sep. Please see our website for details.

EXBURY GARDENS & STEAM RAILWAY
Exbury, Southampton, Hampshire SO45 1AZ
Tel: 023 8089 1203 **Email:** info@exbury.co.uk

HARCOMBE HOUSE
Park Lane, Ropley, Alresford, Hampshire SO24 0BE
Tel: 07796 195550 **Email:** vjeswani@k-capital.net

HIGHCLERE CASTLE, GARDENS & EGYPTIAN EXHIBITION
Highclere Castle, Newbury, Hampshire RG20 9RN
Tel: 01635 253210 **Email:** theoffice@highclerecastle.co.uk

HINTON AMPNER
Bramdean, Alresford, Hampshire SO24 0LA
Tel: 01962 771305 **Email:** hintonampner@nationaltrust.org.uk

JANE AUSTEN'S HOUSE MUSEUM
Chawton, Alton, Hampshire GU34 1SD
Tel: 01420 83262 **Email:** enquiries@jahmsum.org.uk

KING JOHN'S HOUSE & HERITAGE CENTRE
Church Street, Romsey, Hampshire SO51 8BT
Tel: 01794 512200 **Email:** info@kingjohnshouse.org.uk

MOTTISFONT
Mottisfont, Nr Romsey, Hampshire SO51 0LP
Tel: 01794 340757 **Email:** mottisfont@nationaltrust.org.uk

PORTCHESTER CASTLE
Portsmouth, Hampshire PO16 9QW
Tel: 02392 378291 **Email:** customers@english-heritage.org.uk

SIR HAROLD HILLIER GARDENS
Jermyns Lane, Ampfield, Romsey, Hampshire SO51 0QA
Tel: 01794 369318 **Email:** info@hilliergardens.org.uk

TUDOR HOUSE & GARDEN
Bugle Street, Southampton SO14 2AD
Tel: 023 8083 4536 **Email:** museums@southampton.gov.uk

THE VYNE
Sherborne St John, Basingstoke RG24 9HL
Tel: 01256 883858 **Email:** thevyne@nationaltrust.org.uk

WINCHESTER CATHEDRAL
9 The Close, Winchester SO23 9LS
Tel: 01962 857200 **Email:** visits@winchester-cathedral.org.uk

WINCHESTER CITY MILL 🦋
Bridge Street, Winchester SO23 9BH
Tel: 01962 870057 **Email:** winchestercitymill@nationaltrust.org.uk

ST AUGUSTINE'S ABBEY ⊞
Longport, Canterbury, Kent CT1 1TF
Tel: 01227 767345 **Email:** customers@english-heritage.org.uk

BOUGHTON MONCHELSEA PLACE
Boughton Monchelsea, Nr Maidstone, Kent ME17 4BU
Tel: 01622 743120 **Email:** mk@boughtonplace.co.uk

CHILHAM CASTLE
Canterbury, Kent CT4 8DB
Tel: 01227 733100 **Email:** chilhamcastleinfo@gmail.com

COBHAM HALL 🏛ⓔ
Cobham, Kent DA12 3BL
Tel: 01474 823371 **Email:** enquiries@cobhamhall.com

COBHAM WOOD & MAUSOLEUM 🦋
Cobham DA12 3BS
Tel: 01732 810378 **Email:** cobham@nationaltrust.org.uk

DEAL CASTLE ⊞
Victoria Road, Deal, Kent CT14 7BA
Tel: 01304 372762 **Email:** customers@english-heritage.org.uk

DODDINGTON PLACE GARDENS
Doddington, Nr Sittingbourne, Kent ME9 0BB
Tel: 01795 886101

DOVER CASTLE ⊞
Castle Hill, Dover, Kent CT16 1HU
Tel: 01304 211067 **Email:** customers@english-heritage.org.uk

DOWN HOUSE ⊞
Luxted Road, Downe, Kent BR6 7JT
Tel: 01689 859119 **Email:** www.english-heritage.org.uk/darwin

EMMETTS GARDEN 🦋
Ide Hill, Sevenoaks, Kent TN14 6BA
Tel: 01689 859119 **Email:** visits@winchester-cathedral.org.uk

GODINTON HOUSE & GARDENS
Godinton Lane, Ashford Kent TN23 3BP
Tel: 01233 620773 **Email:** info@godinton-house-gardens.co.uk

GOODNESTONE PARK GARDENS 🏛ⓔ
Goodnestone Park, Nr Wingham, Canterbury, Kent CT3 1PL
Tel: 01304 840107 **Email:** enquiries@goodnestoneparkgardens.co.uk

THE GRANGE ▦
St Augustine's Road, Ramsgate, Kent CT11 9NY
Tel: 01628 825925 **Email:** bookings@landmarktrust.org.uk

GREAT COMP GARDEN
Comp Lane, Platt, Borough Green, Kent TN15 8QS
Tel: 01732 886154 **Email:** info@greatcompgarden.co.uk

GROOMBRIDGE PLACE GARDENS
Groombridge, Tunbridge Wells, Kent TN3 9QG
Tel: 01892 861444 **Email:** carrie@groombridge.co.uk

HALL PLACE & GARDENS 🏛
Bourne Road, Bexley, Kent DA5 1PQ
Tel: 01322 526574 **Email:** info@hallplace.org.uk

HEVER CASTLE & GARDENS 🏛ⓔ
Hever Castle, Hever, Edenbridge, Kent TN8 7NG
Tel: 01732 865224 **Email:** info@hevercastle.co.uk

HOLE PARK GARDENS
Hole Park, Benenden Road, Rolvenden, Cranbrook, Kent TN17 4JA
Tel: 01580 241344 **Email:** info@holepark.com

IGHTHAM MOTE 🦋
Mote Road, Ivy Hatch, Sevenoaks, Kent TN15 0NT
Tel: 01732 810378 **Email:** ighthammote@nationaltrust.org.uk

ST JOHN'S JERUSALEM 🦋
Sutton-at-Hone, Dartford Kent DA4 9HQ
Tel: 01732 810378 **Email:** stjohnsjerusalem@nationaltrust.org.uk

KNOLE 🦋
Sevenoaks, Kent TN15 0RP
Tel: 01732 462100 **Email:** knole@nationaltrust.org.uk

LULLINGSTONE CASTLE & WORLD GARDEN
Eynsford, Kent DA4 0JA
Tel: 01322 862114 **Email:** info@lullingstonecastle.co.uk

LULLINGSTONE ROMAN VILLA ⊞
Lullingstone Lane, Eynsford, Kent DA4 0JA
Tel: 01322 863467 **Email:** customers@english-heritage.org.uk

MOUNT EPHRAIM GARDENS 🏛ⓔ
Hernhill, Faversham, Kent ME13 9TX
Tel: 01227 751496 **Email:** info@mountephraimgardens.co.uk

NURSTEAD COURT
Nurstead Church Lane, Meopham, Kent DA13 9AD
Tel: 01474 812368 **Email:** info@nursteadcourt.co.uk

OWLETTS 🦋
The Street, Cobham, Gravesend DA12 3AP
Tel: 01732 810378 **Email:** owletts@nationaltrust.org.uk

PROVENDER HOUSE
Provender Lane, Norton, Nr Faversham, Kent ME13 0ST
Tel: 07773 790872 **Email:** info@provenderhouse.co.uk

QUEX PARK 🏛
Birchington, Kent CT7 0BH
Tel: 01843 841119 **Email:** www.quexpark.co.uk

RIVERHILL HIMALAYAN GARDENS 🏛ⓔ
Sevenoaks, Kent TN15 0RR
Tel: 01732 459777 **Email:** sarah@riverhillgardens.co.uk

ROCHESTER CASTLE ⊞
The Lodge, Rochester-Upon-Medway, Medway ME1 1SW
Tel: 01634 402276 **Email:** customers@english-heritage.org.uk

SCOTNEY CASTLE
Lamberhurst, Tunbridge Wells, Kent TN3 8JN
Tel: 01892 893820 **Email:** scotneycastle@nationaltrust.org.uk

SISSINGHURST CASTLE
Sissinghurst, Cranbrook, Kent TN17 2AB
Tel: 01580 710700 **Email:** sissinghurst@nationaltrust.org.uk

SMALLHYTHE PLACE
Smallhythe, Tenterden, Kent TN30 7NG
Tel: 01580 762334 **Email:** smallhytheplace@nationaltrust.org.uk

TONBRIDGE CASTLE
Castle Street, Tonbridge, Kent TN9 1BG
Tel: 01732 770929 **Email:** tonbridge.castle@tmbc.gov.uk

TUDOR HOUSE
King Street, Margate, Kent CT9 1QE
Tel: 01843 577577 **Email:** visitorinformation@thanet.gov.uk

WALMER CASTLE & GARDENS
Deal, Kent CT14 7LJ
Tel: 01304 364288 **Email:** customers@english-heritage.org.uk

ARDINGTON HOUSE
Wantage, Oxfordshire OX12 8QA
Tel: 01235 821566 **Email:** info@ardingtonhouse.com

CHASTLETON HOUSE
Chastleton, Nr Moreton-In-Marsh, Oxfordshire GL56 0SU
Tel: 01608 674981 **Email:** chastleton@nationaltrust.org.uk

GREYS COURT
Rotherfield Greys, Henley-On-Thames, Oxfordshire RG9 4PG
Tel: 01491 628529 **Email:** greyscourt@nationaltrust.org.uk

MAPLEDURHAM HOUSE & WATERMILL
Mapledurham, Reading RG4 7TR
Tel: 0118 9723350 **Email:** sissinghurst@nationaltrust.org.uk

MILTON MANOR HOUSE
Milton, Abingdon, Oxfordshire OX14 4EN
Tel: 01235 831287

MINSTER LOVELL HALL & DOVECOTE
Minster Lovell, Oxfordshire, OX29 0RR
Tel: 0870 333 1181 **Email:** customers@english-heritage.org.uk

NUFFIELD PLACE
Huntercombe, Henley on Thames RG9 5RY
Tel: 01491 641224 **Email:** nuffieldplace@nationaltrust.org.uk

SULGRAVE MANOR
Manor Road, Sulgrave, Nr Banbury, Oxfordshire OX17 2SD
Tel: 01295 760205 **Email:** enquiries@sulgravemanor.org.uk

WATERPERRY GARDENS
Waterperry, Nr Wheatley, Oxfordshire OX33 1JZ
Tel: 01844 339226 **Email:** office@waterperrygardens.co.uk

CLAREMONT LANDSCAPE GARDEN
Portsmouth Road, Esher, Surrey KT10 9JG
Tel: 01372 467806 **Email:** claremont@nationaltrust.org.uk

GODDARDS
Abinger Common, Dorking, Surrey RH5 6TH
Tel: 01628 825925 **Email:** bookings@landmarktrust.org.uk

HATCHLANDS PARK
East Clandon, Guildford, Surrey GU4 7RT
Tel: 01483 222482 **Email:** hatchlands@nationaltrust.org.uk

LEITH HILL PLACE
Leith Hill Lane, Coldharbour, Dorking, Surrey RH5 6LY
Tel: 01306 711685 **Email:** leithhillplace@nationaltrust.org.uk

LIMNERSLEASE AT THE WATTS GALLERY
Down Lane, Compton, Guildford, Surrey GU3 1DQ
Tel: 01483 810 235 **Email:** info@wattsgallery.org.uk

POLESDEN LACEY
Great Bookham, Nr Dorking, Surrey RH5 6BD
Tel: 01372 452048 **Email:** polesdenlacey@nationaltrust.org.uk

RHS GARDEN WISLEY
Nr Woking, Surrey GU23 6QB
Tel: 0845 260 9000 **Email:** wisley@rhs.org.uk

VANN
Hambledon, Godalming, Surrey GU8 4EF
Tel: 01428 683413 **Email:** vann@caroe.com

1066 BATTLE OF HASTINGS
Battle, Sussex TN33 0AD
Tel: 01424 775705 **Email:** customers@english-heritage.org.uk

ALFRISTON CLERGY HOUSE
The Tye, Alfriston, Nr Polegate, East Sussex BN26 5TL
Tel: 01323 871961 **Email:** alfriston@nationaltrust.org.uk

Anne of Cleves House

52 Southover High Street, Lewes, East Sussex BN7 1JA
At the house you can explore how the Tudors and Elizabethans lived, worked and relaxed at home. **Map Ref:** 4:I5
Tel: 01273 474610 **Email:** anne@sussexpast.co.uk
Website: www.sussexpast.co.uk
Open/Admission: Mon-Sun. For prices and opening times please refer to website.

BATEMAN'S
Burwash, Etchingham, East Sussex TN19 7DS
Tel: 01435 882302 **Email:** batemans@nationaltrust.org.uk

BODIAM CASTLE
Bodiam, Nr Robertsbridge, East Sussex TN32 5UA
Tel: 01580 830196 **Email:** bodiamcastle@nationaltrust.org.uk

CHARLESTON
Firle, Nr Lewes, East Sussex BN8 6LL
Tel: 01323 811626 **Email:** info@charleston.org.uk

CHICHESTER CATHEDRAL
Chichester, West Sussex PO19 1PX
Tel: 01243 782595 **Email:** visitors@chichestercathedral.org.uk

FAIRLIGHT HALL GARDENS
Martineau Lane, Fairlight, Nr Hastings East Sussex TN35 5DR
Tel: 01424 814132 **Email:** admin@fairlighthall.co.uk

FARLEY HOUSE & GALLERY 🏛️ⓕ
Muddles Green, Chiddingly, Nr Lewes, East Sussex, BN8 6HW
Tel: 01825 872856 **Email:** tours@leemiller.co.uk

FISHBOURNE ROMAN PALACE
Salthill Road, Fishbourne, Chichester, Sussex PO19 3QR
Tel: 01243 785859 **Email:** adminfish@sussexpast.co.uk

GLYNDE PLACE 🏛️ⓕ
Glynde, East Sussex BN8 6SX
Tel: 01273 858224 **Email:** info@glynde.co.uk

GREAT DIXTER HOUSE & GARDENS 🏛️ⓕ
Northiam, Rye, East Sussex TN31 6PH
Tel: 01797 252878 **Email:** office@greatdixter.co.uk

HASTINGS CASTLE
Castle Hill Road, West Hill, Hastings, East Sussex TN34 3AR
Tel: 01424 444412 **Email:** bookings@discoverhastings.co.uk

High Beeches Woodland & Water Garden 🏛️ⓕ

High Beeches Lane, Handcross, West Sussex RH17 6HQ
A hidden gem in the High Weald of Sussex sensitively planted with many rare trees and plants.
Map Ref: 4:I4 **Tel:** 01444 400589
Website: www.highbeeches.com
Open: Apr-1 Nov: except Weds, 1-5pm (last adm. 4.30pm). Tours anytime, by appointment only. **Admission:** Adult £8.50

Lewes Castle & Museum

Barbican House, 169 High Street, Lewes, East Sussex BN7 1YE
Climb to the top of this 1000 year old Norman Castle for stunning panoramic views across Sussex and explore the Museum of Sussex Archaeology. **Map Ref:** 4:I6 **Tel:** 01273 486290
Email: castle@sussexpast.co.uk **Website:** www.sussexpast.co.uk
Open/Admission: Daily. For prices and opening times please refer to website.

LEWES PRIORY
Town Hall, High Street, Lewes, East Sussex BN7 2QS
Tel: 01273 486185 **Email:** enquiries@lewespriory.org.uk

Michelham Priory 🏛️ⓕ

Upper Dicker, Hailsham, East Sussex BN27 3QS
England's longest medieval water filled moat surrounds the site which dates back to 1229. **Map Ref:** 4:J6
Tel: 01323 844224 **Email:** adminmich@sussexpast.co.uk
Website: www.sussexpast.co.uk
Open/ Admission: Mon-Sun. For prices and opening times please refer to website.

NYMANS 🌿
Handcross, Haywards Heath, West Sussex RH17 6EB
Tel: 01444 405250 **Email:** nymans@nationaltrust.org.uk

PALLANT HOUSE GALLERY
9 North Pallant, Chichester, West Sussex
Tel: 01243 774557 **Email:** info@pallant.org.uk

PASHLEY MANOR GARDENS 🏛️ⓕ
Pashley Manor, Ticehurst, Wadhurst, East Sussex TN5 7HE
Tel: 01580 200888 **Email:** info@pashleymanorgardens.com

PEVENSEY CASTLE 🏛️
Pevensey, Sussex BN24 5LE
Tel: 01323 762604 **Email:** customers@english-heritage.org.uk

PRESTON MANOR
Preston Drove, Brighton, East Sussex BN1 6SD
Tel: 03000 290900 **Email:** visitor.services@brighton-hove.gov.uk

THE ROYAL PAVILION
Brighton, East Sussex BN1 1EE
Tel: 03000 290900 **Email:** visitor.services@brighton-hove.gov.uk

SACKVILLE COLLEGE
High Street, East Grinstead, West Sussex RH19 3BX
Tel: 01342 323414 **Email:** admin@sackvillecollege.org.uk

SAINT HILL MANOR
Saint Hill Road, East Grinstead, West Sussex RH19 4JY
Tel: 01342 334171 **Email:** info@sainthillmanor.org.uk

SHEFFIELD PARK & GARDEN 🌿
Sheffield Park, Uckfield, East Sussex TN22 3QX
Tel: 01825 790231 **Email:** sheffieldpark@nationaltrust.org.uk

STANDEN 🌿
West Hoathly Road, East Grinstead, West Sussex RH19 4NE
Tel: 01342 323029 **Email:** standen@nationaltrust.org.uk

UPPARK HOUSE & GARDEN 🌿
South Harting, Petersfield, West Sussex GU31 5QR
Tel: 01730 825415 **Email:** uppark@nationaltrust.org.uk

WAKEHURST PLACE
Ardingly Road, North of Ardingly, West Sussex
Tel: 01444 894004 **Email:** wakehurst@kew.org

WEALD & DOWNLAND OPEN AIR MUSEUM
Town Lane, Singleton, Chichester, West Sussex PO18 0EU
Tel: 01243 811363 **Email:** office@wealddown.co.uk

WEST DEAN COLLEGE & GARDENS 🏛️
West Dean, West Dean, West Sussex PO18 0RX
Tel: 01243 818210 **Email:** enquiries@westdean.org.uk

WILMINGTON PRIORY
Wilmington, Nr Eastbourne, East Sussex BN26 5SW
Tel: 01628 825925 **Email:** bookings@landmarktrust.org.uk

WOOLBEDING GARDENS 🌿
Midhurst, West Sussex GU29 9RR
Tel: 0844 249 1895 **Email:** woolbedinggardens@nationaltrust.org.uk

CARISBROOKE CASTLE 🏛️
Newport, Isle Of Wight PO30 1XY
Tel: 01983 522107 **Email:** customers@english-heritage.org.uk

NUNWELL HOUSE & GARDENS 🏛️
Coach Lane, Brading, Isle Of Wight PO36 0JQ
Tel: 01983 407240 **Email:** info@nunwellhouse.co.uk

OSBORNE HOUSE 🏛️
East Cowes, Isle of Wight PO32 6JX
Tel: 01983 200022 **Email:** customers@english-heritage.org.uk

VENTNOR BOTANIC GARDENS
Undercliff Drive, Ventnor, Isle of Wight PO38 1UL
Tel: 01983 855397

SOUTH WEST

CORNWALL • DEVON • DORSET
SOMERSET • WILTSHIRE • GLOUCESTERSHIRE

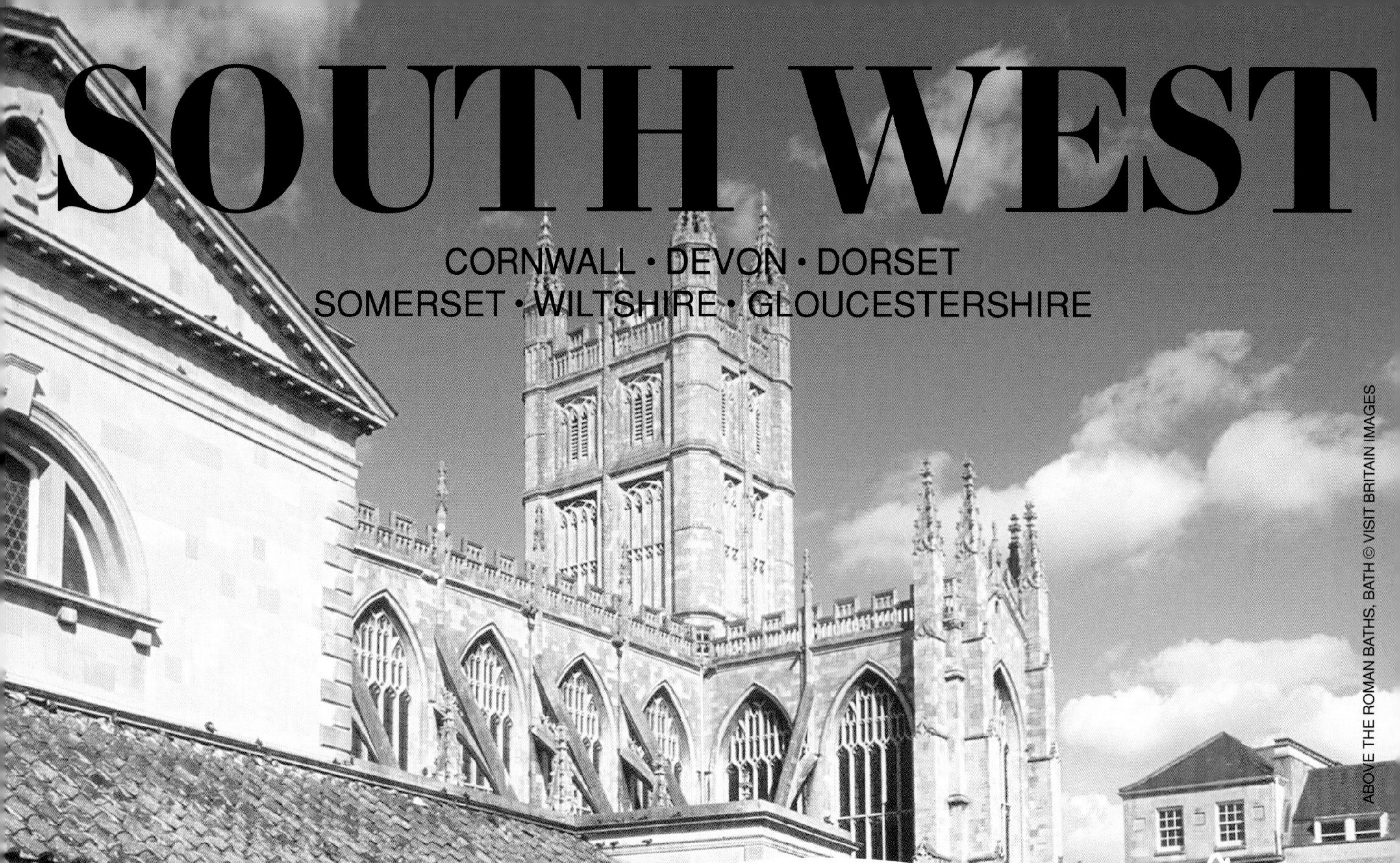

ABOVE THE ROMAN BATHS, BATH © VISIT BRITAIN IMAGES

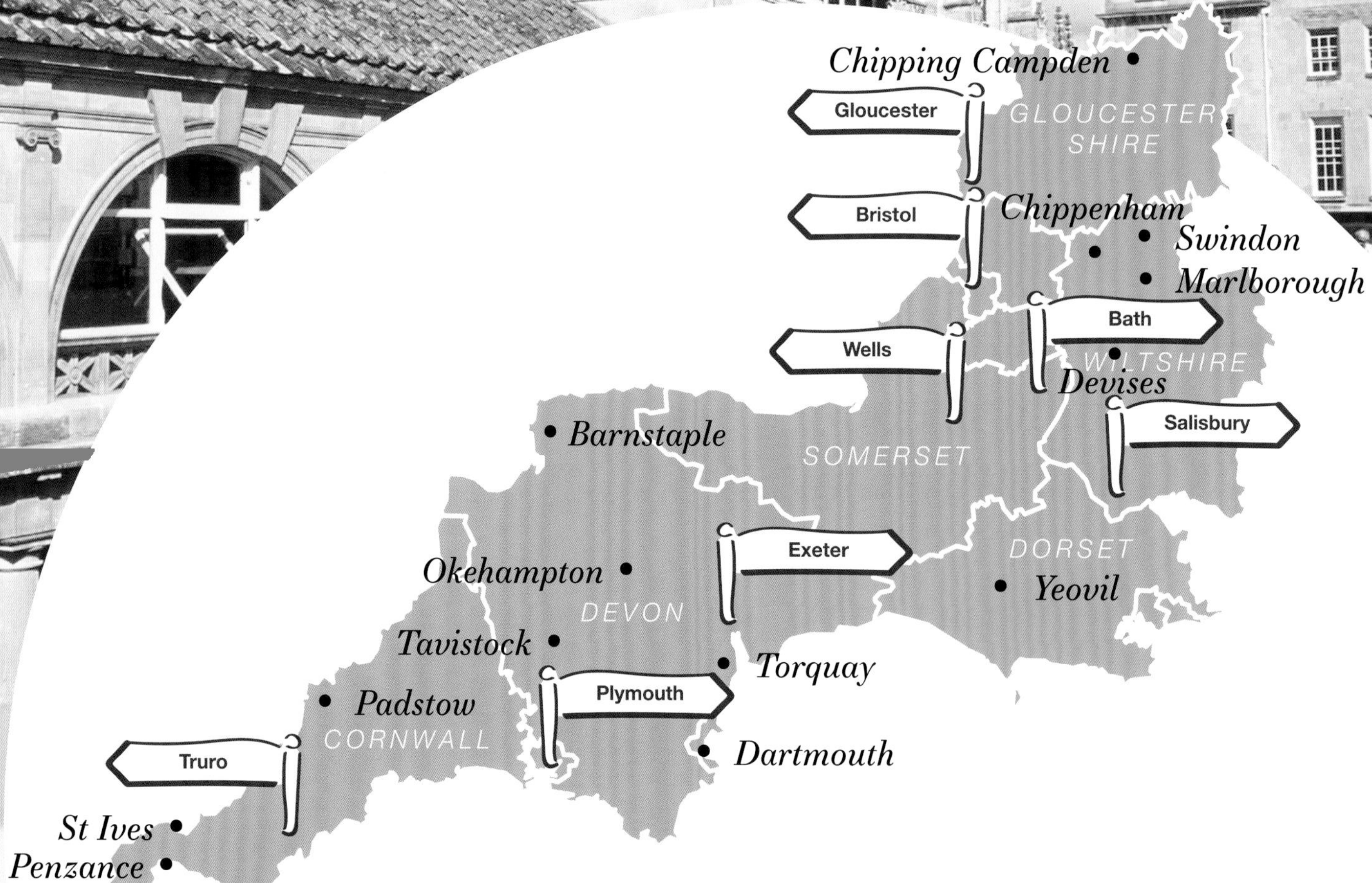
Chipping Campden
Gloucester
GLOUCESTERSHIRE
Bristol
Chippenham
Swindon
Marlborough
Bath
Wells
WILTSHIRE
Devises
Salisbury
Barnstaple
SOMERSET
Exeter
DORSET
Okehampton
Yeovil
DEVON
Tavistock
Torquay
Plymouth
Padstow
CORNWALL
Truro
Dartmouth
St Ives
Penzance

COUNTRYSIDE:

- Jurassic Coast
- Dartmoor, Exmoor, Bodmin Moor
- Atlantic surfing beaches

HERITAGE:

- Drake & Raleigh
- King Arthur
- Tin mining heritage

FOOD:

- Seafood
- Cornish pasties
- Clotted cream

TINTAGEL CASTLE © ENGLISH HERITAGE

ATHELHAMPTON

Late medieval house restored in the 1890s, from when date the eight formal gardens. Beloved of novelist Thomas Hardy, the Great Hall is its glory with a series of linenfold panelled rooms beyond. The West Wing hosts an important collection of the Russian cubist painter Marevna.

Highlights:

- Great Hall
- Yew pyramids in the Great Court
- 17th century dovecot
- Paintings by Marevna

THE IRETON BEDROOM, CHAVENAGE HOUSE

SUDELEY CASTLE

Carefully restored Tudor castle, once home to Henry VIII's last wife, Katherine Parr. Paintings and treasures from Tudor and Civil War history with extensive gardens including a restored Physic Garden and historic rose gardens.

Highlights:

- Books & love letters of Queen Katherine Parr
- Charles I's campaign bed
- Allegory of the Tudor Succession by Lucas de Heere
- Dutch & English Old Masters

DON'T MISS!

TINTAGEL

Legendary site of King Arthur's birthplace, the spectacular ruins of the largely 13th century castle overlay a recently excavated Dark Ages settlement. Dramatic coastal site and new interpretation make this an exciting introduction to Cornish history and myth.

Highlights:

- Crossing the bridge
- Merlin's Cave
- Story stones
- The Beach Café

THE GREAT HALL, ATHELHAMPTON

CHAVENAGE

An E-shaped Elizabethan house with glass and panelling reused from monastic buildings, owned by only 3 families in its history. The house is strangely familiar from a second life as a popular film location.

Highlights:

- Elizabethan carved hall screen
- Cromwell & Ireton bedrooms
- Cromwellian relics
- Mortlake tapestries

THE KNOT GARDEN, SUDELEY CASTLE © VISIT BRITAIN IMAGES

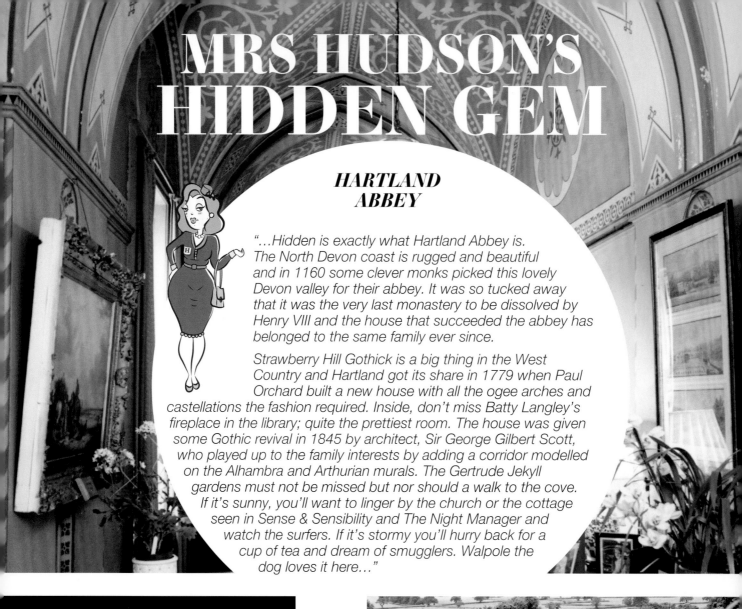

MRS HUDSON'S HIDDEN GEM

HARTLAND ABBEY

"…Hidden is exactly what Hartland Abbey is. The North Devon coast is rugged and beautiful and in 1160 some clever monks picked this lovely Devon valley for their abbey. It was so tucked away that it was the very last monastery to be dissolved by Henry VIII and the house that succeeded the abbey has belonged to the same family ever since.

Strawberry Hill Gothick is a big thing in the West Country and Hartland got its share in 1779 when Paul Orchard built a new house with all the ogee arches and castellations the fashion required. Inside, don't miss Batty Langley's fireplace in the library; quite the prettiest room. The house was given some Gothic revival in 1845 by architect, Sir George Gilbert Scott, who played up to the family interests by adding a corridor modelled on the Alhambra and Arthurian murals. The Gertrude Jekyll gardens must not be missed but nor should a walk to the cove. If it's sunny, you'll want to linger by the church or the cottage seen in Sense & Sensibility and The Night Manager and watch the surfers. If it's stormy you'll hurry back for a cup of tea and dream of smugglers. Walpole the dog loves it here…"

MARK THE YEAR

300 YEARS
TALMAN
Visit William Talman's Dyrham Park 300 years after his death.
- ✔ Dyrham Park

300 YEARS
CHIPPENDALE
Celebrate our greatest furniture maker 300 years after his birth.
- ✔ Corsham Court
- ✔ Saltram House
- ✔ Stourhead

200 YEARS
REPTON
Enjoy the gardens of Humphry Repton 200 years after his death.
- ✔ Antony House
- ✔ Aston Court, Bristol
- ✔ Blaise Castle
- ✔ Corsham Court
- ✔ Dyrham Park
- ✔ Longleat
- ✔ Pentillie Castle

DYRHAM PARK © NATIONAL TRUST IMAGES

CHIPPENDALE CHAIRS IN THE SALOON AT SALTRAM, DEVON © NATIONAL TRUST IMAGES - ANDREAS VON EINSIEDEL

100 YEARS
WOMEN AND SUFFRAGE

1. MAY MORRIS (1862-1938)
Embroiderer, founder of Women's Guild of Arts
at Kelmscott Manor.

2. JANE DIGBY, LADY ELLENBOROUGH (1807-81)
Traveller, libertine, diarist, linguist
at Minterne Gardens.

3. DAME AGATHA CHRISTIE (1890-1976)
Crime novelist & playwright
at Greenway.

MAYFLOWER 2020

The Mayflower sailed for the New World from Plymouth on 16 September 1620 carrying Separatists from Nottinghamshire, Yorkshire and Lincolnshire. Celebrations kick off with the Illuminate Festival of Thanksgiving in November 2019.

DID YOU KNOW?

ST MICHAEL'S MOUNT © VISIT BRITAIN IMAGES

1 ST MICHAEL'S MOUNT

Hitler's foreign minister, von Ribbentrop loved Cornwall and planned to retire to St Michael's Mount if the Nazis won the Second World War.

2 STANWAY HOUSE

Stanway House is home to the highest gravity fed fountain in the world at 300 ft, part of the restored 18th century water gardens.

3 ATHELHAMPTON HALL

The East Wing at 15th century Athelhampton Hall hides a bang-up-to-date cinema with 50 comfortable seats, much enjoyed by locals and visitors to the area.

ATHELHAMPTON'S POPULAR COMMUNITY CINEMA

4 SUDELEY CASTLE

No less than four Tudor Queens of England walked in the gardens at Sudeley Castle - Anne Boleyn, Katherine Parr, Lady Jane Grey and Elizabeth I.

5 LONGLEAT

The world's longest hedge maze is at Longleat. It takes 16,000 English yew trees to line paths 1.69 miles long. It's just one of five mazes at Longleat.

6 BOCONNOC

The legendary Regent diamond, at 410 carats now in the Crown Jewels of France, was sold by ex-Governor of Madras, Thomas Pitt in 1717 to fund his purchase of Boconnoc.

THE HEDGE MAZE, LONGLEAT © CC NIKI ODOLPHE

3 TOP ART COLLECTIONS

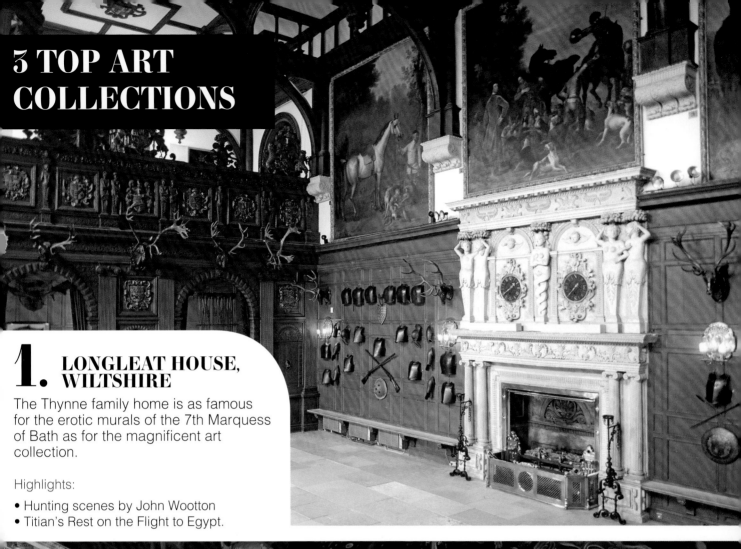

1. LONGLEAT HOUSE, WILTSHIRE

The Thynne family home is as famous for the erotic murals of the 7th Marquess of Bath as for the magnificent art collection.

Highlights:
- Hunting scenes by John Wootton
- Titian's Rest on the Flight to Egypt.

2. WILTON HOUSE, WILTSHIRE

Extensive art collection of the Pembroke family, still patrons of the arts. Works by Rembrandt, Holbein, Hals, Rubens, Reynolds and Brueghel.

Highlights:
- van Dyck portraits in the Single & Double Cube Rooms.

3. CORSHAM COURT, WILTSHIRE

Art collected principally by diplomat, Paul Methuen in the 1740s in purpose built gallery designed by 'Capability' Brown.

Highlights:

- Allegorical portrait of Elizabeth I
- Italian Renaissance masters
- Reynolds portraits

PLACES TO STAY
HISTORIC HOTELS IN THE SOUTH WEST
www.signpost.co.uk

THE MANOR HOTEL, DORSET

Dating back to the 16th century, The Manor at West Bexington, enjoys commanding views over the stunning Jurassic Coast. Overlooking Chesil Beach, The Manor is a true gem that glistens in this beautiful area of Dorset.

BRIDGE HOUSE HOTEL, DORSET

Combining the calm of a 700 year old religious building in the heart of Hardy's Wessex with modern comfort and locally sourced food.

HANNAFORE POINT HOTEL, CORNWALL

With panoramic views of sea, cliffs and St George's Island, Hannafore Point is conveniently placed for sandy beaches, the town of Looe, and, naturally the facilities for deep sea fishing for which the area is famous. Hannafore is on the southwest coastal path and there are several gardens nearby including the Lost Gardens of Heligan, the Eden Project and Cotehele.

133

NORTHCOTE MANOR, DEVON

Northcote Manor is a manor house of 18th century origins, hidden in the heart of the North Devon countryside in a milieu of timeless tranquillity, reflecting its monastic origins. It sits in 20 acres of mature woodlands, lawns and gardens, including a walled secret garden, apple orchards and a Japanese water garden.

PLANTATION HOUSE HOTEL, DEVON

Formerly the parish rectory, this much-loved restaurant with rooms now offers a harmonious blend of relaxed country tranquillity and stylish sophistication, with a personal touch. A gently indulgent sanctuary on the very doorstep of river estuaries, soothing beaches, market towns and the wilderness of Dartmoor.

THE COTTAGE HOTEL, DEVON

The Ireland family have run The Cottage since 1973 and provide a warm, personal service. Set along this Heritage Coastline there are challenging walks affording superb views. The area is famous for its unique flora and fauna, including the Nature Reserve at Slapton Ley.

ALEXANDRA HOTEL, DORSET

Set on a stunning cliff top location, with direct beach access, The Alexandra exudes elegant style, comfort and hospitality, as enjoyed by the most discerning of guests, for over 100 years. The immaculate private grounds overlook the famous Cobb Harbour, Lyme Bay and the World Heritage Coastline.

BERRY HEAD HOTEL, DEVON

Superbly sited coastal hotel built as a Napoleonic hospital in 1803, later home to Henry Francis Lyte, author of popular hymn, Abide with Me.

MORTONS HOUSE, DORSET

Mortons House is a 16th century Grade II Elizabethan manor house hotel and restaurant in beautiful Dorset in the heart of historic Corfe Castle. Built in 1590, Mortons House has retained its unique period features. The hotel's location in the Isle of Purbeck is ideal for guests wishing to enjoy comfort, exceptional food, and a warm welcome.

COTSWOLD HOUSE, GLOUCESTERSHIRE

A superb Regency Grade II townhouse, settled snugly in the heart of Chipping Campden, Cotswolds House Hotel & Spa has overlooked the village square for more than 200 years. As pretty as a picture, the hotel boasts two acres of landscaped gardens, a deluxe award-winning spa and original features throughout.

INN AT FOSSEBRIDGE, GLOUCESTERSHIRE

There has been an inn at Fossebridge on the banks of the River Coln between Northleach and Cirencester, for more than 300 years. Experience exceptional casual dining within a character Cotswold pub with stone walls, flagstone floors and beams.

THE FOUNDING OF AMERICA

Raleigh, Drake and the Mayflower

SHERBORNE CASTLE BUILT BY SIR WALTER RALEIGH IN 1594

The South West of England has an inextricable link with the founding of the United States of America. In 2020 we celebrate the sailing of the Mayflower from Plymouth in Devon to Plymouth Sound in Massachusetts. Meanwhile, 2018 marks 400 years since the death of Sir Walter Raleigh, a towering figure of the Elizabethan age of exploration, whose home was Sherborne Castle in Dorset.

Raleigh's contemporary Sir Francis Drake, whose circumnavigation of the world in 1577 brought him a knighthood and who bought nearby Buckland Abbey with captured Spanish treasure, also had a role to play in the founding of America. In 1586, he stopped at Roanoke Island in North America where Sir Walter Raleigh had first founded a settlement a year before. The colonists had not prospered and returned home with Drake, bringing with them exotic rarities, potatoes, tobacco and maize.

TOBACCO PIPE CARRIED BY SIR WALTER RALEIGH TO THE SCAFFOLD
© SHERBORNE CASTLE

THE ENTRANCE HALL, SHERBORNE CASTLE

Raleigh was granted a royal patent to establish a colony in North America by Elizabeth I in 1585. He had already funded a voyage in 1584 to Roanoke Island which had returned with favourable reports. The first settlers arrived too late for the planting season and lasted only a year, Raleigh's relief expedition did not reach Virginia, named in honour of the Virgin Queen, until after his friend Drake had evacuated the colonists. Raleigh tried again in 1587, sending 104 adults and 11 children but war with Spain intervened and by the time a relief expedition arrived in 1591 there was no trace of the colonists. Raleigh's last, equally abortive attempt to establish a colony was to Chesapeake Bay in 1603. Raleigh's failure was compensated by significant profits from privateering on Spanish shipping. With hindsight, it seems that the Virginia colonies failed because of a poor choice of landing site, internal arguments and an unjustified antagonism towards the locals.

Raleigh's last expeditions, which he led personally, were to find a legendary city of gold on the River Orinoco and finally establish an English presence that could compete with Spain. El Dorado was elusive and, having disobeyed a royal order to avoid conflict with the Spanish, Raleigh was executed by James I on his return in 1618. Raleigh's legacy was transformational. He introduced the potato to our diet, he popularised tobacco smoking, and Raleigh's Seat at Sherborne Castle is one possible location for the famous story of his servant dousing him in ale because he thought his pipe-smoking master was on fire. Most of all he established an idea in the English mind of the possibility of a new life in a new land to the West which inspired the Mayflower Pilgrims.

The core group who sailed on the Mayflower in 1620 were Separatists from the East Midlands, Puritans who wanted an independent Church and State. After years of persecution in England, they chartered the Mayflower and set sail for Virginia in September 1620. There were 102 passengers and a crew of 30; about half were Puritans who called themselves Saints and their fellow travellers, Strangers. Blown off course, they arrived at Cape Cod before establishing a first settlement at Plymouth, Massachusetts under the Mayflower Contract, which allowed for the governance of the colony under the rule of law.

SUNTANNED SIR WALTER RALEIGH ON HIS RETURN FROM THE ORINOCO IN 1618 © SHERBORNE CASTLE

The final success of the Plymouth Colonists marked the beginning of modern America, but visitors to the West Country will first encounter Drake & Raleigh, the swashbuckling heroes who laid the foundations for their enterprise a century earlier. ■

"Raleigh established the possibility of a new life in a new land to the West which inspired the Mayflower Pilgrims"

Boconnoc

www.boconnoc.com

Boconnoc House, the winner of the 2012 HHA/Sotheby's Award for Restoration and the Georgian Group Award, was bought with the proceeds of the Pitt Diamond in 1717. Three Prime Ministers, a history of duels and the architect Sir John Soane play a part in the story of this unique estate. The beautiful woodland garden, the Georgian Bath House, Soane Stable Yard, 15th Century Church and naturesque landscape tempt the explorer.

Exclusive weddings with onsite accommodation for up to 40 people, private hire, film and fashion shoots and corporate days are part of Boconnoc today. Other regular events include the Boconnoc Music Award concert by the Royal College of Music, the Cornwall Garden Society Spring Flower Show and the Boconnoc Steam Fair.

CONTACT
Owner: Boconnoc Trustees
Contact: Sima Hill
Tel: 01208 872507
Email: office@boconnoc.com

LOCATION
Boconnoc, Lostwithiel, Cornwall PL22 0RG
Map Ref: 1:G8 - A38 from Plymouth, Liskeard or from Bodmin to Dobwalls, then A390 to East Taphouse and follow signs.

OPENING TIMES
Garden: 6, 13, 20, 27 May, 2-5pm.
Private Tours: By appointment only.

ADMISSION
House: £14 **Garden:** £6
Child (under 12): Free, Group: 15+ by appointment.

SPECIAL EVENTS
Cornwall Garden Society Spring Flower Show: 7, 8 Apr, Endurance GB Ride 9 & 10 Jun, Boconnoc Music Award concerts with the Royal College of Music 17 & 19 Jul, Steam Fair at Boconnoc 27-29 Jul.

KEY FACTS

 Toilet facilities available.

 Baby changing facilities available.

 Parking available.

 Partial.

 In grounds, on leads.

 18 doubles (9 en suite). Holiday and residential houses to let.

 By appointment during May-Sep.

 By appointment.

 Please see website for conferences with accommodation available.

 Please see the events calendar on the website.

 Church or civil ceremony.

 Perfect film and photography location.

Prideaux Place

www.prideauxplace.co.uk

Tucked away above the busy port of Padstow, the home of the Prideaux family for over 400 years, is surrounded by gardens and wooded grounds overlooking a deer park and the Camel estuary to the moors beyond. The house still retains its 'E' shape Elizabethan front and contains fine paintings and furniture. Now a major international film location, this family home is one of the brightest jewels in Cornwall's crown. The historic garden is undergoing major restoration work and offers some of the best views in the county. A cornucopia of Cornish history under one roof.

KEY FACTS

 Open air theatre, open air concerts, car rallies, art exhibitions, charity events.

 Toilet and Baby changing facilities available.

 By arrangement.

 Parking available.

 Partial. Ground floor and grounds.

 Dogs welcome on leads.

 Obligatory.

 By arrangement.

 Terrace Tea Room situated in what was once the Old Schoolroom. Fully licensed.

 Gift shop.

 By arrangement.

 Please see website for upcoming special events.

 Wedding ceremonies and receptions.

The historical context & architecture of Prideaux Place makes it one of the most sought after film locations.

CONTACT
Owner: Peter Prideaux-Brune Esq
Contact: The Administrator
Tel: 01841 532411 **Fax:** 01841 532945
Email: office@prideauxplace.co.uk

LOCATION
Padstow, Cornwall PL28 8RP
Map Ref: 1:E8 - 5m from A39 Newquay/Wadebridge link road. Signposted by Historic House signs.

TYPICALLY OPEN
Easter Sun 16 Apr-Thu 5 Oct
(closed Sun 30 Apr-Wed 3 May).
Grounds and Tea Room: 12.30pm-5pm
House Tours: 1.30pm-4pm (last tour)

ADMISSION
House & Grounds
Adult: £9, Child (12-16 yrs): £5, Under 12yrs: Free, Groups: 15+ (discounts apply).
Grounds only
Adult: £4, Child (12-16 yrs): £2, Under 12yrs: Free, Groups: 15+ (discounts apply).

St Michael's Mount

www.stmichaelsmount.co.uk

©NATIONAL TRUST IMAGES/ST MICHAEL'S MOUNT

This beautiful island has become an icon for Cornwall and has magnificent views of Mount's Bay from its summit. The church and castle, whose origins date from the 12th Century, have at various times acted as a Benedictine priory, a place of pilgrimage, a fortress, a home to the St Aubyn family, and is now a magnet for visitors from all over the world.

Striding the causeway or crossing by boat. Treading medieval pathways or exploring tropical gardens. Climbing to the castle or uncovering stories of harbour, legend and family home.

Marvel at the views, hear the islanders' tales and unearth a history that lives on in every step - through time and tide the Mount creates moments to remember.

©NATIONAL TRUST IMAGES/ST MICHAEL'S MOUNT

CONTACT
Owner: National Trust **Contact:** St Aubyn Estates
Tel: 01736 710265 **Additional Tel:** 01736 710507
Email: enquiries@stmichaelsmount.co.uk

LOCATION
Marazion, Nr Penzance, Cornwall TR17 0EL
Map Ref: 3:G5 - Marazion, Near Penzance.
TRANSPORT ROUTES - Car l Bike l Bus

TYPICALLY OPEN
Castle
Sun 18 Mar-Fri 29 Jun:10.30am-5pm
Sun 1 Jul-Fri 31 Aug: 10am-5.30pm
Sun 2 Sep-Fri 26 Oct:10.30am-5pm
Garden
Mon 16 Ap-Fri 29 Jun:10.30am-5pm (Mon-Fri)
Thu 5 Jul-Fri 31 Aug:10am-5.30pm (Thu & Fri)
Thu 6 Sep-Fri 28 Sep:10.30am-5pm (Thu & Fri)

Please note that there are limited opening times during the winter. Please check the website for full opening times.

ADMISSION
Please see website for all admission prices.

KEY FACTS

 Please refer to the website for all up to date information regarding events and activities.

 WC's and disabled toilets on the island.

 Baby changing facilities available.

 Coach and car parking on the mainland is available. Not National Trust - charges apply.

 Partial - see website for access statement. Assistance dogs allowed in the castle & garden.

 Dogs are permitted in the village and harbour area, but not in the castle or garden.

 By prior arrangement.

 By prior arrangement.

 Island Cafe offers expansive sea views from its garden. Pasties, sandwiches, cream teas.

 Sail Loft serves fresh Newlyn fish specials, homebaked cakes, cream teas and local ales.

 Visit the Island Shop or Courtyard Shop for unique product ranges, accessories and gifts.

 Plant sales available.

 Events throughout the year - see website for details.

Prideaux Place

Trewithen Gardens & Parks

trewithengardens.co.uk

Trewithen means 'house of the trees' and the name truly describes this early Georgian house in its wood and parkland setting. The 30 acre garden is an International Camellia Society Garden of Excellence (1 of only 5 in the UK) and is also renowned for its rhododendrons, magnolias and Champion Trees.

CONTACT
Owner: Mr S T J Galsworthy
Contact: Liz White
Contact: Gary Long
Tel: 01726 883647
Email: secretary@ trewithenestate.co.uk

LOCATION
Grampound Road, Nr Truro, Cornwall TR2 4DD
Map Ref: 1:E9 - On the A390 between Truro & St Austell.

OPENING TIMES
Gardens: Mar 1-Jun 30 daily 10am-4.30pm.
House: Mar-Jun Mon & Tue afternoons 2pm-4pm (guided tours only - booking advisable).

ADMISSION
Adult: £8.50, Child U12: Free. Combined entry, group rates & concessions available.

KEY FACTS

 No photography inside.

 Toilet facilities available, including a disabled toilet.

 Parking available including for coaches.

 Partially, mostly level gravel paths.

 Dogs welcome but must be on leads at all times.

 Please contact for guided tour details.

 The Tea Shed, shop & plant centre.

Boconnoc

South West

Cadhay

www.cadhay.org.uk Ⓕ

Cadhay is approached by an avenue of lime-trees, and stands in an extensive garden, with herbaceous borders and yew hedges, with excellent views over the original medieval fish ponds. The main part of the house was built in about 1550 by John Haydon who had married the de Cadhay heiress. He retained the Great Hall of an earlier house, of which the fine timber roof (about 1420-1460) can be seen. An Elizabethan Long Gallery was added by John's successor at the end of the 16th Century, forming a unique courtyard with statues of Sovereigns on each side, described by Sir Simon Jenkins as one of the 'Treasures of Devon'.

KEY FACTS

 Parking available.

 Ground floor and grounds.

 Luxury self-catering holiday accommodation for 22 in an historic Elizabethan manor.

 Obligatory.

 The Apple Store is now a Tea Room.

Plant sales.

Venue to celebrate a landmark birthday, anniversary, reunion or other special occasions.

Please see the news section of the website for all events.

A unique venue for a Devon wedding; atmospheric & individual.

CONTACT
Owner: Mr R Thistlethwayte
Contact: Jayne Covell
Tel: 01404 813511

LOCATION
Ottery St Mary, Devon EX11 1QT **Map Ref:** 2:L6
1 mile North West of Ottery St Mary. From West take A30 & exit at Pattesons Cross, follow signs for Fairmile & then Cadhay. From East, exit at the Iron Bridge & follow signs as above.

OPENING TIMES
May-Sep, Fri 2pm-5pm. Also, late May & Summer Bank Holiday Sat-Sun-Mon. Last tour 4pm.

ADMISSION
House (Guided tour) & Gardens - Adult: £8, Child: £3.
Garden only - Adult: £4, Child: £1.
Groups: 15+ by prior arrangement.

Hartland Abbey

www.hartlandabbey.com Ⓕ

Built in 1160, Hartland Abbey is a hidden gem on the stunning North Devon coast. Passing down generations from the Dissolution, it remains a fascinating, lived-in family home: architecture from 1160 to 1850 by Meadows and Sir George Gilbert Scott; murals, important paintings and furniture, porcelain, early photographs, documents and family memorabilia. Exhibitions: 'Filming at Hartland Abbey since 1934' and 'William Stukeley-Saviour of Stonehenge'. Woodland gardens and walks lead to the Jekyll designed Bog Garden and Fernery, restored 18th Century Walled Gardens of flowers, fruit and vegetables, the Summerhouse, Gazebo and the beach at Blackpool Mill. Location for BBC's 'Sense and Sensibility', 'The Night Manager' and 'Guernsey' in 2017. Beautiful daffodils, bluebells and tulips in spring. Delicious home cooking in The Old Kitchens Tea Room. 1 mile from Hartland Quay. 2016 Winner 'Best Garden and/or Country House in N Devon'. Coaches very welcome. Special Events - see website.

KEY FACTS

 Parking adjacent to house.

 Partial. Disabled WC.

 Dogs in grounds, on leads.

 Conducted tours by arrangement.

Homemade lunches & cream teas.

Small shop in the museum selling a wide range of gifts.

Plants for sale produced in our gardens.

Wedding receptions. Corporate events.

Five separate venues.

CONTACT
Owner: Sir Hugh Stucley Bt **Contact:** Theresa Seligmann
Tel: 01237 441496/234 / 01884 860225
Email: ha_admin@btconnect.com

LOCATION
Nr Bideford, North Devon EX39 6DT **Map Ref:** 1:G5
OS Ref: SS240 249 - 15m W of Bideford, 15m N of Bude off A39 between Hartland and Hartland Quay on B3248.

OPENING TIMES
House, Gardens, Grounds & Beachwalk: Sun 25 Mar- 30 Sept, Sun-Thu 11am-5pm. (House 2pm-5pm - last admission 4pm).
Tearoom, Light lunches & cream teas: 11am-5pm.

ADMISSION
House, Gardens, Grounds & Beachwalk
Adult: £12.50, Child (5-15ys): £5, Under 5: Free,
Registered disabled: £8.50, Family (2+2): £30.
Gardens, Grounds, Beachwalk & Exhibition
Adult: £8.50, Child (5-15ys): £4, Under 5: Free,
Registered disabled: £5, Family (2+2): £23.
Groups & coaches: Concs 20+. Open at other dates & times.
Booking essential. Large car park adjacent to the house.

Fursdon House & Gardens

www.fursdon.co.uk

Fursdon House is at the heart of a small estate where the family has lived for over 750 years. Set within a hilly and wooded landscape the gardens and grounds are attractive with walled and open areas with far reaching views. Family memorabilia with fine costumes and textiles are displayed on informal guided tours.

Two spacious apartments and a restored Victorian cottage offer stylish holiday accommodation.

CONTACT
Owner: Mr & Mrs E D Fursdon **Contact:** Mrs C M Fursdon
Tel: 01392 860860 **Email:** admin@fursdon.co.uk

LOCATION
Cadbury, Nr Thorverton, Exeter, Devon EX5 5JS
Map Ref: 2:K6 - Off A3072 between Bickleigh & Crediton. 9 miles North of Exeter signposted through Thorverton from A396 Exeter to Tiverton Road.

OPENING TIMES
Gardens & Tea Room: Easter-Sep Weds, Thus & BH Mons.
House: Open for guided tours Jun-Aug, Weds, Thus & BH Mons 2.30pm & 3.30pm. Group tours at other times by arrangement. Some special openings on Suns. See website for details.

ADMISSION
House & Garden
Adult: £8.50 (Garden only: £4.50), Child: Free.

KEY FACTS

Caters for conferences. No photography or video.

Toilet facilities available.

Baby changing facilities available.

Ample parking but limited for coaches.

Partial. Please see our access statement for all access details.

Dogs on leads are allowed in the gardens.

3 self-catering holiday properties.

Obligatory.

Coach Hall Tea Room serving cream teas & selection of cakes, when the gardens & house open.

Coach Hall suitable for small meetings & conferences. Max 40 seated.

Please see the 'News & Events' section of the website for all the upcoming events.

Fursdon hosts a very small number of unique and special wedding receptions each year.

Tiverton Castle

www.tivertoncastle.com

Part Grade I Listed, part Scheduled Ancient Monument, few buildings evoke such immediate feeling of history. Originally built 1106, but later altered. Home of medieval Earls of Devon & Princess Katherine Plantagenet. Captured by Fairfax during English Civil War.

For fun; children try on armour, listen to ghost stories, explore secret passages, experience the medieval loos and enjoy the beautiful walled gardens, interesting furniture and pictures.

Super holiday accommodation - modern comforts in medieval surroundings. Make a Castle your home.

CONTACT
Owner: Mr and Mrs A K Gordon
Contact: Mrs A Gordon
Tel: 01884 253200 **Alt Tel:** 01884 255200
Fax: 01884 254200 **Email:** info@tivertoncastle.com

LOCATION
Park Hill, Tiverton, Devon EX16 6RP
Map Ref: 2:K5 - 7 mile from J25 on M5 along A361 towards Tiverton follow Castle signs.

OPENING TIMES
Easter-end Oct: Sun, Thu, BH Mon, 2.30pm-5.30pm. Last admission 5pm. Open to groups (12+) by prior arrangement at any time.

ADMISSION
Adult: £7, Child (7-16yrs): £3, Under 7's: Free.
Garden: £2

KEY FACTS

Excellent loo facilities.

Limited for coaches. Free parking for visitors in the drive. 20 spaces.

Partial. Please see website for further information.

Make a castle your home and stay in one of the lovely 5 self-catering holiday properties on site.

Private house within the courtyard, by arrangement. Tour parties welcome all year when not open.

Great fun for children; welcoming school parties, specially if the children come in period costume.

Tiny shop selling inexpensive, good quality souvenirs mainly relating to the Castle.

Plant sales available.

Please see the 'What's on' section of the website to see all local attractions.

Castle Hill Gardens

castlehilldevon.co.uk

Set in the rolling hills of Devon, Castle Hill Gardens offers a tranquil visit. Stroll through the spectacular gardens, dotted with mystical temples, follies, statues, vistas and a sham castle. The path through the Woodland Gardens, filled with flowering shrubs, leads you down to the river, the magical Satyr's temple and Ugley Bridge.

KEY FACTS

 Daily except Saturdays.

 Free parking.

 Partial. WC's.

 On leads.

 Groups and coach parties are welcome at all times by prior arrangement.

 Refreshments are available from Apr-Sep.

CONTACT
Owner: The Earl and Countess of Arran
Contact: Marie Tippet
Tel: 01598 760421 / 01598 760336 Ext 1
Email: gardens@castlehill-devon.com
LOCATION
Filleigh, Barnstaple, Devon EX32 0RQ
Map Ref: 2:I14 - A361, take B3226 to South Molton. Follow brown signs to Castle Hill.
OPENING TIMES
Daily except Sats.
Apr-Sep 11am-5pm.
Oct-Mar 11am-dusk.
ADMISSION
Please see website for prices.

Sand

sandsidbury.co.uk

Sand is one of East Devon's hidden gems. The beautiful valley garden extends to six acres and is the setting for the lived-in Tudor house, the 15th Century Hall House, and the 16th Century Summer House. The family, under whose unbroken ownership the property has remained since 1560, provide guided house tours.

KEY FACTS

 No photography in house.

 Toilet facilities available.

 Parking available.

 Partial.

 Dogs welcome on leads.

 Guided tours obligatory.

 The tea room offers light refreshments only.

CONTACT
Owner: Roger Huyshe
Contact: Stella & Stephen Huyshe-Shires
Tel: 01395 597230
Email: info@sandsidbury.co.uk
LOCATION
Sidbury, Sidmouth EX10 0QN **Map Ref:** 2:L7
Well signed, 400 yards off A375 between Honiton and Sidmouth. Do not rely on SatNav by postcode.
OPENING TIMES
Suns & Mons in Jun & BH Suns & Mons. For other dates see website. Open 2pm-6pm last tour 5pm. Groups by appt.
ADMISSION
House & Garden
Adult: £7.50, Child/Student: £1.
Garden only
Adult: £3, Accompanied Child (under 16): Free.

Hemerdon House

hemerdonhouse.co.uk

Built in the late 18th Century by the current owners' ancestors, Hemerdon House is a trove of local history, containing naval and military mementos, books, paintings, furniture, china and silver collected through many generations. Family members offer tours of the interior on certain days of the year - please see website for details - and visitors are welcome to explore the grounds on those days.

KEY FACTS

 Parties of 6 or more please contact us in advance; parties of 10 or more by prior arrangement only.

 Toilet facilities available.

 Free parking.

 Partial access - please see website for details.

 Dogs on leads are permitted in the grounds while the house is open.

 Two tours, approximately 1 hour 15 minutes each, starting at 2.30pm and 4pm.

CONTACT
Tel: 07704 708416
Email: hemerdon.house@gmail.com

LOCATION
Plympton, Devon PL7 5BZ
Map Ref: 2:I9
SatNav directions may be misleading so please see website for directions.

OPENING TIMES
See website for dates.

ADMISSION
HHA Member: £5
Adult: £7.50
Child: Free (Under 12)

The Alhambra Corridor, Hartland Abbey

Minterne Gardens
www.minterne.co.uk

Landscaped in the manner of 'Capability' Brown, Minterne's unique garden has been described by Simon Jenkins as 'a corner of paradise'. 20 wild, woodland acres of magnolias, rhododendrons and azaleas providing new vistas at each turn, with small lakes, streams and cascades. Private House tours, dinners, corporate seminars, wedding and events. As seen on BBC Gardeners' World. Voted one of the ten Prettiest Gardens in England by The Times.

CONTACT
Owner/Contact: The Hon Mr & Mrs Henry Digby
Tel: 01300 341370
Email: enquiries@minterne.co.uk

LOCATION
Minterne Magna, Nr Dorchester, Dorset DT2 7AU
Map Ref: 2:O6 - On A352 Dorchester/Sherborne Road, 2 miles North of Cerne Abbas.

OPENING TIMES
Mid Feb-9 Nov: daily, 10am-6pm.

ADMISSION
Adult: £6
Child: (accompanied by an adult): Free
RHS members: Free

KEY FACTS

 Gardens open daily from 10am-6pm, Feb-Nov.

 Toilet facilities available.

 Parking is free for visitors in the car park opposite St Andrews Church. Picnic tables in car park.

 Features various steep and uneven surfaces and are therefore NOT advised for wheelchairs.

 In grounds on leads.

 By arrangement, with a minimum of 20 in the party. Tours personally guided by Lord Digby.

 Café on East Terrace open from 10.30am, Apr-Oct (weather permitting). Light lunches & cream teas.

 Serves as a spectacular venue for guests seeking a private dining experience.

 Please see website for details on plant sales .

 Seminars/Team Building/ Away Days.

 Offering a small & intimate wedding venue for licensed civil ceremonies or large reception for your wedding.

 Minterne has been featured in films, television, radio, broadsheet newspapers and books.

Sherborne Castle & Gardens
sherbornecastle.com

Built by Sir Walter Raleigh in 1594. Home of the Digby family since 1617. View magnificent staterooms, nationally important collections of art, furniture & porcelain, Raleigh's kitchen and a museum with a 'Capability Brown' exhibition. 2018 marks the 400th anniversary of Raleigh's execution - new Sir Walter Raleigh exhibition. Explore 42 acres of English landscape gardens designed by 'Capability Brown' and discover a 50 acre lake, herbaceous borders, magnificent specimen trees and sweeping vistas.

CONTACT
Owner: Edward Wingfield Digby **Contact:** Robert Smith
Tel: 01935 812072 **Email:** enquiries@sherbornecastle.com

LOCATION
New Road, Sherborne, Dorset DT9 5NR
Map Ref: 2:O5 - 1/4m from town and main line railway station. Follow brown signs from A30 or A352. ½m S of the Old Castle.

OPENING TIMES
Castle, Gardens, Gift Shop & Tea Rooms: Good Friday 30 Mar-28 Oct 2018; daily except Mon & Fri; Gardens from 10am, Tearoom from 10.30am, Castle & Gift Shop from 11am.

ADMISSION
Castle & Gardens
Adult: £12, Senior: £11.50, Child: Free (max 4 per full paying adult).
Gardens only
Adult/Senior: £6.50, Child: Free (max of 4 per adult).
Groups: 15+ discount options available on application.

KEY FACTS

 Visitors are welcome to picnic in the gardens. Picnic tables are provided in the designated areas.

 Internal and external toilets include facilities for wheelchairs and baby changing.

 Unlimited free parking for coaches and cars.

 Access to the ground floor only. A slide show runs showing the inaccessible rooms.

 Dogs are welcome in the gardens provided they are kept on a short lead at all times.

 Pre-booked private & self-guided tours of the castle are available for groups.

 School & language student groups are accepted as private or self-guided tours.

 Tea Room offers coffees, traditional light lunches & afternoon teas with a wide selection of cakes. Free Wi-Fi.

 Gift Shop offers a wide variety of gifts, souvenirs & Sherborne Castle Wine to remind you of your visit.

 The Orangery & Ginkgo Lawn are available for corporate & private functions. Please contact for details.

 Sherborne Castle hosts a wide variety of public events throughout the open season.

A wonderful venue for civil marriage ceremonies, civil partnerships and wedding receptions.

South West

Deans Court

www.deanscourt.org

An historic private house and garden that has been lived in for 1,300 years.
Guided Tours
Weekdays at 10am,12pm. Suns & Bank Holidays at 2pm, 4pm. Meet at gate on Deans Court Lane.
NGS Openings May 21, Jun 19. See NGS website.

KEY FACTS

 Parking available only on NGS open days.

 Contact for further details.

 Dogs welcome on NGS open days only not tours.

 Holiday houses sleep from 4-26 people.

 Weekdays 10am, 12pm. Suns & BHs 2pm, 4pm. Meet at gate on Deans Court Lane.

 20 pers. max.

 Healthfood Café.

 Homestore.

 The venue hire fee covers everything you need to hold a Country Wedding in a marquee.

CONTACT
Owner:
Sir William & Lady Hanham
Contact: Jonathan Cornish
Tel: 01202 849314
Email: info@deanscourt.org
LOCATION
Deans Court Lane, Wimborne, Dorset BH21 1EE
Map Ref: 3:B6 - Follow signs to Wimborne Town Centre; pass through the Square, at the end of the High St. cross the junction (opposite Holmans TV shop) into Deans Court Ln.
OPENING TIMES
May 3, 10, 17, 20, 21, 28, 31
Jun 7, 14, 17, 19, 24, 28
Jul 1, 5, 12, 19, 26
Aug 2, 5, 9,12, 16, 19, 23,26, 27, 30
ADMISSION
Adults: £8, Senior & Disabled: £6, Child (under-16) & HHA Friends: Free

Wolfeton House

A fine medieval and Elizabethan manor house lying in the water-meadows near the confluence of the rivers Cerne and Frome. It was embellished around 1580 and has splendid plaster ceilings, fireplaces and panelling. To be seen are the Great Hall, Stairs and Chamber, Parlour, Dining Room, Chapel & Cyder House.

KEY FACTS

 Catering for groups by prior arrangement.

 Groups by appointment throughout the year.

 Limited for coaches.

 Accessible.

 Guided tours by arrangement.

 Educational and school visits by arrangement.

 Corporate functions by arrangement.

CONTACT
Owner:
Capt N T L L T Thimbleby
Contact: The Steward
Tel: 01305 263500
Email: kthimbleby.wolfeton@gmail.com

LOCATION
Nr Dorchester, Dorset DT2 9QN

Map Ref: 2:O6

1½m from Dorchester on the A37 towards Yeovil. Indicated by Historic House signs.

OPENING TIMES
Jun-end Sep: Mon, Wed & Thu, 2pm-5pm.

Groups by appointment throughout the year.

ADMISSION
£8

Sandford Orcas Manor House

Tudor manor house with gatehouse, fine panelling, furniture, pictures. Terraced gardens with topiary and herb garden. Personal conducted tour by owner.

KEY FACTS

 Parking is available.

 Unsuitable.

 Dogs welcome in grounds, on leads.

 Person conducted tours are obligatory.

CONTACT
Owner/Contact:
Sir Mervyn Medlycott Bt
Tel: 01963 220206

LOCATION
Sandford Orcas, Sherborne, Dorset DT9 4SB **Map Ref:** 2:O5
2½m North of Sherborne, Dorset 4m South of A303 at Sparkford. Entrance next to church.

OPENING TIMES
Easter Mon, 10am-5pm.
May & Jul-Sep:
Suns & Mons, 2pm-5pm.

ADMISSION
Adult: £5, Child: £2.50.
Groups (10+)
Adult: £4, Child: £2.

Minterne Garden

Kelmscott Manor

www.kelmscottmanor.org.uk Ⓕ

'The loveliest haunt of ancient peace'. Kelmscott Manor, a Grade I listed Tudor farmhouse adjacent to the River Thames, was William Morris's summer residence from 1871 until his death in 1896. Morris loved Kelmscott Manor, which seemed to him to have 'grown up out of the soil'. Its beautiful gardens with barns, dovecote, meadow and stream provided a constant source of inspiration. The house contains an outstanding collection of the possessions and work of Morris, his family and associates, including furniture, textiles, pictures, carpets and ceramics.

CONTACT
Owner: Society of Antiquaries of London
Tel: 01367 252486 **Email:** admin@kelmscottmanor.org.uk

LOCATION
Kelmscott, Nr Lechlade, Gloucestershire GL7 3HJ
(West Oxfordshire)
Map Ref: 6:P12 - At South East end of the village, 2 miles due East of Lechlade, off the Lechlade - Faringdon Road.

OPENING TIMES
House & Garden: Apr-Oct, Weds and Sats, 11am-5pm
(Ticket office opens 10.30am). Last admission to the house, 4pm.
Limited advance bookings on public open days.
House has limited capacity; timed ticket system operates.
Group visits: Apr-Oct, Thurs. Must be booked in advance.

ADMISSION
Adult: £9.50, Child/Student: £5, Family: £26.
Garden only: £3.50. Carer accompanying disabled person free.

KEY FACTS

 No flash photography, protruding lenses & tripods or "selfie sticks" in house.

 Toilets available, including accessible toilet for the disabled

 Baby changing facilities are available in the accessible toilet next to the Tearoom.

 Ample free parking 10 minutes' walk. Limited for coaches.

 Partial. Good access to the ground floor of the house, gardens, shop and Tearoom for wheelchair users.

Well-behaved dogs on leads; except in the formal gardens & manor house. Assistant dogs welcome.

 Group tours by arrangement.

 Educational visits by arrangement.

 Enjoy freshly prepared delicious homemade food in our licensed Tearoom.

 Gift Shop selling a wide range of items based on William Morris designs.

Please see the 'What's On' section of the website for events, exhibitions, workshops & lectures etc.

Sezincote

www.sezincote.co.uk  Ⓕ

Exotic oriental water garden by Repton and Daniell.

Large semi-circular orangery.

House by S P Cockerell in Indian style was the inspiration for Brighton Pavilion.

CONTACT
Contact: Dr E Peake
Tel: 01386 700444 **Email:** enquiries@sezincote.co.uk

LOCATION
Moreton-In-Marsh, Gloucestershire GL56 9AW
Map Ref: 6:P10 -2 miles west of Moreton-in-Marsh on the A44 opposite entrance to Batsford Arboretum.

OPENING TIMES
Garden: Thus, Fridays & BH Mons, 2pm-6pm except Dec.
House: As above May-Sep. Teas in Orangery when house open.

ADMISSION
House
Adult: £10 (guided tour).
Garden
Adult: £5, Child: £1.50 (Under 5s: Free).
Groups: Welcomed weekdays, please contact for details.

KEY FACTS

 Please see our website for up-to-date events and special openings.

 Garden open all year apart from Dec.

 For full information for disabled visitors please email enquiries@sezincote.co.uk.

 Properties to rent from larger, 6 bed farm houses to 3 bed cottages to quirky 2 bedroom period cottages.

 Obligatory.

 Tea and cake served May to Sep.

 Sezincote is a theatrical and magical summer venue and hosts six weddings a year.

 Civil and religious ceremonies and wedding receptions.

South West

Stanway House & Water Garden

www.stanwayfountain.co.uk

'As perfect and pretty a Cotswold manor house as anyone is likely to see' (Fodor's Great Britain 1998 guidebook). Stanway's beautiful architecture, furniture, parkland and village are complemented by the restored 18th Century water garden and the magnificent fountain, 300 feet, making it the tallest garden and gravity fountain in the world. The Watermill in Church Stanway, now fully restored as a working flour mill, was recently re-opened by HRH The Prince of Wales. Its massive 24-foot overshot waterwheel, 8th largest waterwheel in England, drives traditional machinery, to produce stoneground Cotswold flour.

KEY FACTS

 Toilet facilities available.

 Group visits all year round.

 Parking available.

 Welcomes people with disabilities but you are advised to telephone for full details of access available.

 Dogs are welcome in the grounds of Stanway. Please keep on leads.

 Audio tours available.

 Group visits, coach parties & personal tours can be prior arranged at any time of year.

 School tours of the Water Mill by arrangement.

 Teas, cold drinks and ice cream available.

 Gift shop selling beers.

 Please contact for all corporate enquiries.

 For all upcoming events please see the 'News & Events' section of the website.

 The perfect venue for wedding receptions.

 Film and photographic location.

CONTACT
Owner: The Earl of Wemyss and March
Contact: Debbie Lewis
Tel: 01386 584528 **Tours:** 07850 585539
Fax: 01386 584688
Email: stanwayhse@btconnect.com

LOCATION
Stanway, Cheltenham, Gloucestershire GL54 5PQ
Map Ref: 6:O10 - North of Winchcombe, just off B4077.

OPENING TIMES
House & Garden: Jun-Aug: Tue & Thu, 2pm-5pm.
Private Tours: By arrangement at other times.

ADMISSION
Please see website for up-to-date admission prices.

Kiftsgate Court Gardens

www.kiftsgate.co.uk

Magnificently situated garden on the edge of the Cotswold escarpment with views towards the Malvern Hills. Many unusual shrubs and plants including tree peonies, abutilons, specie and old-fashioned roses. Winner HHA/ Christie's Garden of the Year Award 2003.

KEY FACTS

 The toilets are in the courtyard, the entrance to which is on the right as you leave the main car park.

 Limited for coaches.

 Partial. A map showing the easiest route is available free of charge at the entrance.

 No dogs in the garden. There is an area next to the overflow car park where dogs can stretch their legs.

 The Tea Room serves cream teas, delicious cakes, biscuits and a selection of sandwiches.

The small shop next to the plant sales area offers a range of garden related gifts.

Plants grown in the garden and propagated in our own nursery are available to buy.

CONTACT
Owner: Mr & Mrs J G Chambers
Contact: Mr J G Chambers
Tel: 01386 438777
Email: info@kiftsgate.co.uk

LOCATION
Chipping Campden, Gloucestershire GL55 6LN
Map Ref: 6:O9 - 4 miles North East of Chipping Campden. ¼ mile West of Hidcote Garden.

OPENING TIMES
May, Jun, Jul, Sat-Wed, 12 noon-6pm. Aug, Sat-Wed, 2pm-6pm. Apr & Sep, Sun, Mon & Wed, 2pm-6pm.

ADMISSION
Adult: £8.50, Child: £2.50. Groups (20+): £7.50.

Water Willow by D G Rossetti at Kelmscott Manor

Fairfield

Elizabethan and medieval house. Occupied by the same family (Acland-Hoods and their ancestors) for over 800 years. Woodland garden. Views of Quantocks and the sea.

House described in Simon Jenkins' book 'England's Thousand Best Houses'.

CONTACT
Tel: 01278 732617 / 01278 732251

LOCATION
Stogursey, Bridgwater, Somerset TA5 1PU
Map Ref: 2:L4 - 1m W Bridgwater, 8m East Williton. From A39 Bridgwater/ Minehead turn North. House 1m West Stogursey.

OPENING TIMES
Mar-Sep. Bank Holiday Mons 2.30pm-4.30pm.
Gardens also open.
Advisable to contact to confirm dates / details on further dates.
ADMISSION
£6 in aid of Stogursey Church.

KEY FACTS

 No inside photography.

 No coach parking.

 Accessible.

 Guide dogs only.

 Guided tours obligatory.

Glastonbury Abbey

glastonburyabbey.com

A hidden jewel in the heart of Somerset, Glastonbury Abbey is traditionally associated with the earliest days of Christianity in Britain. It is also the resting place for the legendary King Arthur.

CONTACT
Owner:
Glastonbury Abbey Estate
Tel: 01458 832267
Email: info glastonburyabbey.com
Twitter: @glastonburyabbe
LOCATION
Magdalene Street, Glastonbury BA6 9EL
Map Ref: 2:N4 - 50 yards from the Market Cross, in centre of Glastonbury.
OPENING TIMES
Nov-Feb 9am-4pm
Mar-May 9am-6pm
Jun-Aug 9am-8pm
Sep-Oct 9am-6pm
ADMISSION
For pricing details visit the website - reduced tickets online up until 6pm the day before you visit.

KEY FACTS

 All year except 25 December.

 Pay and display nearby.

 Please see the access statement online for further details or contact prior to your visit.

 Dogs welcome on leads.

 Mar-Oct (groups pre-book Nov-Feb).

 Primary to University, RE, History, workshops & activities 01458 8361103.

 Summer.

 The Glastonbury Abbey Shop is just beside the Ticket Office and Main Entrance of the abbey.

 Events held throughout year.

Stanway House & Water Garden

Longleat
www.longleat.co.uk

Set within 900 acres of 'Capability' Brown landscaped grounds, Longleat House is widely regarded as one of the best examples of high Elizabethan architecture in Britain and one of the most beautiful stately homes open to the public.

Visited by Elizabeth I in 1547, Longleat House was built by Sir John Thynne from 1568 and is currently home of the 7th Marquess of Bath. Many treasures are included within; the fine collection of paintings ranges from English portraits dating from the 16th Century to Dutch landscapes and Italian Old Masters. The ceilings are renowned for their ornate paintings and abundance of gilt made by the firm of John Dibblee Crace in the 1870s and 1880s. The furniture collection includes English pieces from as early as the 16th Century, fine French furniture of the 17th and 18th Centuries and a collection of major Italian pieces.

Don't miss the Safari Drive-Through, Animal Discovery and Adventure Zone for a fun-filled day out for all the family as well as spectacular seasonal events.

CONTACT
Owner: Marquess of Bath
Tel: 01985 844400
Email: enquiries@longleat.co.uk

LOCATION
Longleat, Warminster BA12 7NW
Map: 2:P4 - Just off the A36 between Bath-Salisbury (A362 Warminster-Frome) 2 hours from London following M3, A303, A36, A362 or M4/J18. A46, A36.

TRANSPORT ROUTES
Car I Bike

OPENING TIMES
Feb-Oct. Please see website for more details.

Limited House route available during Christmas period; selected dates from Nov-Jan.

Please see website for details.

ADMISSION
Please see website for details: www.longleat.co.uk

KEY FACTS

 Guest services / Lost persons.

 Toilet facilities available.

 Baby changing facilities available.

 When the park is closed VIP Safari Park tours are available for a closer view.

 Free parking available.

 The park and attractions are made as accessible as possible. See the website for further details.

 Longleat Hotels are an exclusive collection of opulent South West hotels and accommodation.

 House tours from 12 noon daily; private chattels tours on advertised dates.

 For learning opportunities please see the school section of the website.

 Orangery.

 The Cellar Café.

 Lady Bath's Shop; Emma's Kitchen.

 Book indoor and outdoor events from 45 -500+.

 Please see the 'What's On' section of the website for all seasonal events and exhibitions.

Wilton House

www.wiltonhouse.com

Wilton House has been the Earl of Pembroke's ancestral home for nearly 500 years. Inigo Jones and John Webb rebuilt the house in the Palladian style after the 1647 fire whilst further alterations were made by James Wyatt from 1801. Recipient of the 2010 HHA/Sotheby's Restoration Award, the chief architectural features are the 17th Century state apartments (Single and Double Cube rooms) and the 19th Century Cloisters.

The House contains one of the finest art collections in Europe and is set in magnificent landscaped parkland featuring the Palladian Bridge.

A large adventure playground provides hours of fun for younger visitors. The Gift Shop offers a varied range of presents and souvenirs and the Palladian Restaurant provides refreshments, lunches and teas.

KEY FACTS

 No photography in the house. Open 5 days a week during the season. Guide dogs only.

 Toilets and disability WC's available.

 Facilities provided.

 Space for 200 cars and 12 coaches (free coach parking and coach driver meal voucher).

 In the house, grounds, shop & restaurant.

 By arrangement only (15+). Grounds guided tour £8.50.

 National Curriculum KS1/2. Sandford Award Winner 2002 and 2008.

 Licensed.

 Licensed. Group bookings available 20+.

 Gift shop.

 Antiques Fair, Equestrian Event, Country Fair, Vehicle Rallies and Charity Sponsored Walks.

 Film location.

CONTACT
Contact: The Estate Office
Owner: The Earl and Countess of Pembroke
Tel: 01722 746728 **General Enquiries:** 01722 746700
Email: tourism@wiltonhouse.com

LOCATION
Wilton, Salisbury, Wiltshire SP2 0BJ
Map Ref: 3:B4 - Wilton House is situated 3 miles west of Salisbury, just off the A30 and 9 miles from Stonehenge, 37 miles from Bath and 90 miles from London.
TRANSPORT ROUTES Car l Bus l Train l Bike

OPENING TIMES
House: 30 Mar-2 Apr inclusive; 5 May-2 Sep, Suns-Thus & BH Sats only, 11.30am-5pm, last admission 4.30pm.
*Please check website for up-to-date information.
Grounds: 30 Mar-15 Apr; 5 May-9 Sep, Suns-Thus & BH Sats only, 11am-5.30pm.
Private groups at other times by arrangement.

ADMISSION

House & Ground	Grounds	Group Admission
Adult: £15.50	Adult: £6.50	Adult: £13
Child (5-15): £8	Child (5-15): £5	Child (5-15): £6.50
Conc: £13.25	Conc: £6	Conc: £11
Family: £38.50	Family: £18	

*Includes admission to Dining & South Ante Rooms when open.

Bowood House & Gardens

www.bowood.org

©ANNASTOWE/BOWOOD 2016

Bowood House & Gardens; home to the Marquis and Marchioness of Lansdowne, surrounded by 2,000 acres of Grade 1 listed 'Capability' Brown parkland, an award winning Walled Garden and a 30 acre spring Woodland Garden. Visit the Georgian House and discover over 250 years of art and historical memorabilia and the laboratory where Joseph Priestley discovered oxygen gas. There's an adrenalin fuelled children's adventure playground, an educational petting farm and acres of beautiful grounds.

KEY FACTS

 For further information please see the website.

 Toilets accessible in the House, near the Soft Play Area and in the Treehouse Café.

 Baby changing facilities are available within the Treehouse Café.

 Free ample parking.

 Limited disabled parking spaces near House and WC available.

 In the heart of the Bowood Estate in the Wiltshire countryside the luxury hotel is ideal for a range of breaks.

 Pre-booked guided tours available for a minimum of 15 guests.

 A haven for children, stimulating their imaginations and educational.

 Treehouse Café has a full range of freshly prepared hot and cold food, sweets and ice cream.

 The Stables Restaurant in the house is also open every day for lunch and afternoon tea.

 The Terrace Gift Shop has a wide range or affordable Bowood souvenirs, to remind you of your wonderful time.

 An exceptional venue for corporate & private events in Wiltshire, offering extensive meeting facilities.

 Please see the 'What's on' section of the website all events.

 Offers a range of wedding packages to suit your tailored needs for the perfect wedding.

CONTACT
Owner: The Marquis of Lansdowne
Tel: 01249 812102
Email: houseandgardens@bowood.org

LOCATION
Calne, Wiltshire SN11 0LZ
Map Ref: 3:A2

Follow the brown tourist signs 'Bowood House & Gardens'. The entrance is through the white gates just off Derry Hill. If using a Satnav please use the postcode SN11 9NF.

OPENING TIMES / ADMISSION
Apr-Oct, 11am-6pm.
See website for up-to-date opening & admission details.

Iford Manor: The Peto Garden

www.ifordmanor.co.uk

Unique Grade 1 Italian-style garden set on a romantic hillside above the River Frome. Home to the famous Edwardian garden architect Harold Peto from 1899-1933, this Grade 1 listed garden represents his inspirational 'Tuscan dream', featuring terraces, colonnades, cloisters, casita, statuary, evergreen planting and magnificent rural views. The garden has recently undergone extensive replanting following major restoration of the structures. Winner of 2017 Group Travel "Little Treasures of Britain" Award.

KEY FACTS

 No professional photography without permission. Children under 10yrs preferred weekdays for safety.

 Toilet and disabled WC facilities available.

 On-site parking available for cars. Coaches by appointment only.

 Partial step-free access. Please call in advance for information.

 National Routes 4 and 254 run within 1 mile.

 Dogs welcome on leads.

 Available for groups by appointment.

 Tea and cake available during open hours.

 Iford Arts opera and jazz concerts May to Aug.

Manolo: The Boy Who Made Shoes for Lizards (2017).

CONTACT
Owner/Contact: Mr William Cartwright-Hignett
Contact: Mr Geoff Parkes (Administrator)
Tel: 01225 863146 **Email:** info@ifordmanor.co.uk

LOCATION
Lower Westwood, Bradford-on-Avon, Wiltshire BA15 2BA
Map Ref: 2:P3 - 2 miles SW of Bradford on Avon, signed from B3109. 6 miles S of Bath, signed from A36.
Coaches / campervans: Should call in advance for directions.
Train: Freshford (& 20 min walk) or Bradford on Avon (& taxi).

OPENING TIMES
Apr 1-Sep 30: Weds-Sun & BH Mons, 11am-4pm.
ADMISSIONS
Adult: £6, Conc: £5.20, Children (under 2yrs): Free.
Groups: 15+ Please contact for details.

Lydiard Park

www.lydiardpark.org.uk

Lydiard Park is the ancestral home of the Viscounts Bolingbroke. The Palladian house contains original family furnishings and portraits, exceptional plasterwork and rare 17th Century window. The Georgian ornamental Walled Garden has beautiful seasonal displays of flowers and unique garden features. Exceptional monuments, including the Golden Cavalier, in the church.

CONTACT
Owner: Swindon Borough Council
Contact: Lydiard Park
Tel: 01793 466664
Email: lydiardpark@swindon.gov.uk

LOCATION
Lydiard Tregoze, Swindon, Wiltshire SN5 3PA
Map Ref: 3:B1- 4 miles West of Swindon, 1½ miles North M4/J16.

OPENING TIMES
House: Wed-Sun between Easter & Christmas, 11am-4pm.
Lydiard Park is open every day from 7.30am to dusk.

ADMISSIONS
Adult: £6.50, Child (3-16 yrs): £3.50, Senior: £6.

KEY FACTS

 For further information please visit the website.

 Toilet & accessible WC inside the Coach House, next to the Tea Rooms.

 The park is open all year round.

 Car parking charges apply. Coach parking near Lydiard House accessed via the Hay Lane entrance.

 Designated parking, There is wheelchair access to the House, Church and Visitor Centre.

 Outside of Apr-Sep dogs allowed off lead in the majority of the Park.

Audio tours available.

 Guided tours (subject to availability and must be booked in advance).

 Educational visits by arrangement.

 Forest Café open all year & Coach House Tea Rooms opens depending on the weather conditions.

 Small gift shop.

 Seasonal heritage plants available to purchase from Coach House Tea Rooms.

 Conference Centre, run by the Chartridge Conference Company is available.

 Please see the 'Events' section of the website for all upcoming events.

Longleat

Corsham Court

corsham-court.co.uk

Historic collection of paintings and furniture. Extensive gardens.

Tours by arrangement.

Sign-posted from the A4, approximately 4 miles West of Chippenham.

CONTACT
Owner: Lord Methuen
Contact: The Curator
Tel: 01249 712214 \ 01249 701610
Email: staterooms@ corsham-court.co.uk

LOCATION
Corsham, Wiltshire SN13 0BZ
Map Ref: 3:A2

OPENING TIMES
Tue, Wed, Thu, Sat, Sun
20 Mar-30 Sep, 2pm-5.30pm.
Weekends only: 1 Oct-19 Mar, 2pm-4.30pm (Closed Dec).
ADMISSION
House & Gardens
Adult: £10, Child: £5.
Gardens only
Adult: £5, Child: £2.50.

KEY FACTS

 No photography in house.

 Open all year by arrangement.

 120yds from house. Coaches may park in Church Square. Coach parties must book in advance.

 Platform lift and WC.

 Dogs on leads welcome in the gardens.

 Max 45. If requested the owner may meet the group. Morning tours preferred.

Available: rate negotiable. A guide will be provided.

 Guide books, postcards, etc. at the cash desk.

ANTONY HOUSE & GARDEN ❧
Torpoint, Cornwall PL11 2QA
Tel: 01752 812191 **Email:** antony@nationaltrust.org.uk

CAERHAYS CASTLE & GARDEN 🏛ⓕ
Caerhays, Gorran, St Austell, Cornwall PL26 6LY
Tel: 01872 5013101 **Email:** enquiries@caerhays.co.uk

ST CATHERINE'S CASTLE ⌗
St Catherine's Cove, Fowey, Cornwall PL23 1JH
Tel: 0370 333 1181 **Email:** customers@english-heritage.org.uk

CHYSAUSTER ANCIENT VILLAGE ⌗
Nr Newmill, Penzance, Cornwall TR20 8XA
Tel: 07831 757934 **Email:** customers@english-heritage.org.uk

COTEHELE ❧
Saint Dominick, Saltash, Cornwall PL12 6TA
Tel: 01579 351346 **Email:** cothele@nationaltrust.org.uk

LANHYDROCK ❧
Lanhydrock, Bodmin, Cornwall PL30 5AD
Tel: 01208 265950 **Email:** lanhydrock@nationaltrust.org.uk

LAUNCESTON CASTLE ⌗
Castle Lodge, Launceston, Cornwall PL15 7DR
Tel: 01566 772365 **Email:** customers@english-heritage.org.uk

LAWRENCE HOUSE MUSEUM ❧
9 Castle Street, Launceston, Cornwall PL15 8BA
Tel: 01566 773277 **Email:** lawrencehousemuseum@yahoo.co.uk

THE LOST GARDENS OF HELIGAN
Pentewan, St Austall, Cornwall PL26 6EN
Tel: 01726 845100 **Email:** info@heligan.com

ST MAWES CASTLE ⌗
St Mawes, Cornwall TR2 5DE
Tel: 01326 270526 **Email:** stmawes.castle@english-heritage.org.uk

MOUNT EDGCUMBE HOUSE & COUNTRY PARK
Cremyll, Torpoint, Cornwall PL10 1HZ
Tel: 01752 822236

PENCARROW HOUSE & GARDENS 🏛ⓕ
Washaway, Bodmin, Cornwall PL30 3AG
Tel: 01208 841369 **Email:** info@pencarrow.co.uk

PENDENNIS CASTLE ⌗
Falmouth, Cornwall TR11 4LP
Tel: 01326 316594 **Email:** pendennis.castle@english-heritage.org.uk

PENTILLIE CASTLE & ESTATE
Paynters Cross, St Mellion, Saltash, Cornwall PL12 6QD
Tel: 01579 212002 **Email:** contact@pentillie.co.uk

PORT ELIOT HOUSE & GARDENS 🏛ⓕ
St. Germans, Saltash, Cornwall PL12 5ND
Tel: 01503 230211 **Email:** info@porteliot.co.uk

RESTORMEL CASTLE ⌗
Lostwithiel, Cornwall PL22 0EE
Tel: 01208 872687 **Email:** customers@english-heritage.org.uk

TINTAGEL CASTLE ⌗ ◇
Tintagel, Cornwall PL34 0HE
Tel: 01840 770328 **Email:** tintagel.castle@english-heritage.org.uk

TREBAH GARDEN 🏛
Mawnan Smith, Nr Falmouth, Cornwall TR11 5JZ
Tel: 01326 252200 **Email:** mail@trebah-garden.co.uk

TRELISSICK GARDEN ❧
Feock, Truro, Cornwall TR3 6QL
Tel: 01872 862090 **Email:** trelissick@nationaltrust.org.uk

TRERICE ❧
Kestle Mill, Nr Newquay, Cornwall TR8 4PG
Tel: 01637 875404 **Email:** trerice@nationaltrust.org.uk

A LA RONDE ❧
Summer Lane, Exmouth, Devon EX8 5BD
Tel: 01395 265514 **Email:** alaronde@nationaltrust.org.uk

ARLINGTON COURT ❧
Nr Barnstaple, North Devon EX31 4LP
Tel: 01271 850296 **Email:** arlingtoncourt@nationaltrust.org.uk

BERRY POMEROY CASTLE ⌗
Totnes, Devon TQ9 6LJ
Tel: 01803 866618 **Email:** customers@english-heritage.org.uk

BUCKLAND ABBEY ❧
The National Trust, Yelverton, Devon PL20 6EY
Tel: 01822 853607 **Email:** bucklandabbey@nationaltrust.org.uk

CASTLE DROGO ❧
Drewsteignton, Nr Exeter EX6 6PB
Tel: 01647 433306 **Email:** castledrogo@nationaltrust.org.uk

CHAMBERCOMBE MANOR 🏛ⓕ
Ilfracombe, Devon EX34 9RJ
Tel: 01271 862202 **Email:** chambercombemanor@btconnect.com

CLOVELLY
Nr Bideford, N Devon EX39 5TA
Tel: 01237 431781 **Email:** visitorcentre@clovelly.co.uk

COLETON FISHACRE ❧
Brownstone Road, Kingswear, Dartmouth TQ6 0EQ
Tel: 01803 842382 **Email:** coletonfishacre@nationaltrust.org.uk

COMPTON CASTLE ❧
Marldon, Paighton TQ3 1TA
Tel: 01803 843235 **Email:** compton@nationaltrust.org.uk

DARTMOUTH CASTLE ⌗
Castle Road, Dartmouth, Devon TQ6 0JN
Tel: 01803 833588 **Email:** dartmouth.castle@english-heritage.org.uk

DOWNES 🏛
Crediton, Devon EX17 3PL
Tel: 01363 775142 **Email:** info@downes.co.uk

THE GARDEN HOUSE
Buckland Monachorum, Yelverton PL20 7LQ
Tel: 01822 854769 **Email:** office@the gardenhouse.org.uk

GREAT FULFORD
Dunsford, Nr. Exeter, Devon EX6 7AJ
Tel: 01647 24205 **Email:** francis@greatfulford.co.uk

GREENWAY �
Greenway Road, Galmpton, Nr Brixham, Devon TQ5 0ES
Tel: 01803 842382 **Email:** greenway@nationaltrust.org.uk

KILLERTON �</br>
Broadclyst, Exeter EX5 3LE
Tel: 01392 881345 **Email:** killerton@nationaltrust.org.uk

KNIGHTSHAYES �</br>
Bolham, Tiverton, Devon EX16 7RQ
Tel: 01884 254665 **Email:** knightshayes@nationaltrust.org.uk

POWDERHAM CASTLE 🏛ⓔ
Kenton, Nr Exeter, Devon EX6 8JQ
Tel: 01626 890243 **Email:** castle@powderham.co.uk

RHS GARDEN ROSEMOOR
Great Torrington, Devon EX38 8PH
Tel: 01805 624067 **Email:** rosemooradmin@rhs.org.uk

SALTRAM �</br>
Plympton, Plymouth, Devon PL7 1UH
Tel: 01752 333500 **Email:** saltram@nationaltrust.org.uk

SHILSTONE 🏛
Modbury, Devon PL21 0TW
Tel: 01548 830888 **Email:** events@shilstonedevon.co.uk

TOTNES CASTLE ⌗
Castle Street, Totnes, Devon TQ9 5NU
Tel: 01803 864406 **Email:** customers@english-heritage.org.uk

UGBROOKE HOUSE & GARDENS 🏛ⓔ
Chudleigh, Devon TQ13 0AD
Tel: 01626 852179 **Email:** info@ugbrooke.co.uk

ABBOTSBURY SUBTROPICAL GARDENS 🏛ⓔ
Abbotsbury, Weymouth, Dorset DT3 4LA
Tel: 01305 871387 **Email:** info@abbotsbury-tourism.co.uk

ATHELHAMPTON HOUSE & GARDENS 🏛ⓔ
Athelhampton, Dorchester, Dorset DT2 7LG
Tel: 01305 848363 **Email:** enquiry@athelhampton.co.uk

Church Of Our Lady & St Ignatius

North Chideock, Bridport, Dorset DT6 6LF
A gem of English Catholicism and the Shrine of the Dorset Martyrs
built in 1874 in Italian Romanesque style. **Map Ref:** 2:A7
OS ref: SY090 786 - A35 to Chideock, turn into N Rd & ¼ mile on right.
Tel: 01308 488348 **Email:** info@chideockmartyrschurch.org.uk
Website: www.chideockmartyrschurch.org.uk
Open: All year: 10am-4pm. **Admission:** Donations welcome.

CLAVELL TOWER ▣
Kimmeridge, Nr Wareham, Dorset BH20 5PE
Tel: 01628 825925 **Email:** bookings@landmarktrust.org.uk

CORFE CASTLE �</br>
Wareham, Dorset BH20 5EZ
Tel: 01929 477062 **Email:** corfecastle@nationaltrust.org.uk

EDMONDSHAM HOUSE & GARDENS 🏛ⓔ
Cranborne, Wimborne, Dorset BH21 5RE
Tel: 01725 517207 **Email:** edmondsham.estateoffice@homeuser.net

FORDE ABBEY & GARDENS 🏛ⓔ
Forde Abbey, Chard, Somerset TA20 4LU
Tel: 01460 221290 **Email:** info@fordeabbey.co.uk

ST GILES HOUSE 🏛
Wimborne St Giles, Dorset BH21 5NA
Tel: 01725 517214 **Email:** catherine@stgileshouse.com

HIGHCLIFFE CASTLE
Highcliffe-On-Sea, Christchurch BH23 4LE
Tel: 01425 278807 **Email:** enquiries@highcliffecastle.co.uk

HIGHER MELCOMBE 🏛
Melcombe Bingham, Dorchester, Dorset DT2 7PB
Tel: 01258 880251 **Email:** mc.woodhouse@hotmail.co.uk

KINGSTON LACY �</br>
Wimborne Minster, Dorset BH21 4EA
Tel: 01202 883402 **Email:** kingstonlacy@nationaltrust.org.uk

LULWORTH CASTLE & PARK 🏛ⓔ
East Lulworth, Wareham, Dorset BH20 5QS
Tel: 01929 400352 **Email:** info@lulworth.com

MAPPERTON 🏛ⓔ
Beaminster, Dorset DT8 3NR
Tel: 01308 862645 **Email:** office@mapperton.comk

PORTLAND CASTLE ⌗
Castletown, Portland, Weymouth, Dorset DT5 1AZ
Tel: 01305 820539 **Email:** customers@english-heritage.org.uk

STOCK GAYLARD HOUSE 🏛ⓔ
Nr Sturminster Newton, Dorset DT10 2BG
Tel: 01963 23511 **Email:** office@stockgaylard.com

ABLINGTON MANOR
Bibury, Cirencester, Gloucestershire GL7 5NY
Tel: 01285 740363 **Email:** prue@ablingtonmanor.com

BATSFORD ARBORETUM
Batsford, Moreton-in-Marsh, Gloucestershire GL56 9QB
Tel: 01386 701441 **Email:** arboretum@batsfordfoundation.co.uk

BERKELEY CASTLE 🏛ⓔ
Berkeley, Gloucestershire GL13 9BQ
Tel: 01453 810303 **Email:** info@berkeley-castle.com

BOURTON HOUSE GARDEN
Bourton-on-the-Hill, Gloucestershire GL56 9AE
Tel: 01386 700754 **Email:** info@bourtonhouse.com

CHAVENAGE HOUSE 🏛ⓔ
Chavenage, Tetbury, Gloucestershire GL8 8XP
Tel: 01666 502329 **Email:** info@chavenage.com

CHEDWORTH ROMAN VILLA �</br>
Yanworth, Cheltenham, Gloucestershire GL54 3LJ
Tel: 01242 890256 **Email:** chedworth@nationaltrust.org.uk

CIRENCESTER PARK GARDENS 🏛ⓕ
Cirencester, Gloucestershire GL7 2BU
Tel: 01285 653135

DYRHAM PARK ❧
Dyrham, Nr Bath, Gloucestershire SN14 8ER
Tel: 0117 9372501 **Email:** dyrhampark@nationaltrust.org.uk

Frampton Court 🏛 ✦
Frampton on Severn, Gloucestershire GL2 7EX
Built in 1731 & now run as a luxury B&B, Frampton Court has a superb panelled interior, antique furniture & the 'Frampton Flora' watercolours.
Map Ref: 6:M12 - 2 miles from M5 J13 via A38 & B4071.
Tel: 01452 740268 **Email:** themanor@framptoncourtestate.co.uk
Website: www.framptoncourtestate.co.uk
Open: By appointment for groups (10+). **Admission:** £10

Frampton Manor
Frampton on Severn, Gloucestershire GL2 7EP
Said to be the birthplace of 'Fair Rosamund' Clifford mistress of Henry II.
Walled Garden. **Map Ref:** 6:M12 - 2 miles from M5 J13 via A38 & B4071.
Tel: 01452 740268 **Email:** themanor@framptoncourtestate.co.uk
Website: www.framptoncourtestate.co.uk **Open:** House by appt for groups 10+. Garden only Mon & Fri 23 Apr-27 Jul, 2.30-4.30pm.
Admission: House £10, Garden £5, 16th Century Wool Barn £3.

HARDWICKE COURT 🏛ⓕ
Gloucester, Gloucestershire GL2 4RS
Tel: 01452 720212

HIDCOTE MANOR GARDEN ❧
Hidcote Bartrim, Nr Chipping Campden, Gloucestershire GL55 6LR
Tel: 01386 438333 **Email:** hidcote@nationaltrust.org.uk

HIGHGROVE GARDENS
The Garden Tours Office, The Barn, Close Farm, Gloucestershire GL8 8PH
Tel: 03031 237310 **Email:** customerservices@highgroveshop.com

NEWARK PARK ❧
Ozleworth, Wotton-Under-Edge, Gloucestershire GL12 7PZ
Tel: 01453 842644 **Email:** newarkpark@nationaltrust.org.uk

OWLPEN MANOR 🏛
Uley, Nr Dursley, Gloucestershire GL11 5BZ
Tel: 01453 860261 **Email:** sales@owlpen.com

PAINSWICK ROCOCO GARDEN 🏛ⓕ
Painswick, Gloucestershire GL6 6TH
Tel: 01452 813204 **Email:** info@rococogarden.org.uk

RODMARTON MANOR 🏛ⓕ
Cirencester, Gloucestershire GL7 6PF
Tel: 01285 841442 **Email:** enquiries@rodmarton-manor.co.uk

DR JENNER'S HOUSE & GARDEN 🏛ⓕ
The Chantry, Church Lane, Berkeley, Gloucestershire GL13 9BN
Tel: 01453 810631 **Email:** info@edwardjenner.co.uk

MISARDEN PARK GARDEN 🏛ⓕ
Stroud, Gloucestershire GL6 7JA
Tel: 01285 821303 **Email:** estate.office@miserdenestate.co.uk

SUDELEY CASTLE & GARDENS 🏛
The Cotswolds, Gloucestershire GL54 5JD
Tel: 01242 604244 **Email:** enquiries@sudeley.org.uk

Whittington Court 🏛ⓕ
Cheltenham, Gloucestershire GL54 4HF
Elizabethan & Jacobean manor house with church.
Map Ref: 6:N11 - 4m E of Cheltenham on N side of A40.
Tel: 01242 820556
Email: lucy@whittingtoncourt.co.uk
Open: 31 Mar-15 Apr inclusive & 11-27 Aug inclusive: 2-5pm.
Admission: Adult: £5, Child: £1, OAP: £4.

SNOWSHILL MANOR ❧
Snowshill, near Broadway, Gloucestershire WR12 7JU
Tel: 01386 852410 **Email:** snowshillmanor@nationaltrust.org.uk

WOODCHESTER MANSION 🏛ⓕ
Stonehouse, Gloucestershire GL10 3TS
Tel: 01453 861541 **Email:** info@woodchestermansion.org.uk

ACTON COURT 🏛ⓕ
Latteridge Road, Iton Acton, Bristol, Gloucestershire BS37 9TL
Tel: 01454 228224 **Email:** info@actoncourt.com

THE AMERICAN MUSEUM & GARDENS
Claverton Manor, Bath BA2 7BD
Tel: 01225 460503 **Email:** info@americanmuseum.org

ASSEMBLY ROOMS
Bennett Street, Bath BA1 2QH
Tel: 01225 477785 **Email:** costume_enquiries@bathnes.gov.uk

COMBE SYDENHAM COUNTRY PARK
Monksilver, Taunton, Somerset TA4 4JG
Tel: 01643 702259 **Email:** bcsources@aol.com

BARRINGTON COURT ❧
Barrington, Nr Ilminster, Somerset TA19 0NQ
Tel: 01460 241938 **Email:** barringtoncourt@nationaltrust.org.uk

COTHAY MANOR & GARDENS
Greenham, Wellington, Somerset TA21 0JR
Tel: 01823 672283 **Email:** cothaymanor@btinternet.com

DODINGTON HALL
Nr Nether Stowey, Bridgwater, Somerset TA5 1LF
Tel: 01278 741400

DUNSTER CASTLE ❧
Dunster, Nr Minehead, Somerset TA24 6SL
Tel: 01643 821314 **Email:** dunstercastle@nationaltrust.org.uk

FARLEIGH HUNGERFORD CASTLE ⌗
Farleigh Hungerford, Bath, Somerset BA2 7RS
Tel: 01225 754026 **Email:** customers@english-heritage.org.uk

HESTERCOMBE GARDENS 🏛ⓕ
Cheddon Fitzpaine, Taunton, Somerset TA2 8LG
Tel: 01823 413923 **Email:** info@hestercombe.com

KENTSFORD
Washford, Watchet, Somerset TA23 0JD
Tel: 01984 632309 **Email:** wyndhamest@btconnect.com

MONTACUTE HOUSE ❧
Montacute, Somerset TA15 6XP
Tel: 01935 823289 **Email:** montacute@nationaltrust.org.uk

ORCHARD WYNDHAM 🏛
Williton, Taunton, Somerset TA4 4HH
Tel: 01984 632309 **Email:** wyndhamest@btconnect.com

PRIOR PARK LANDSCAPE GARDEN ❧
Ralph Allen Drive, Bath BA2 5AH
Tel: 01225 833422 **Email:** priorpark@nationaltrust.org.uk

ROMAN BATHS
Abbey Church Yard, Bath BA1 1LZ
Tel: 01225 477785 **Email:** romanbaths_bookings@bathnes.gov.uk

TYNTESFIELD ❧
Wraxall, North Somerset BS48 1NX
Tel: 0844 800 4966 **Email:** tyntesfield@nationaltrust.org.uk

ABBEY HOUSE GARDENS
Malmesbury, Wiltshire SN16 9AS
Tel: 01666 827650 **Email:** info@abbeyhousegardens.co.uk

ARUNDELLS
59 Cathedral Close, Salisbury, Wiltshire SP1 2EN
Tel: 01722 326546

LACOCK ABBEY ❧
Lacock, Nr Chippenham, Wiltshire SN15 2LG
Tel: 01249 730459 **Email:** lacockabbey@nationaltrust.org.uk

THE MERCHANT'S HOUSE
132 High Street, Marlborough, Wiltshire SN8 1HN
Tel: 01672 511491 **Email:** admin@merchantshousetrust.co.uk

MOMPESSON HOUSE ❧
Cathedral Close, Salisbury, Wiltshire SP1 2EL
Tel: 01722 335659 **Email:** mompessonhouse@nationaltrust.org.uk

Newhouse 🏛©

Redlynch, Salisbury, Wiltshire SP5 2NX
A brick, Jacobean 'Trinity' House, c1609, with 2 Georgian wings & a basically Georgian interior. **Map Ref:** 3:B5 - 9m S of Salisbury between A36 & A338. **Tel:** 01725 510055 **Email:** events@newhouseestate.co.uk
Website: www.newhouseestate.co.uk
Open: 1 Mar-6 Apr, Mon-Fri, & 27 Aug. **Admission:** Adult: £5, Child: £3, Conc: £5. Groups (15+): Adult: £4, Child: £3, Conc: £4.

Norrington Manor

Alvediston, Salisbury, Wiltshire SP5 5LL
Built in 1377 it has been altered and added to in every century since, with the exception of the 18th Century.
Map Ref: 3:AS - Signposted to N of Berwick St John & Alvediston rd (half way between the 2 villages). **Tel:** 01722 780 259
Open: By appointment in writing.
Admission: A donation to the local churches is asked for.

OLD WARDOUR CASTLE ⌗
Nr Tisbury, Wiltshire SP3 6RR
Tel: 01747 870487 **Email:** customers@english-heritage.org.uk

STONEHENGE ⌗
Wiltshire SP4 7DE
Tel: 08703 331181 **Email:** customers@english-heritage.org.uk

STOURHEAD ❧
Stourton, Nr Warminster BA12 6QD
Tel: 01747 841152 **Email:** stourhead@nationaltrust.org.uk

Wilton House ©Britain on view

EAST OF ENGLAND

BEDFORDSHIRE · CAMBRIDGESHIRE · ESSEX
HERTFORDSHIRE · NORFOLK · SUFFOLK

Cromer

Wells-next
-the-Sea

Norwich

NORFOLK

Peterborough

Ely

Huntingdon

*CAMBRIDGE
SHIRE*

Cambridge

Bedford

SUFFOLK

Ipswich

*BEDFORD
SHIRE*

Hertford

Letchworth

*HERTFORD
SHIRE*

Chelmsford

Luton

ESSEX

St Albans

🌲 COUNTRYSIDE:

- The Fens
- The Broads
- Constable Country

⧗ HERITAGE:

- Oliver Cromwell
- Wool churches
- Garden cities

🍴 FOOD:

- Cromer crab
- Norfolk turkeys
- Mustard

DON'T MISS!

AUDLEY END

Important Jacobean house with Jacobean revival interiors and rooms by Robert Adam. Displays, largely from the Victorian life of the house, include nurseries, below stairs and working stables.

Highlights:

- Old Master collection
- Victorian taxidermy
- Stables and servants
- Polish wartime history

AUDLEY HOUSE AND HORSES STABLES

CAMBRIDGE COLLEGES

You can see Cambridge's historic college buildings and gardens, generally outside term times or from a punt on the Cam. They range from Peterhouse's medieval hall of 1290 to 2016's quirky up-turned 'pot'-ting shed in Jesus' garden taking in every architectural style in between.

Highlights:

- King's College Chapel
- Pepys Library at Magdalene College
- Queens' College
- Modern colleges at St John's & Faculty of History

THE LONG GALLERY, HATFIELD HOUSE

CAMBRIDGE QUEEN'S COLLEGE - GATEHOUSE

HATFIELD HOUSE

A Jacobean prodigy house, built by Robert Cecil, chief minister to James I, and behind it, The Old Palace, childhood home of Queen Elizabeth I. Fine Jacobean interiors are filled with works of art while outside the 17th century gardens were designed by John Tradescant.

Highlights:

- James I mantelpiece in Drawing Room
- Gilded Long Gallery ceiling
- The Grand Staircase
- Portraits & possessions of Elizabeth I

THE MARBLE HALL, HOLKHAM HALL

HOLKHAM HALL

This great Palladian house is a tribute to the Grand Tour, that essential travel for all young men in the 18th century. Both builder, Thomas Coke, 1st Earl of Leicester and his great nephew, agricultural reformer Coke of Norfolk, were Grand Tourists so the house is resplendent with Old Masters, Italian landscapes and antique statuary in an interior of restrained elegance.

Highlights:

- William Kent furnishings
- The Marble Hall
- Thomas Coke of Norfolk by Thomas Gainsborough
- Field to Fork exhibition

WOBURN ABBEY

The home of the powerful Russell family, Earls & Dukes of Bedford, is a Palladian mansion built by Henry Flitcroft in 1744, housing an exceptional collection of works of art and set in an ancient deer park and recently restored gardens.

Highlights:

- The Canaletto Room
- Chinoiserie
- Shell Grotto
- Gold & silver vaults

THE SHELL GROTTO, WOBURN ABBEY © BEDFORD ESTATES

MRS HUDSON'S HIDDEN GEM

HINDRINGHAM HALL

"…East Anglia has some of the most delicious little moated manor houses straight out of a story book. One of my favourites belongs to Charles and Lynda Tucker at Hindringham. The house is warm brick and cool flint reached by a little brick bridge across a moat that has gone all the way round since the 12th century. It all belonged to the church then, so the priors of Norwich must have had lots of fat carp to eat on fast days from the fish ponds that have just been restored in the garden.

The house is Tudor, built around 1538 by a courtier who had got rich in the service of Henry VIII's illegitimate son, Henry Fitzroy. It was in decline before Gerald Gosselin, a man with a good eye for oak beams, restored it in 1900. Mrs Tucker has worked tirelessly to revitalise the gardens which are open regularly during the Summer, though the house is only open for a few days. But make an effort to get there, the roses are fragrant, the black swans elegant, the tea homemade and it's the sort of place where you feel history stops and you step off the road of time…"

MARK THE YEAR

200 YEARS
REPTON

Enjoy the gardens of Humphry Repton 200 years after his death.

- ✔ *Woburn Abbey*
- ✔ *Sheringham Park*
- ✔ *Hylands House*
- ✔ *Catton Park*

SHERINGHAM PARK

REPTON GROUNDS AT HYLANDS HOUSE

WOBURN ABBEY GARDENS

100 YEARS
WOMEN & SUFFRAGE

1. ELIZABETH I (1533-1603)
Charismatic Queen of England at Hatfield House.

ELIZABETH I - THE RAINBOW PORTRAIT AT HATFIELD HOUSE

ILLUSTRATION FROM THE CHILDREN AT GREEN KNOWE BOOKS BY LUCY M BOSTON DRAWN BY HER SON PETER

2. LUCY M BOSTON
Novelist and gardener at The Manor House, Hemingford Grey.

LADY CONSTANCE LYTTON © KNEBWORTH ESTATES

3. LADY CONSTANCE LYTTON (1897-1923)
Suffragette at Knebworth House.

DID YOU KNOW?

EASTERN LIBRARY ELTONHALL

1 COPPED HALL

A Midsummer Night's Dream, Shakespeare's most popular play, was written for the wedding of Sir Thomas Heneage & Mary, Countess of Southampton in 1594 and performed specially for them in the Long Gallery at Copped Hall.

2 WOBURN ABBEY

Afternoon tea was invented by Anna Maria, 7th Duchess of Bedford of Woburn Abbey to counteract a "sinking feeling" she felt at 4 o'clock once dinner times moved to evening in the 1840s. It became THE fashionable social event for women.

3 ELTON HALL

The impressive library at Elton Hall started in the 1660s by Sir Thomas Proby includes a prayer book owned by Henry VIII, a gift from his last wife, Katherine Parr.

DUCHESS ANNA MARIA

SOMERLEYTON HALL

THE UNDERPANTS MICK JAGGER WORE IN 1976 © KNEBWORTH ESTATES

4 KNEBWORTH

Knebworth, which has the largest festival field in the UK, has been the home of rock music since The Bucolic Frolic of 1974 featuring the Allman Brothers, Van Morrison and the Doobies. Mick Jagger of the Rolling Stones left his underpants behind in 1976.

5 SOMERLEYTON HALL

Millionaire Victorian railway developer Samuel Morton Peto lavished money on his new house at Somerleyton Hall, employing only the best for house and garden. Peto went spectacularly bust in 1866, died in obscurity and is buried in Tunbridge Wells.

6 LAYER MARNEY TOWER

The unusual brick and terracotta Tudor gatehouse at Layer Marney Tower, the tallest in the country at 80 foot, was badly damaged in an earthquake in 1884.

3 TOP SPOTS FOR WALKS

SANDRINGHAM COUNTRY PARK

1.

SANDRINGHAM, NORFOLK

600 acre country park. Nature trails. Bird hide.

🐕 *Dogs on leads.*

2.

ICKWORTH, SUFFOLK

Walks of varying lengths. Great War walking trail.

🐕 *Dogs on leads.*

WALKS AT ICKWORTH

3.

HOLKHAM HALL, NORFOLK

Winner, Best Family Day Out & Best Place to Shop, Hudson's Heritage Awards 2017

Well marked estate walks & nature trails. Red & fallow deer.

🐕 *Dogs on leads.*

🚲 *Bike to hire.*

HOLKHAM WALKS NATURE TRAIL

WENTWORTH HOUSE HOTEL, SUFFOLK

The Pritt family have been the owners of this charming Victorian hotel for over 90 years. The Wentworth Hotel is ideally situated on the seafront in the historic town of Aldeburgh, a centre for music lovers worldwide.

HINTLESHAM HALL, SUFFOLK

Elegant Georgian façade hiding an Elizabethan house, decorated with fine plasterwork and antiques. Once owned by both TV chef Robert Carrier and TV hotel inspector Ruth Watson.

THE PHEASANT, NORFOLK

The Pheasant is a newly opened mock-Georgian mansion of great comfort, standing in its own parkland just off the A149 North Norfolk Coast Road. It is part of the family owned Kelling Estate, which also comprises woodlands, a stud as well as a productive farm, which provides much of the hotel's fresh and seasonal fare.

THE PIER AT HARWICH, ESSEX

Once a stopover for passengers travelling to the Continent, now a harbourside hotel with a distinct nautical flavour, a reputation for seafood and views across the water.

NORFOLK MEAD HOTEL, NORFOLK

Set in over 8 acres of lovingly kept private grounds to enjoy while staying at the Norfolk Mead. From the expansive front lawn to the gardens that circle the hotel and extend right to the banks of the River Bure. Swans, geese and other wildfowl can be spotted on the private lake.

HOTEL FELIX, CAMBRIDGESHIRE

Built in 1852 as a family home by a well-known surgeon at nearby Addenbrooke's Hospital, Hotel Felix is a blend of Victorian architecture and contemporary comfort. It was Cambridge's first independent boutique hotel, just a mile from the city centre and set in three acres of grounds.

KESGRAVE HALL HOTEL, SUFFOLK

Kesgrave Hall is a country house located in woodlands north of the suburban village of Kesgrave on the eastern outskirts of Ipswich. Constructed in 1812 by William Cunliffe-Shawe, it was transformed into a luxurious 4* boutique hotel in 2014.

OLD RECTORY, NORFOLK

Chris & Sally Entwistle are very much 'hands on' hosts at this charming Grade II Listed Old Rectory, just two miles from Norwich City Centre and set in the residential Conservation Area of Thorpe St Andrew.

THE CHEQUERS INN, NORFOLK

Dating back to the 16th century, The Chequers Inn situated in the pretty village of Thornham is perfectly placed for exploring the subtle beauty of the North Norfolk coast.

MAISON TALBOOTH, ESSEX

Maison Talbooth is a Victorian house which has been owned by the Milsom family for over 40 years and is now one of the leading hotels of East Anglia. It is situated on the Essex/Suffolk border, ½ mile from the picturesque village of Dedham and overlooking beautiful Dedham Vale, famous Constable country.

BROOM HALL COUNTRY HOTEL, NORFOLK

Broom Hall is a charming family run Victorian house in the heart of the Breckland, established in 1994 by the current family owners Angela and her son Simon Rowling .

YOU ARE WELCOME

By Sheila Charrington, Chairman, Invitation to View

For the curious and adventurous, Invitation to View offers a chance to visit interesting buildings; many not normally open to visitors. The scheme, started 20 years ago by the Suffolk Tourist Board, follows a simple formula; owners of houses taking part put dates when they can offer tours in an annual brochure and online; visitors can easily see when each house is open and book a tour on that specific day. Just like booking tickets for the theatre. Larger groups can still book direct.

When the Tourist Board withdrew, participating owners organised themselves into a committee, engaged an administrator and ran it themselves. It quickly spread all over East Anglia, moved into the South West and then Welsh Marches and it is still growing, Yorkshire hopefully being next. There are currently 90 properties on the Invitation to View list.

There is a hugely diverse range of buildings to choose from. Some are stately like Brynkinalt Hall near Wrexham, Kelly House in Devon which has been in the same family for 900 years, or tiny like Letheringham. Lodge near Woodbridge, the smallest occupied moated site in the country. We have a council house in Essex, that the Sunday Times called "Britain's most extraordinary home" and Pitchford Hall in Shropshire, which is a restoration work in progress. None of the buildings can be said to be typical, some are purely family homes, and others have to work hard for their living. Our house, Layer Marney Tower in Essex, is one of the latter. It is a wedding venue, hosts corporate events and school visits, glamping in the woods and has a busy summer events programme for visitors. Started around 1520 by Henry 1st Lord Marney, it was a statement Tudor palace that he failed to finish before his death in 1523. Quite large enough, today we have a 150ft front façade with the tallest Tudor gatehouse in the country, a stable block converted 150 years ago to a Long Gallery, a mediaeval barn and church. An Invitation to View tour to Layer Marney Tower includes visiting the private side of the house. I generally show people around and I chat about the history and some of the stories attached to running it. Most Invitation to View tours are led by the owners, which gives a particularly personal and intimate insight into the house and its history. Our buildings have a past, a present and a future. They are not museums only looking back at a great past. You will find family photos on the tables, and family memorabilia, the minutiae of life, although we do aim to have a good tidy up before our visitors arrive!

OLD HALL, NORFOLK

BELLE GROVE, SUFFOLK

THE HALL OF MIRRORS, TALLISTON, ESSEX

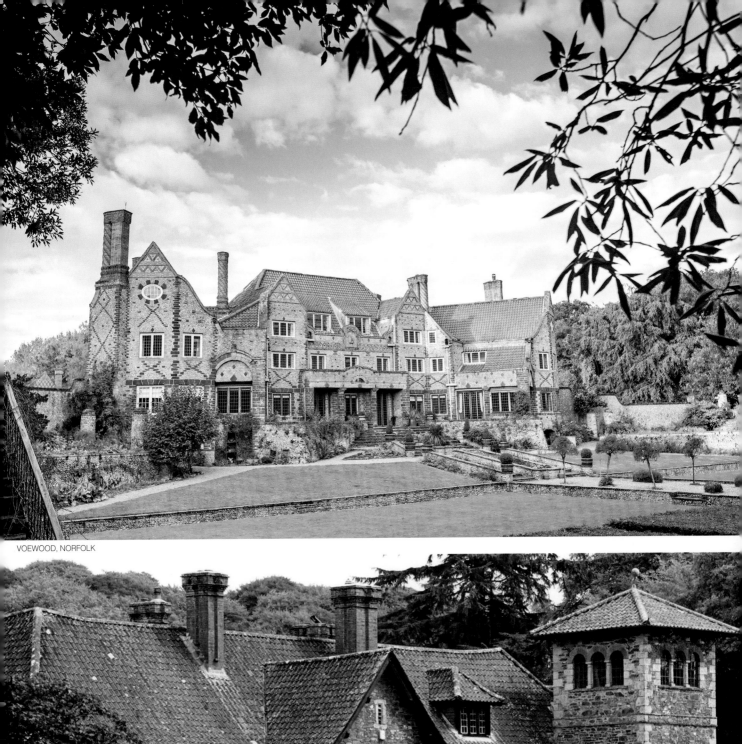

VOEWOOD, NORFOLK

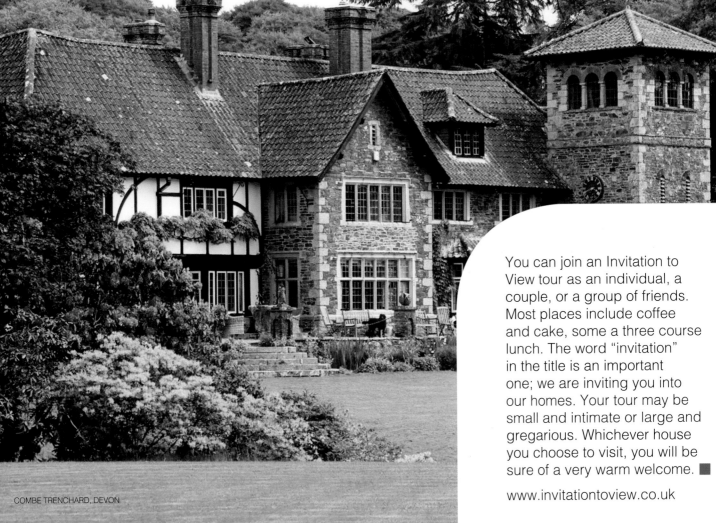

COMBE TRENCHARD, DEVON

You can join an Invitation to View tour as an individual, a couple, or a group of friends. Most places include coffee and cake, some a three course lunch. The word "invitation" in the title is an important one; we are inviting you into our homes. Your tour may be small and intimate or large and gregarious. Whichever house you choose to visit, you will be sure of a very warm welcome. ■

www.invitationtoview.co.uk

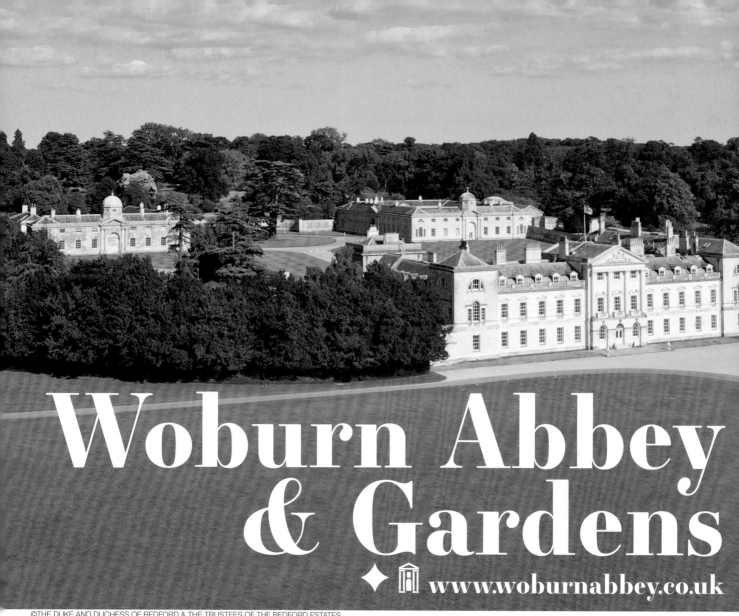

Woburn Abbey & Gardens

◆ 🏛 www.woburnabbey.co.uk

©ROCKERY AND PAVILION WOBURN ABBEY GARDENS

Step inside Woburn Abbey and immerse yourself in 500 years of history, explore 28 acres of award-winning gardens and enjoy a drive through the extensive deer park.

Home of the Duke and Duchess of Bedford, Woburn Abbey was gifted to the family by Henry VIII in his will of 1547. Explore nearly 500 years of one family's history, including the popularisation of afternoon tea, a Royal pardon, political reform and Royal visits.

Discover an art collection including an unrivalled group of 16th and 17th Century portraits, works by Reynolds and Van Dyck and the largest private collection of Canaletto's Venetian views on public display, together with a treasury of silver, porcelain and fine English and French furniture.

In 2018 celebrate Humphry Repton's bicentennial year with us – Repton considered that of all of his landscape designs, none were more fully realised than at Woburn. Repton's most elaborate Red Book will be on display for the first time, as part of our new exhibition in the Abbey.

The 28 acres of Woburn Abbey Gardens are exceptional. Enjoy elegant horticultural designs, woodland glades, ponds and architectural features; much of which were the inspiration of Humphry Repton. The restoration of Repton's original Pleasure Grounds from 200 years ago continues today.

©WOBURN QUEEN VICTORIA'S BEDROOM

OWNER
The Duke and Duchess of Bedford &
The Trustees of the Bedford Estates

CONTACT
Woburn Abbey

Tel: 01525 290333
Email: admissions@woburn.co.uk

LOCATION
Woburn, Bedfordshire MK17 9WA

Map Ref: 7:D10

Signposted from M1 J12/J13 and A4012.
Easy access from A5 via Hockliffe, follow signs to Woburn village.

OPENING TIMES
Woburn Abbey, Gardens & Deer Park.

Please call or visit our website for details.

ADMISSION
Please call or visit our website for details.

Group rates available.

SPECIAL EVENTS
Please visit our website for a full list of our events, guided tours and study days.

Don't miss the Woburn Abbey Garden Show: 23 & 24 Jun 2018.

Set against the stunning backdrop of Woburn Abbey, 'The Gardener's Garden Show' offers visitors an informative day out.

Carriage Tours
Available monthly from Apr-Aug, please check the website for details.

KEY FACTS

 Photography is not permitted inside the Abbey & we ask that mobile phones are switched to silent.

 Please telephone for details.

 Toilet facilities available.

 Licensed Tea Room. Freshly prepared, homemade meals, snacks, sweet treats and afternoon tea.

 Baby changing facilities available.

 Gift and souvenir shop.

 Free parking.

 Woburn grown plants available to buy throughout the main season.

 Very limited access in the house. Good access in the gardens.

 Conferences, exhibitions, banqueting, luncheons & dinners.

 Except assistance dogs in gardens only.

 www.woburnabbey.co.uk/events

 The Woburn Hotel in the village of Woburn.

 Weddings are held in the Sculpture Gallery, visit website or call for more information.

 By arrangement.

Victoria Wood's Nice Cup of Tea', 'Masterchef', 'Heston's Great British Food', 'Countryfile' & 'The One Show'.

Elton Hall

www.eltonhall.com

Elton Hall is a fascinating mixture of styles and has evolved as a family house since the late 15th Century. The house contains wonderful furniture, porcelain and magnificent paintings. Artists represented in the collection include Gainsborough, Constable, Reynolds and Old Masters from the early Italian Renaissance. The library is one of the largest in private ownership and contains such treasures as

Henry VIII's prayer book. The formal gardens have been restored during the last 30 years and include a Gothic Orangery, a Flower Garden with spectacular fountain, Shrub Garden and Box Walk. Billowing borders surround the lily pond, while topiary, parterres and immaculately kept lawns and paths give structure to the many unusual plants.

CONTACT
Owner: Sir William Proby Bt, CBE
Contact: Jane Jones
Tel: 01832 280468
Email: events@eltonhall.com

LOCATION
Elton Hall & Gardens, Elton, Cambridgeshire PE8 6SH
Map Ref: 7:E7
Close to A1 in the village of Elton, off A605 Peterborough - Oundle Road.

OPENING TIMES
2pm-5pm, May, last May BH, Sun & Mon. Jun & Jul, Wed, Thu. Aug, Wed, Thu, Sun & BH Mon. Private groups by arrangement daily May-Sep.
Opening days subject to change, please check the website or call before visiting.

ADMISSION
Please see website www.eltonhall.com for current house and garden prices. Children under 16 free. Or call 01832 280468.

KEY FACTS

 No photography in house.

 Lavatories & disabled WC facilities at both the Walled Garden and the Hall.

 Baby changing facilities available.

 At Walled Garden & Tearooms adjacent to Elton Hall.

 Garden suitable. Ample room with provision for disabled parking.

 Obligatory. Except Bank Holidays when room guides. Tours approx. 1 hour.

 Contact events@eltonhall.com

 Tearooms provide delicious lunches, teas and light refreshments.

 Walled Garden Plant Centre and Tearoom.

 The Garden Centre offers plant sales.

 For meetings and dinners, Parkland for outdoor activities.

 Please see the 'What's On' section of the website for all the upcoming events such as 'The Angel Fair'.

The romantic Orangery and the grand Billiard Room are licensed for wedding ceremonies.

 Provides the perfect backdrop for filming or stylish photo-shoots.

Kimbolton Castle
www.kimbolton.cambs.sch.uk/castle

Vanbrugh and Hawksmoor's 18th Century adaptation of 13th Century fortified house. Katherine of Aragon's last residence. Tudor remains still visible. Courtyard by Henry Bell of King's Lynn. Outstanding Pellegrini murals. Gatehouse by Robert Adam. Home of Earls and Dukes of Manchester, 1615-1950. Family portraits in State Rooms. Wooded grounds with fine Wellingtonia avenue. Now owned by Kimbolton School.

Children's animal, Tudor and Victorian trails and dressing-up box. Light refreshments available.

Group tours by prior arrangement: special rates apply.

The Castle can be booked for weddings and other events.

KEY FACTS

 Toilet facilities are available in the Castle.

 Ample coach parking, with free admission for coach drivers. Visitors may park in the castle grounds.

 A tour of the interior of the Castle takes approximately 1½ hours and 2 hours with the exterior included.

School groups are admitted to the Castle free of charge, by special arrangement.

 Postcards, guidebooks and a limited range of souvenirs are on sale to visitors.

 Highly experienced in hosting a wide variety of formal and informal celebrations and functions.

 The perfect setting for wedding ceremonies and receptions.

CONTACT
Owner: Governors of Kimbolton School
Contact: Mrs N Butler **Tel:** 01480 860505
Email: reception@kimbolton.cambs.sch.uk
Additional Email: ncb@kimbolton.cambs.sch.uk

LOCATION
Kimbolton, Huntingdon, Cambridgeshire PE28 0EA
Map Ref: 7:E8 - 7 miles North West of St Neots on B645.

OPENING TIMES
2018 Dates: 4 Mar at 1pm-4pm and 4 Nov at 1pm-4pm

ADMISSION
Adult: £5
Child: £2.50
Over 60s: £4
Groups: Tours by arrangement throughout the year, including evenings, subject to Kimbolton School use. Min charge £60.

The Manor, Hemingford Grey

www.greenknowe.co.uk

One of the oldest continuously inhabited houses in Britain built about 1130. The three walls of The Music Room have seen and heard nearly nine hundred years of family life. The house was made famous as 'Green Knowe' by the author Lucy M. Boston.
The internationally known patchwork collection sewn by Lucy Boston is also shown. Surrounded by a moat and on the fourth side by a river the four acre garden, laid out by Lucy Boston, has topiary, old roses, award-winning irises and herbaceous borders.

KEY FACTS

 No photography in house.

 The garden is open all year and the House is open throughout the year but strictly by appointment.

 Cars: Disabled plus a few spaces if none in High Street. Coaches: Nearby.

 Partial. Access to hall and dining room only. Garden has some gravel areas.

 Obligatory.

 Particularly suitable for children.

 Cafés in the village.

 The Cock pub in village.

 Cash, cheque or bank transfer payments only.

 Plants sales available.

 Please see homepage for all events and shows.

 Film location.

CONTACT
Owner/Contact: Diana Boston
Tel: 01480 463134 **Email:** diana_boston@hotmail.com

LOCATION
Norman Court, High Street, Hemingford Grey, Cambridgeshire PE28 9BN **Map Ref:** 7:F8 - A14, 3m SE of Huntingdon. 12m NW of Cambridge. Access via small gate on riverside.

OPENING TIMES
House: All year to individuals or groups by prior arrangement. Also in May guided tours daily at 2pm (booking advisable).
Garden: All year, daily, 11am-5pm (4pm in winter).

ADMISSION
House & Garden
Adult: £8, Concessions: £7, Child: £3, Family: £22.
Garden only
Adult: £5, Concessions: £4.50, Child: Free.

Elton Hall

Copped Hall

www.coppedhalltrust.org.uk

Mid-18th Century Palladian mansion under restoration. Situated on ridge overlooking landscaped park. Ancillary buildings including stables and racquets court. Former elaborate gardens being rescued from abandonment. Large 18th Century walled kitchen garden - adjacent to site of 16th Century mansion where 'A Midsummer Night's Dream' was first performed. Ideal film location.

CONTACT
Owner: The Copped Hall Trust
Contact: Alan Cox
Tel: 020 7267 1679
Mobile: 07799 473 108
Email: coxalan1@aol.com

LOCATION
Crown Hill, Epping, Essex CM16 5HS **Map Ref:** 7:G12
4 miles South West of Epping, North of M25. Satnav postcode for entry is CM16 5HR.

OPENING TIMES
Ticketed events and special open days. See website for dates. Private tours by appointment.

ADMISSION
Open Days: £8
Guided Tour Days: £8
Gardens Only: £5

KEY FACTS

 Parking available.

 Partial access.

 Dogs welcome in grounds on leads. No dogs in mansion.

 Guided tours on the third Sun of every month except Dec. 2 1/2 - 3 hours. Access 10am-11am only.

 Workshops and study days.

 Pudding evening & afternoon tea.

 Purchase a variety of goods in the shop appealing to all tastes.

 Please see the calendar on the website for all upcoming events, concerts and theatre.

Ingatestone Hall

ingatestonehall.com

16th Century mansion, with 11 acres of grounds (formal garden and wild walk), built by Sir William Petre, Secretary of State to four Tudor monarchs, which has remained in his family ever since. Furniture, portraits and memorabilia accumulated over the centuries - and two Priests' hiding places.

CONTACT
Owner/Contact: The Lord Petre
Tel: 01277 353010
Email:
house@ingatestonehall.co.uk

LOCATION
Hall Lane, Ingatestone, Essex CM4 9NR **Map Ref:** 7:H12
Off A12 between Brentwood & Chelmsford. From London end of Ingatestone High Street, take Station Lane, cross level crossing & continue for ½ mile.

OPENING TIMES
1 Apr-30 Sep 2018 Wed, Suns & BHs, 12pm-5pm.

ADMISSION
Adult: £7, Child: £3,
Under 5yrs: Free, Conc: £6.
Groups: 20+ Booked in advance.
Adult: £6, Child: £2, Conc: £5.

KEY FACTS

 No photography in house.

 Free parking.

 Partial. WC's.

 Available out of normal hours by arrangement.

 Teas & light lunches are served in the Summer Parlour whenever the house is open without pre-booking.

 A wide range of gifts and souvenirs are on sale in the shop.

 Capacity for receptions - 100. Capacity for dinners - 65.

 Celebrate your wedding in the company of 20 or 200 of your friends and family at the hall.

Audley End

177

Hatfield House

www.hatfield-house.co.uk

Over 400 years of culture, history and entertainment.

Hatfield House is the home of the 7th Marquess and Marchioness of Salisbury and their family. The Estate has been in the Cecil family for over 400 years. Superb examples of Jacobean craftsmanship can be seen throughout the House.

In 1611, Robert Cecil, 1st Earl of Salisbury built his fine Jacobean House adjoining the site of the Old Palace of Hatfield. The House was splendidly decorated for entertaining the Royal Court, with State Rooms rich in paintings, fine furniture and tapestries.

Superb examples of Jacobean craftsmanship can be seen throughout Hatfield House such as the Grand Staircase with its fine carving and the rare stained glass window in the private chapel. Displayed throughout the House are many historic mementos collected over the centuries by the Cecils', one of England's foremost political families.

The garden at Hatfield House dates from the early 17th Century when Robert Cecil employed John Tradescant the Elder to collect plants for his new home. Tradescant was sent to Europe where he found and brought back trees, bulbs, plants and fruit trees, which had never previously been grown in England.

In the Park, an oak tree marks the place where the young Princess Elizabeth first heard of her accession to the throne. Visitors can enjoy extensive walks in the park, following trails through the woods and along the Broadwater. The Veteran Tree Trail also provides the opportunity to learn more about our ancient oaks.

OWNER
The 7th Marquess of Salisbury
CONTACT
Visitors Department **Tel:** 01707 287010
Email: visitors@hatfield-house.co.uk
Website: www.hatfield-house.co.uk

LOCATION
Hatfield House, Hatfield Hertfordshire AL9 5NQ
Map Ref: 7:F11
Car: 21 miles north of London, M25 Jct 23, A1(M) Jct 4. Pedestrian Entrance directly opposite Hatfield Railway Station.
Bus: Nearest stop at Hatfield Station, also regular buses from surrounding towns.
Rail: Kings Cross to Hatfield 22mins. Station is opposite entrance to Park. Underground links to main line at Finsbury Park.

OPENING TIMES
Hatfield House, Park & Gardens
Sat 31 Mar-Sat 29 Sep 2018.
Hatfield House: Weds-Sun & BH 11am-5pm.
Hatfield Park & Gardens: Tues-Sun 10am-5:30pm.
Hatfield Park Farm
Tues 20 Mar-Sun 28 Oct 2018.
Tues-Sun & BH 10am-5pm.
Stable Yard Shops & Restaurants
Open throughout the year Tues-Sun & BH 10am-5pm (please check with individual retailers).

ADMISSION
House, Park and West Garden
Adult: £19
Seniors: £18
Child: £9
Group rates available
East Garden
Wed only: £4 per person
West Garden and Park only
Adult: £11
Seniors: £10
Child: £7
Group rates available

KEY FACTS

 No flash photography in house. Tours of Old Palace when building is not in use.

 Toilet, disabled toilet and baby changing facilities available.

 Free car and coach parking available.

 All floors of House accessible via lift.

 Cycling is not permitted however there are cycle racks available, if you choose to cycle to the house.

 Dogs are permitted in the Park only. Assistance dogs, are allowed in the House and Gardens.

 Audio tours of house.

 Group tours by arrangement, please call 07107 287052.

 Living History Schools programme.

 Morning coffee, afternoon tea, cakes, hot & cold lunches. Tel: 01707 262030.

 The Coach House Restaurant. Tel: 01707 262030.

 Newly refurbished Stable Yard home to variety of independent retailers & Hatfield House Gift Shop.

 Weddings, banquets and conferences venue and catering. Tel 01707 262055.

 There are a number of events held throughout the year, please see the website for more details.

 Wedding venue available, please contact for further information.

Hatfield House is a popular choice for productions & is close to Pinewood, Leavesden & Elstree studios.

East of England

Knebworth House

www.knebworthhouse.com

A fantastic day out for all the family. Home of the Lytton family since 1490, Knebworth's romantic gothic exterior hides a much earlier Tudor house. Explore the delightful formal gardens with dinosaur trail, wilderness garden, walled garden and a huge adventure playground in the historic deer park. Events programme throughout the year. Knebworth is well known for its rock concerts and as a popular TV/feature film location. Knebworth Barns are open all year for weddings and corporate hospitality.

KEY FACTS

 Photography of the exterior and gardens & park permitted, but no photography or video films inside.

 Toilet facilities available.

 Ample parking free of charge.

 See Access statement online for full details.

 Dogs are welcome in the Park, on leads. Assistance Dogs permitted in the House, Gardens & Dino Trail.

 See website for list of local accommodation. Novotel adjoins the Park.

 Audio tour available to download from the website to bring along with your device & headphones.

 Admission generally by guided tour. See website for details of free flow days.

 See Education section of Website. Sandford award winning programmes.

 Garden Terrace Tea Room offers delicious refreshments in a delightful oak barn.

 The popular gift shop stocks a full range of Knebworth souvenirs, such as toys and books.

 Purchase plants & cuttings from Knebworth Gardens Plant Shop.

 Knebworth Barns Conference and Banqueting Centre is open all year round for all forms of entertaining.

 For all upcoming events such as fairs, shows and trails please see the 'Events' section of the website.

 If you are planning a wedding or celebration, take a look at some of the offers at Knebworth Barns.

Prides itself on being film friendly, with a history of working with film & TV crews for over 40 years.

CONTACT
Contact: The Estate Office
Tel: 01438 812661 **Email:** info@knebworthhouse.com

LOCATION
Knebworth Park, Knebworth, Hertfordshire SG1 2AX
Map Ref: 7:E11 - Direct access off the A1(M) J7 Stevenage, SG1 2AX, 28m N of London, 15m N of M25/J23.

OPENING TIMES
Mar-Sep, Please check website for open dates and times for Knebworth House, Gardens & Park. Knebworth Barns are open all year for events, corporate and social functions.

ADMISSION
See website for current prices. Children under 3 admitted free of charge. HHA members free on non-event days. RHS Partner Garden. Discount admission for Art Fund members.

Hatfield House

Hatfield House

Holkham Hall

◆ 🏛 **www.holkham.co.uk**

WILDLIFE CORRIDORS

LIVING ON THE EDGE

A breathtaking Palladian house with an outstanding art collection, panoramic landscapes and the best beach in England.

Holkham is a special place where a stunning coastal landscape meets one of England's great agricultural estates. At the heart of this thriving, privately-owned, 25,000 acre estate stands Holkham Hall, an elegant 18th century Palladian-style mansion. The Marble Hall, with its 50ft domed ceiling, is a spectacular entrance, with stairs leading to the magnificent state rooms displaying superb collections of ancient statuary, original furniture, tapestries and paintings.

Visitors can enjoy the Field to Fork Experience which tells the fascinating story of Holkham's unique farming heritage through engaging, interactive displays and even a tractor simulator to learn to drive and plough the fields! Or there is the tranquillity and colourful plantings of the 6 acre, 18th century walled garden; a peaceful haven to visit. For shopping and refreshments, the cobbled courtyard houses a spacious gift shop and café, both showcasing the work and produce of local artisans and suppliers. Discover the wildlife and landscape of Holkham park with walks and cycle or boat hire. Families will love the children's woodland play area, with its tree houses, rope walkways, zip wire and a fun model combine harvester with tunnels and slides.

At the north entrance to the park lies Holkham village with the estate-owned inn, The Victoria, several shops and the entrance to Holkham Beach and National Nature Reserve, with its golden sands and panoramic vista, perfect for bird-watching or for a day on the beach.

OWNER
Trustees of the Holkham Estate
Home of the Earls of Leicester

CONTACT
Contact: Marketing Manager Laurane Herrieven
Tel: 01328 710227
Email: enquiries@holkham.co.uk

LOCATION
Holkham Estate, Wells-next-the-Sea,
Norfolk, NR23 1AB **- Map Ref:** 8:14
Car: London 120m, Norwich 35m, King's Lynn 30m. Sat Nav: NR23 1RH. OS Ref: TF885 428
Bus: Coasthopper from King's Lynn to Cromer.
Rail: Norwich 35m. King's Lynn 30m.
Air: Norwich Airport 32m.

OPENING TIMES
Hall: 25 Mar-31 Oct, 12pm-4pm, Sun, Mon, Thu. Plus Good Fri & Easter Sat, 26 & 27 Oct for Halloween. NB Chapel, Libraries & Strangers' Wing, open at family's discretion.
Field to Fork, Walled Garden, Woodland Play Area, Courtyard Gift Shop & Café:
25 Mar-31 Oct, 10am-5pm, every day.
For winter opening & admission see website.
Cycle Hire & Lake Activities: See website.

ADMISSION
Holkham Hall, Field to Fork & Walled Garden
Adult: £16, Child (5-16yrs): £8, Family: £44
Field to Fork & Walled Garden
Adult: £7.50, Child (5-16yrs): £3.75, Family: £21
Field to Fork Only
Adult: £5, Child (5-16yrs): £2.50, Family: £13.50
NB Family ticket = 2 adults & up to 3 children.

Car parking: £3 per day, redeemable in gift shop on £12+ purchases.
Pre-booked groups: 15+ 20% discount, free parking, organiser ticket free, coach driver free refreshments.
Private Guided Tours: 12+ £22 per person.

KEY FACTS

 Photography allowed for personal use, no drones. Full access statement on Holkham website.

 Lavatories, including accessible facilities in the courtyard. Lavatories also in the hall & walled garden.

 Baby changing facilities are located in the courtyard.

 Open for events and functions outside of main visitor season.

 Ample. Parking charge.

 Main courtyard only. Stair-climbing machine in hall offers access for most manually operated wheelchairs.

 Cycle hire centre on site. Check website for details. Sustrans Route No: 1.

 On leads in park. Assistance dogs only in the hall.

 The Victoria Inn, Holkham village.

 Private guided tours by arrangement.

 All year round comprehensive educational programme.

 Courtyard Café. Licensed. Local produce.

 The Victoria Inn, Holkham village. Licensed.

 Courtyard Gift Shop. Local Norfolk produce and items.

 Plant sales in gift shop and walled garden.

 Hall, Lady Elizabeth Wing and grounds.

 Events and functions all year round. Please see full events programme.

 Civil ceremonies and partnerships.

Castle Rising Castle

www.castlerising.co.uk

Castle Rising Castle is one of the most famous 12th Century castles in England. The stone keep, built in around 1140 AD, is amongst the finest surviving example of its kind anywhere in the country and, together with the massive surrounding earthworks, ensures that Rising is a castle of national importance. In its time Rising has served as a hunting lodge, royal residence, and for a brief time in the 18th Century even housed a mental patient.

The most famous period in its history was when it came to the mother of Edward III, Queen Isabella, following her part in the murder of her husband Edward II. The castle passed to the Howard family in 1544 and it remains in their hands today, the current owner being a descendant of William D'Albini II, the Norman baron who raised the castle.

KEY FACTS

 Picnic area.

 Toilet facilities adjoining the car park.

 Closed 24-26 Dec.

 Large car park.

 Suitable. Disabled access to the shop and grounds only.

 There is an audio guide available to guide you around the Castle.

 School visits welcome. Pre-booking is essential.

 Gift shop.

 Please see the 'Events' section of the website for all upcoming activities.

CONTACT
Owner: Lord Howard
Contact: The Custodian
Tel: 01553 631330 **Fax:** 01533 631724
Email: thecastle@castlerising.com

LOCATION
Castle Rising, King's Lynn, Norfolk PE31 6AH
Map Ref: 7:H5 - Located 4m NE of King's Lynn off A149.

OPENING TIMES
1 Apr-1 Nov, daily, 10am-6pm (closes at dusk if earlier in Oct).
2 Nov-31 Mar, Wed-Sun, 10am-4pm.

ADMISSION
Adult: £4.50, Child: £3, Concession: £3.80,
Family (2 adults + 2 children): £14.
Groups: 11+ (15% discount for groups).
Opening times and prices are subject to change.

Houghton Hall & Gardens

www.houghtonhall.com

Houghton Hall is one of the finest examples of Palladian architecture in England. Built in the 1720s for Sir Robert Walpole, Britain's first Prime Minister. Original designs by James Gibbs & Colen Campbell, interior decoration by William Kent. The hall is currently home to the 7th Marquess of Cholmondeley, Walpole's descendant, and his family.

The award-winning 5-acre walled garden is divided into themed areas and includes a double-sided herbaceous border, formal rose parterre, mixed kitchen garden, fountains and statues. Contemporary sculptures by world renowned artists including Jeppe Hein, Stephen Cox, Zhan Wang, Richard Long, Rachel Whiteread, Anya Gallaccio, Phillip King and James Turrell are displayed in the gardens and grounds.

KEY FACTS

 Toilet facilities available and a disabled WC in the stable block.

 Allocated disabled parking near the House.

 Lift to 1st floor State Rooms. For further details see the 'Disabled Access' section of the website.

 2 hour private guided tour of the House – between 10am-12noon. Subject to availability.

 Provides opportunities for local schools & educational groups to discover and explore.

 The fully licensed Stables Café offers a range of seasonally inspired hot & cold food, afternoon teas etc.

 The Gift Shop is located in The Stables.

 Please see the website for upcoming events and exhibitions.

CONTACT
Owner: The Marquess of Cholmondeley
Contact: The Estate Office
Tel: 01485 528569 **Fax:** 01485 528167
Email: info@houghtonhall.com

LOCATION
Houghton, King's Lynn, Norfolk PE31 6UE

Map Ref: 8:15
13m E of King's Lynn, 10m W of Fakenham, 1½m N of A148.

OPENING TIMES
See website www.houghtonhall.com

ADMISSION
See website for prices / booking details.

Raveningham Gardens

www.raveningham.com

Superb herbaceous borders, 19th Century walled kitchen garden, Victorian glasshouse, herb garden, rose garden, time garden, contemporary sculptures, Millennium lake, arboretum with newly created stumpery, 14th Century church, all in a glorious parkland setting surrounding Raveningham Hall. Tea Room serving homemade cake and refreshments.

KEY FACTS

 Visitors welcome to browse through The Raveningham Centre offering antiques, rugs, arts, gifts and crafts.

 The Raveningham Estate has various properties, both residential and commercial, available to let.

 Toilet facilities available.

 Tea Room, homemade cakes, quiches & other refreshments.

 Parking is available.

 Plants from the Garden on sale at the Tearoom.

Disabled toilet, gardens accessible via gravel paths.

 Corporate functions available.

 Well behaved dogs on leads welcome.

 Please see the website for all upcoming Garden Events.

CONTACT
Owner: Sir Nicholas Bacon Bt OBE DL
Contact: Dr Barbara Linsley
Tel: 01508 548480 **Email:** barbara@raveningham.com

LOCATION
Raveningham, Norwich, Norfolk NR14 6NS **Map Ref:** 8:L7
Between Norwich & Lowestoft off A146 then B1136.

OPENING TIMES
Snowdrop season: Feb, Sun-Fri (closed Sats) 11am-4pm.
NGS opening: Sun 11 Mar-Mothering Sunday.
Main season: Sun 1 Apr-Fri 31 Aug, Wed-Fri, 11am-4pm.
Suns: 15, 22 & 29 Jul, 5, 12, 19 & 26 Aug.
Bank Holidays: Sun/Mon 1 & 2 Apr, Sun/Mon 6 & 7 May, Sun/Mon 27 & 28 May, Sun/Mon 26 & 27 Aug.

ADMISSION
Adult: £5, Child (under 16yrs): Free, Concessions: £4.50.
Groups welcome by prior arrangement.

Holkham Hall

Mannington
Gardens & Countryside
manningtongardens.co.uk

Gardens known for large collection of classic roses also feature trees and shrubs and other plants surrounding medieval moated manor with lake, board walk across meadow with bird hide and interesting events programme.

CONTACT
Owner: Lord & Lady Walpole
Contact: Lady Walpole
Tel: 01263 584175
E-mail: admin@walpoleestate.co.uk

LOCATION
Mannington Hall, Norwich NR11 7BB **Map Ref:** 8:K5

OPEN
Walks open every day of the year. Events from Apr and Gardens from late May-Aug; Suns 12pm-5pm, Wed, Thu & Fri 11am-5pm. Party visits and appointments may be possible on other days.

ADMISSION
Please see website.

KEY FACTS

 £2 car park fee (walkers only).

 Grounds. WC's.

 Dogs welcome in park only.

 Guided tours of the garden and ground floor of the hall by arrangement.

The Mannington Minnows Nature Club runs in the school holidays (usually Tue & Thu) for 6 + yrs old.

 Greedy Goose Tearoom serves refreshments and homemade treats when the garden is open.

 Shop is stocked with souvenirs, crafts, drinks and snacks.

 Purchase plants at the gift shop.

In 2018 there will be the usual wide variety of events.

Ickworth House, Parkland, Woodland & Gardens

nationaltrust.org.uk/ickworth

Unconventional and unforgettable. An Italianate Palace in the heart of Suffolk. Enjoy an entertaining day at this beautiful country estate. The grand Rotunda is full of treasures collected by the Hervey family and sits in 1800 acres of tranquil parkland. Walk around a truly unique Italianate garden, complete with a magical stumpery, and explore a working Walled garden which supplies the Cafés with home grown produce. Explore 1930s life in restored Servants Quarters and take part in a calendar of events throughout the year.

KEY FACTS

 Toilet facilities available.

 Baby changing facilities available. Front-carrying baby slings and hip-carrying infant seats for loan.

 Property closed Christmas Eve & Christmas Day.

 Parking 200 yards from West Wing and house. Parking for coaches.

 Lift in main house. Mobility scooters available. West Wing drop off point.

 Assistance dogs only in Italianate gardens. All dogs on leads on the Estate.

 5 Holiday cottages available.

 Basement audio tour on selected days.

 Tours available daily. Free regular park and garden tours subject to availability.

 Drinks, snacks and outside seating area at the Porter's Lodge outdoor café. Open 10am-5pm.

 Seasonal menu in our friendly, self-service West Wing restaurant.

 Sweets, treats, ice creams, toys, gifts & books in the West Wing gift shop. Open 10.30am-5pm.

 Plant and garden centre conveniently near the car park. Open 11am-5pm.

Please see the 'What's On' section of the website for all upcoming events.

CONTACT
Owner: National Trust **Contact:** Business Support Officer **Tel:** 01284 735270 **Email:** ickworth@nationaltrust.org.uk

LOCATION
The Rotunda, Horringer, Bury St Edmunds, Suffolk IP29 5QE
Map Ref: 8:19 - From A14 take junction 42 towards Westley; on West side of A143. For all other routes head towards Horringer. Please don't use our postcode for your SatNav, follow signs to Horringer instead.

OPENING TIMES
House - 1 Jan-3 Mar 11am-3pm, 4 Mar-28 Oct 11am-5pm, 29 Oct-31 Dec 11am-3pm. Tours only 11am-12pm & 4pm-5pm.
Parkland & Gardens: All year 9am-5.30pm.
Shop & Cafe: 1 Jan-3 Mar 10.30am-4pm, 4 Mar-28 Oct 10.30am-5pm, 29 Oct-31 Dec 10.30am-4pm.

ADMISSION
House, Park & Gardens - Adult: £15, Child: £7.50, Family: £37.50, Group prices available. .

Otley Hall

Otley Hall

www.otleyhall.co.uk

The outstanding late medieval house in East Suffolk. Stunning medieval Moated Hall (Grade I) frequently described as 'one of England's loveliest houses'. Noted for its richly carved beams, superb linenfold panelling and 16th Century wall paintings.

The unique 10 acre gardens include historically accurate Tudor re-creations and voted among the top 10 gardens to visit in Great Britain.

CONTACT
Owner: Dr Ian & Reverend Catherine Beaumont
Contact: Karen Gwynne-Vince
Tel: 01473 890264
Email: events@otleyhall.co.uk

Facebook: facebook.com/otleyhallsuffolk
Twitter: @OtleyHall

LOCATION
Hall Lane, Otley, Suffolk IP6 9PA
Map Ref: 8:K9
7 miles North of Ipswich, off the B1079.

OPENING TIMES
Gardens & Café: May-Sep, 11am-5pm, every Weds.

ADMISSION
£3 entrance fee. By appointment only.

KEY FACTS

 No commercial photography.

 Tours by appointment all year round.

 Grounds open all year round.

 Café serving light lunches and afternoon tea.

 Available.

 Private & corporate events are available. Please contact for more information.

 Partial.

 Please see website for events.

 In grounds only and on a short lead.

 Exclusive access to the house & grounds for wedding ceremonies and receptions.

Framlingham Castle

Gainsborough's House

www.gainsborough.org

Gainsborough's House is the childhood home of the artist Thomas Gainsborough, R.A. (1727–1788) and shows the most comprehensive collection of his paintings, drawings and prints on display within a single setting. A varied programme of temporary exhibitions is also shown throughout the year. The historic house dates back to the 16th Century and has an attractive walled garden filled with 18th Century plant species.

CONTACT
Owner: Gainsborough's House Society
Contact: Liz Cooper
Tel: 01787 372958
Email: mail@gainsborough.org

LOCATION
46 Gainsborough Street, Sudbury, Suffolk CO10 2EU
Map Ref: 8:I10 - From Sudbury town centre head down Gainsborough Street towards Weaver's Lane.

OPEN
All year: Mon-Sat, 10am-5pm; Sun, 11am-5pm. Closed: Good Friday & Christmas to New Year.

ADMISSION
Please call for price details or see our website.

KEY FACTS

 No photography in the Exhibition Gallery.

 Suitable WC's.

 By arrangement.

 Shop offers a range of themes based on the heritage of Gainsborough and the Georgian period.

 A small selection of plants from Gainsborough's Garden are available for sale.

CECIL HIGGINS ART GALLERY
Castle Lane, Bedford MK40 3RP
Tel: 01234 718618 **Email:** thehiggins@bedford.gov.uk

HOUGHTON HOUSE ⌗
Ampthill, Bedford, Bedfordshire MK45 2EZ
Tel: 01223 582700 **Email:** customers@english-heritage.org.uk

THE LUTON HOO WALLED GARDEN
Luton Hoo Estate, Luton, Bedfordshire LU1 3TQ
Tel: 01582 879089 **Email:** office@lhwg.org.uk

MOGGERHANGER PARK 🏛ⓕ
Park Road, Moggerhanger, Bedfordshire MK44 3RW
Tel: 01767 641007 **Email:** enquiries@moggerhangerpark.com

QUEEN ANNE'S SUMMERHOUSE ▦
Shuttleworth, Old Warden, Bedfordshire SG18 9DU
Tel: 01628 825925 **Email:** bookings@landmarktrust.org.uk

SWISS GARDEN
Old Warden Park, Bedfordshire SG18 9EP
Tel: 01767 627927 **Email:** enquiries@shuttleworth.org

Turvey House 🏛ⓕ
Turvey, Bedfordshire MK43 8EL
A neo-classical house set in picturesque parkland bordering the River Great Ouse; with a fine collection of 18th & 19th Century antiques.
Map Ref: 7:D9 - Between Bedford and Northampton on A428.
Tel: 01234 881621 **Email:** danielhanbury@hotmail.com
Website: www.turveyhouse.co.uk **Open:** The House and Gardens will be closed to the public throughout 2018 and will reopen in 2019.

WREST PARK ⌗
Silsoe, Luton, Bedfordshire MK45 4HS
Tel: 01525 860000 **Email:** customers@english-heritage.org.uk

ANGLESEY ABBEY, GARDENS & LODE MILL ❧
Quy Road, Lode, Cambridgeshire CB25 9EJ
Tel: 01223 810080 **Email:** angleseyabbey@nationaltrust.org.uk

CAMBRIDGE UNIVERSITY BOTANIC GARDEN
1 Brookside, Cambridge CB2 1JE
Tel: 01223 336265 **Email:** enquiries@botanic.cam.ac.uk

DENNY ABBEY ⌗
Ely Road, Chittering, Waterbeach, Cambridgeshire CB25 9PQ
Tel: 01223 860988 **Email:** info@farmlandmuseum.org.uk

ELY CATHEDRAL
The Chapter House, The College, Ely, Cambridgeshire CB7 4DL
Tel: 01353 667735 ext.261

ISLAND HALL 🏛
Godmanchester, Cambridgeshire PE29 2BA
Tel: 01480 459676 **Email:** enquire@islandhall.com

LONGTHORPE TOWER ⌗
Thorpe Road, Longthorpe, Cambridgeshire PE1 1HA
Tel: 01733 864663 **Email:** customers@english-heritage.org.uk

PECKOVER HOUSE & GARDEN ❧
North Brink, Wisbech, Cambridgeshire PE13 1JR
Tel: 01945 583463 **Email:** peckover@nationaltrust.org.uk

WIMPOLE ESTATE ❧
Arrington, Royston, Cambridgeshire SG8 0BW
Tel: 01223 206000 **Email:** wimpolehall@nationaltrust.org.uk

AUDLEY END ⌗
Audley End House, Audley End, Saffron Walden, Essex CB11 4JF
Tel: 01799 522842 **Email:** customers@english-heritage.org.uk

BOURNE MILL ❧
Bourne Road, Colchester, Essex CO2 8RT
Tel: 01206 549799 **Email:** bournemill@nationaltrust.org.uk

COPPED HALL
Crown Hill, Epping, Essex CM16 5HS
Tel: 020 7267 1679 **Email:** coxalan1@aol.com

HEDINGHAM CASTLE ✦
Castle Hedingham, Halstead, Essex, CO9 3DJ
Tel: 01787 460261 **Email:** mail@hedinghamcastle.co.uk

HILL HALL ⌗
Theydon Mount, Essex CM16 7QQ
Tel: 01799 522842 **Email:** customers@english-heritage.org.uk

HYLANDS ESTATE
Hylands Park, London Road, Chelmsford CM2 8WQ
Tel: 01245 605500 **Email:** hylands@chelmsford.gov.uk

LAYER MARNEY TOWER 🏛ⓕ
Nr Colchester, Essex CO5 9US
Tel: 01206 330784 **Email:** info@layermarneytower.co.uk

THE MUNNINGS ART MUSEUM 🏛ⓕ
Castle House, Castle Hill, Dedham, Essex CO7 6AZ
Tel: 01206 322127 **Email:** enquiries@munningsmuseum.org.uk

PAYCOCKE'S HOUSE & GARDEN ❧
25 West Street, Coggeshall, Essex CO6 1NS
Tel: 01376 561305 **Email:** paycockes@nationaltrust.org.uk

RHS HYDE HALL
Creephedge Lane, Rettendon, Chelmsford, Essex CM3 8ET
Tel: 08452 658071 **Email:** hydehall@rhs.org.uk

ASHRIDGE GARDENS 🏛ⓕ
Berkhamsted, Hertfordshire HP4 1NS
Tel: 01442 843491 **Email:** reception@ashridge.org.uk

BENINGTON LORDSHIP GARDENS 🏛ⓕ
Benington Lordship, Benington, Stevenage, Hertfordshire SG2 7BS
Tel: 01438 869668 **Email:** garden@beningtonlordship.co.uk

GORHAMBURY 🏛ⓕ
St Albans, Hertfordshire AL3 6AH
Tel: 01727 854051 **Email:** office@grimstontrust.co.uk

SHAW'S CORNER ❧
Ayot St Lawrence, Welwyn, Hertfordshire AL6 9BX
Tel: 01438 829221 **Email:** shawscorner@nationaltrust.org.uk

BACONSTHORPE CASTLE ⌗
Hall Lane, Baconsthorpe, Norfolk NR25 9LN
Tel: 01223 582700 **Email:** customers@english-heritage.org.uk

BLICKLING ESTATE ⚘
Blickling, Norwich, Norfolk NR11 6NF
Tel: 01263 738030 **Email:** blickling@nationaltrust.org.uk

CASTLE ACRE PRIORY ⌗
Stocks Green, Castle Acre, King's Lynn, Norfolk PE32 2XD
Tel: 01760 755394 **Email:** customers@english-heritage.org.uk

CLIFTON HOUSE
Queen Street, King's Lynn PE30 1HT
Email: anna@kingstaithe.com

DRAGON HALL
115-123 King Street, Norwich, Norfolk NR1 1QE
Tel: 01603 663922 **Email:** info@dragonhall.org

EUSTON HALL
Thetford, Suffolk IP24 2QP
Tel: 01842 766366 **Email:** info@euston-estate.co.uk

FAIRHAVEN WOODLAND & WATER GARDEN
School Road, South Walsham, Norfolk NR13 6DZ
Tel: 01603 270449 **Email:** fairhavengarden@btconnect.com

FELBRIGG HALL ⚘
Felbrigg, Norwich, Norfolk NR11 8PR
Tel: 01263 837444 **Email:** felbrigg@nationaltrust.org.uk

HINDRINGHAM HALL & GARDENS 🏛ⓕ
Blacksmiths Lane, Hindringham, Norfolk NR21 0QA
Tel: 01328 878226 **Email:** info@hindringhamhall.org

KIMBERLEY HALL
Wymondham, Norfolk NR18 0RT
Tel: 01603 759447 **Email:** events@kimberleyhall.co.uk

NORWICH CASTLE MUSEUM & ART GALLERY
Norwich, Norfolk NR1 3JU
Tel: 01603 493625 **Email:** museums@norfolk.gov.uk

OXBURGH HALL ⚘
Oxborough, King's Lynn, Norfolk PE33 9PS
Tel: 01366 328258 **Email:** oxburghhall@nationaltrust.org.uk

SANDRINGHAM
The Estate Office, Sandringham, Norfolk PE35 6EN
Tel: 01485 545408 **Email:** visits@sandringhamestate.co.uk

SHERINGHAM PARK ⚘
Upper Sheringham, Norfolk NR26 8TL
Tel: 01263 820550 **Email:** sheringhampark@nationaltrust.org.uk

WALSINGHAM ABBEY GROUNDS & THE SHIREHALL MUSEUM 🏛ⓕ
Common Place, Walsingham, Norfolk NR22 6BP
Tel: 01328 820510 **Email:** museum@walsinghamabbey.com

BELCHAMP HALL
Belchamp Walter, Sudbury, Suffolk CO10 7AT
Tel: 01787 881961

BRUISYARD HALL
Bruisyard, Saxmundham, Woodbridge IP17 2EJ
Tel: 01728 639000 **Email:** info@bruisyardhall.com

FLATFORD ⚘
Bridge Cottage, East Bergholt, Suffolk CO7 6UL
Tel: 01206 298260 **Email:** flatfordbridgecottage@nationaltrust.org.uk

FRAMLINGHAM CASTLE ⌗
Framlingham, Suffolk IP13 9BP
Tel: 01728 724189 **Email:** customers@english-heritage.org.uk

FRESTON TOWER ▪
Nr Ipswich, Suffolk IP9 1AD
Tel: 01628 825925 **Email:** bookings@landmarktrust.org.uk

GLEMHAM HALL 🏛ⓕ
Little Glemham, Woodbridge, Suffolk IP13 0BT
Tel: 01728 746704 **Email:** events@glemhamhall.co.uk

Haughley Park 🏛ⓕ

Stowmarket, Suffolk, IP14 3JY
Grade 1 Jacobean manor house of 1620 set in gardens, park and woodland. 17th C. Barn Wedding Venue. **Map Ref:** 8:J8 - Signed at J47a and J49 on A14, 10m west of Bury St Eds. **Tel:** 01359 240205 **Email:** robert@haughleypark.co.uk **Website:** www.haughleypark.co.uk **Open:** Gardens & Woods: Bluebell Sundays (last In Apr. first in May). **Admission:** Adults £4. See website for events. Groups by arrangement.

HELMINGHAM HALL GARDENS 🏛ⓕ
Helmingham, Stowmarket, Suffolk IP14 6EF
Tel: 01473 890799 **Email:** events@helmingham.com

KENTWELL HALL & GARDENS 🏛ⓕ
Long Melford, Suffolk CO10 9BA
Tel: 01787 310207 **Email:** info@kentwell.co.uk

LANDGUARD FORT ⌗
Felixstowe, Suffolk IP11 3TX
Tel: 01394 675900 **Email:** customers@english-heritage.org.uk

LAVENHAM: THE GUILDHALL OF CORPUS CHRISTI ⚘
The Market Place, Lavenham, Sudbury CO10 9QZ
Tel: 01787 247646 **Email:** lavenhamguildhall@nationaltrust.org.uk

MELFORD HALL ⚘
Long Melford, Sudbury, Suffolk CO10 9AA
Tel: 01787 379228 **Email:** melford@nationaltrust.org.uk

ORFORD CASTLE ⌗
Orford, Woodbridge, Suffolk IP12 2ND
Tel: 01394 450472 **Email:** customers@english-heritage.org.uk

THE RED HOUSE - ALDEBURGH
Golf Lane, Aldeburgh, Suffolk IP15 5PZ
Tel: 01728 452615 **Email:** enquiries@brittenpears.org

SOMERLEYTON HALL & GARDENS 🏛ⓕ
Somerleyton, Lowestoft, Suffolk NR32 5QQ
Tel: 08712 224244 **Email:** info@somerleyton.co.uk

SUTTON HOO ⚘
Woodbridge, Suffolk IP12 3DJ
Tel: 01394 389700 **Email:** suttonhoo@nationaltrust.org.uk

WYKEN HALL GARDENS
Stanton, Bury St Edmunds, Suffolk IP31 2DW
Tel: 01359 250287

EAST MIDLANDS

DERBYSHIRE • LEICESTERSHIRE & RUTLAND • LINCOLNSHIRE
NORTHAMPTONSHIRE • NOTTINGHAMSHIRE

Lincoln

• Buxton • Bakewell

DERBYSHIRE

• Matlock

Derby

Nottingham

• Newark

LINCOLNSHIRE

NOTTINGHAM
SHIRE

• Southwell

Grantham •

Boston •

Loughborough • • Melton Mowbray

LEICESTER
SHIRE

Leicester

RUTLAND

NORTHAMPTON
SHIRE

• Northampton

© VISIT BRITAIN · VISIT PEAKS AND DERBYSHIRE · DANIEL BOSWORTH · JAMES PAINE'S BRIDGE AT CHATSWORTH

⚘ COUNTRYSIDE:

- Peak District
- Robin Hood Country
- Rutland Water

⧗ HERITAGE:

- Elizabethan prodigy houses
- English Civil War
- Magna Carta at Lincoln Castle

🍴 FOOD:

- Grantham gingerbread
- Melton Mowbray pork pies
- Bakewell tart

DON'T MISS!

BURGHLEY HOUSE

The pinnacled palace of William Cecil, chief adviser to Queen Elizabeth I, is the ultimate of the so-called 'prodigy' houses, extravagant mansions built by her courtiers. Most of the lavish interiors belong to the time of his descendants who scoured Europe for the best Old Master paintings, sculpture, tapestries and furniture to fill it.

Highlights:

- Turtle skulls from past pots of turtle soup
- The Hell Staircase
- The Garden of Surprises
- Sir Thomas Lawrence's portrait of The 1st Marquess of Exeter & his wife Sarah. She was a farmer's daughter with whom he fell in love while living incognito.
- Japanese porcelain

© WWW.BURGHLEY.CO.UK. - THE HELL STAIRCASE, BURGHLEY HOUSE

COTTESBROOKE HALL & GARDENS

Inside a modest Queen Anne house of 1702, set in an 18th century park with vistas to Saxon Brixworth church, is one of the best collections of English sporting art in the world. Depictions of horses, dogs and the English at play by all the masters, including Stubbs, Herring and Munnings vie for attention with fine English furniture and porcelain.

Highlights:

- The Woolavington Collection of Sporting Art
- French 19th bronzes
- Arts & Crafts gardens

191

MRS HUDSON'S HIDDEN GEM

APETHORPE PALACE

"…I do love a makeover show. In the world of Heritage the rescue of Apethorpe Palace is like reinventing Susan Boyle as a Duchess. In 2004, Apethorpe was unloved and leaking from every pipe and spout. After a makeover by English Heritage, the restored house now has a new life as a family home. Imagine living in James I's favourite palace!

Lots of cool things happened at Apethorpe. It looks like Queen Elizabeth signed the death warrant of her cousin Mary, Queen of Scots in the Great Hall; feeling terrible about it of course. James I did love a masque and Apethorpe was a favourite place to stage these extravaganzas of dressing up and dancing. The house's best secret of all was discovered during restoration. Everyone knows that James I was hopelessly in love with the glamorous Duke of Buckingham but until a door connecting their bedrooms at Apethorpe was found, no one quite knew how far it had gone. Clearly, the court of James I was ok with cross dressing and corridor creeping. Apethorpe is open for guided tours by appointment in July and August so book in now…"

MARK THE YEAR

200 YEARS
REPTON
Enjoy the gardens of Humphry Repton 200 years after his death.
- ✔ Clumber Park
- ✔ Scrivelsby Walled Garden
- ✔ Thoresby Park
- ✔ Wollaton Hall

300 YEARS
TALMAN
Visit the masterpiece of architect William Talman 300 years after his death.
- ✔ Chatsworth House

PLEASURE GROUNDS, CLUMBER PARK © NATIONAL TRUST IMAGES/ANDREW BUTLER

CHATSWORTH

100 YEARS
WOMEN & SUFFRAGE

1.

GEORGIANA, DUCHESS OF DEVONSHIRE (1767-1806)
Socialite and political campaigner for the Whig party
at Chatsworth.

2.

BESS OF HARDWICK (c. 1527-1608)
Elizabeth Talbot, Countess of Shrewsbury
Builder of Chatsworth and Hardwick Hall, of fortunes
and a family dynasty.

NANCY LANCASTER IN 1913

3.

NANCY LANCASTER (1897-1994)
Interior designer and pioneer of 'British Country
House Style' at Kelmarsh Hall.

LILFORD PARK

RENISHAW HALL GARDENS

400 YEARS
MAYFLOWER 2020

It is welcome news that the important Jacobean house at Lilford Park, once home to the Browne family, is undergoing restoration. Robert Browne (1550-1633) was founder of the first radical 'Separatist' church (separate from the Church of England that is). The Pilgrim Fathers who set off on the Mayflower in 1620 to found the Plymouth Colony followed Brownist teachings, so Browne is known as "the Father of the Pilgrims".

100 YEARS
WORLD WAR 1

Renishaw Hall, home to the literary and artistic Sitwell family, has a collection of WW1 art and letters which chart Edith's patronage of poet Wilfred Owen, killed in the last days of the War, and brother Osbert and Sacheverell's encouragement of war artists including Paul Nash and William Roberts. Works by all 3 can be seen at Renishaw.

DID YOU KNOW ?

1 TISSINGTON HALL

Tissington Hall sees the ancient practice of well dressing every May. The well is decorated with flower petals in a ceremony dating back beyond Christianity.

2 LAMPORT HALL

The first garden gnome in Britain is at Lamport Hall, one of many small figures from Nuremburg added to his new rockery by Sir Charles Isham in 1847.

3 ROCKINGHAM CASTLE

The Elephant Hedge at Rockingham Castle has nothing to do with elephants but is so old that it has grown into a shape that resembles a line of tuskers nose to tail.

WELL DRESSING AT TISSINGTON HALL

LAMPORT GNOME

THE ELEPHANT HEDGE - ROCKINGHAM CASTLE

4 WOOLSTHORPE MANOR

At Woolsthorpe Manor you can see the apple tree that inspired Sir Isaac Newton to discover gravity.

5 RENISHAW HALL

In 1798, the superbly named Sitwell Sitwell of Renishaw Hall, first in a long line of eccentrics, shot a tiger in Sheffield; it had escaped from a circus.

6 KIRBY HALL AND HOLDENBY HALL

East Midlanders had some of the most admired legs in the land. Sir Christopher Hatton, built Kirby Hall and Holdenby Hall, but it was his legs that were admired by Queen Elizabeth I and apparently Queen Victoria felt the same about the shapely legs of Frederick, 4th Earl Spencer of Althorp.

3 TOP CYCLING SPOTS

WOODLAND CYCLE TRAILS AT GRIMSTHORPE CASTLE

1. GRIMSTHORPE CASTLE

Cycling trails through the park with views of the castle, along the track of Lord Willoughby d'Eresby's private railway. Trace an old drove road and pass through mature oak woodlands.

🐕 *Dogs welcome on leads.*

🚲 *Cycle tracks and bike hire.*

2. CLUMBER PARK

3,000 acres of parkland, woods and heathland through the estate of the Duke of Newcastle, now run by the National Trust.

🐕 *Dogs welcome on leads.*

🚲 *Cycle tracks & bike hire.*

FAMILY CYCLING AT CLUMBER PARK © NATIONAL TRUST IMAGES

CHOOSE A CYCLE TRAIL AT DODDINGTON HALL

3. DODDINGTON HALL

Winner, Best Place to Shop & Best Innovation, UK Heritage Awards 2016

Cycle trails of varying lengths and difficulties through the parkland and beyond.

🐕 *Dogs welcome on leads.*

🚲 *Cycle tracks & bikes to hire.*

RUSHTON HALL HOTEL, NORTHAMPTONSHIRE

16th century country house hotel, once home to the catholic Tresham family, builders of Rushton Triangular Lodge as a symbol of the Trinity. The estates were forfeit after the Gunpowder Plot.

WASHINGBOROUGH HALL, LINCOLNSHIRE

A beautiful Grade II listed, Georgian manor house hotel. Set in three acres of mature gardens, in the heart of pretty Washingborough village, 2 miles east of the historic City of Lincoln.

LANGAR HALL, NOTTINGHAMSHIRE

A country house hotel of 1837 that is also a family home. Barbara Cartland, Penelope Keith and Jools Holland have been guests; Ed and Justine Milliband were married here. Family home of the heroic Admiral Howe, victor of the Glorious First of June, the largest fleet action of the Napoleonic Wars.

BARNSDALE LODGE HOTEL, RUTLAND

Overlooking Rutland Water and the undulating hills of England's smallest county, this former 17th century farmhouse, adjacent to the estate of the Earl of Gainsborough, is an idyllic retreat for anyone wishing to escape.

BRIDGE HILL HOUSE, DERBYSHIRE

Bridge Hill House sits high above the Derwent Valley in Belper, overlooking The Derwent Mills World Heritage site, one of the landmarks of the Industrial Revolution. The many attractions of the town, including the North Mill Museum and the River Garden are all within walking distance.

PETWOOD HOTEL, LINCOLNSHIRE

The Petwood started life in the early 19th century when springs were discovered below it, giving the Spa to Woodhall and heralding the arrival of many Victorian visitors. Over the year's kings and queens, opera singers and actors have stayed. In 1942 the hotel became the headquarters of RAF squadron 617 The Dambusters.

GLENDON GUEST HOUSE, DERBYSHIRE

The house forms part of a picturesque Victorian terrace, built in 1857, looking onto Knowleston Gardens. An ideal base to explore the Peak District, Chatsworth, Haddon Hall and other historic houses.

LOSEHILL HOUSE HOTEL & SPA, DERBYSHIRE

This 1914 Arts and Crafts gem redeveloped as a boutique country hotel and spa occupies a secluded spot on the side of Losehill with stunning views overlooking Win Hill. Situated near Hope, equidistant from the wonderful villages of Castleton and Edale, all in the midst of some of the best walking and outdoor activity countryside in England.

BIGGIN HALL HOTEL, DERBYSHIRE

A dog-friendly 17th century manor house nestling into the rocky hillsides of the Derbyshire Peak District. Good location for visiting heritage places and for walks or cycling.

IZAAK WALTON HOTEL, DERBYSHIRE

Lord Tennyson subscribed his name to the visitor's book in 1882, and declared "Dovedale was one of the most unique and delicious places in England".

SURPRISE!

When James Miller stepped down as head of global auctioneers, Sotheby's, he may have imagined that, like innumerable other Northamptonshire gentlemen in past centuries, he would retire quietly to the countryside, visit a few friends and doze in a deckchair. But he received a surprise request.

The Queen's new Lord Lieutenant of the county, David Laing, wanted to get Northamptonshire noticed, so he set up a group of deputies to help make a difference. He asked James Miller, who quickly teamed up with another Northamptonshire resident, James Lowther, also newly retired, this time as Creative Director of global advertising agency Saatchi & Saatchi and Chairman of M&C Saatchi, and took on the task of promoting local culture.

CROWDS AT THE ANNUAL ALTHORP LITERARY FESTIVAL, HELD IN OCTOBER.

Dominic Wilcox's GPS shoes prove that innovation is still part of Northamptonshire's leather industry.

Their first step was to discover that it is certainly not that Northamptonshire lacks culture, rather that nobody knows about it. Like many counties, Northamptonshire has quite a distinctive style and history but it is also cleaved by three main roads, the M1, M14 and A43. People simply pass on through. It is also rather lovely so sometimes the residents quite like it being a secret but as James Miller points out "That's no good for the local economy".

They have pooled their skills to launch a website, Britain's Best Surprise, promoting all that Is good about the county. And it turns out that is it quite an extraordinary county after all. It started out well, good grazing brought a booming wool trade in medieval times, and the fact that there was no dominant monastic house meant that as land was parcelled out after the Dissolution of the Monasteries, it could be divided between several of the aspirant Tudor lawyers looking to become country gentlemen. The county ended up with more than its fair share of Elizabethan prodigy houses which James Miller calls "plutocratic masterpiles". William Cecil built at Burghley and Christopher Hatton at Kirby and Holdenby and their local churches filled up with grand Renaissance tombs.

MARKET SQUARE AT DUSK

WELLAND RAILWAY VIADUCT, THE LONGEST MASONRY VIADUCT IN BRITAIN COMPLETED IN 1878.

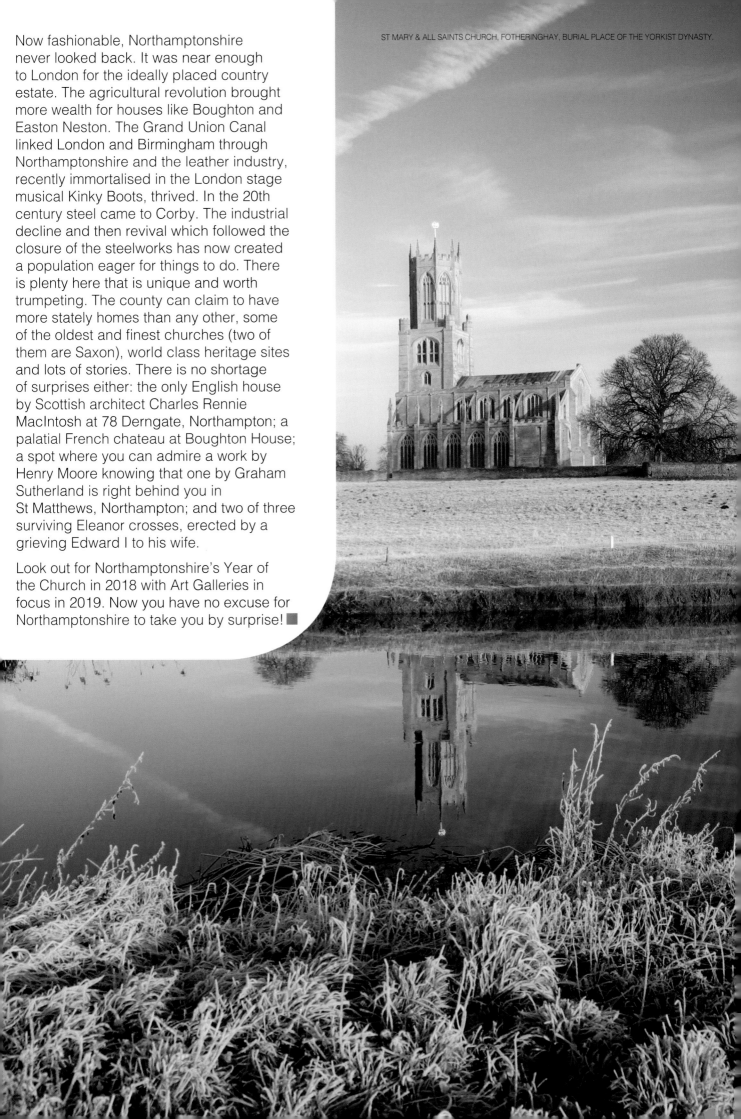

Now fashionable, Northamptonshire never looked back. It was near enough to London for the ideally placed country estate. The agricultural revolution brought more wealth for houses like Boughton and Easton Neston. The Grand Union Canal linked London and Birmingham through Northamptonshire and the leather industry, recently immortalised in the London stage musical Kinky Boots, thrived. In the 20th century steel came to Corby. The industrial decline and then revival which followed the closure of the steelworks has now created a population eager for things to do. There is plenty here that is unique and worth trumpeting. The county can claim to have more stately homes than any other, some of the oldest and finest churches (two of them are Saxon), world class heritage sites and lots of stories. There is no shortage of surprises either: the only English house by Scottish architect Charles Rennie MacIntosh at 78 Derngate, Northampton; a palatial French chateau at Boughton House; a spot where you can admire a work by Henry Moore knowing that one by Graham Sutherland is right behind you in St Matthews, Northampton; and two of three surviving Eleanor crosses, erected by a grieving Edward I to his wife.

Look out for Northamptonshire's Year of the Church in 2018 with Art Galleries in focus in 2019. Now you have no excuse for Northamptonshire to take you by surprise! ■

Chatsworth

www.chatsworth.org

Chatsworth, home of the Duke and Duchess of Devonshire is set in the heart of the Peak District. Explore the historic house for fascinating stories and one of Europe's most significant art collections. In the garden, discover water features, giant sculptures and beautiful flowers set in Britain's most stunning and surprising country estate. Or come face to face with our farm animals in our working farmyard and enjoy adventurous fun in the playground.

KEY FACTS

 Toilet facilities available.

 Baby changing facilities available.

 Open until 7pm. Online bookings free parking. £4 per vehicle. Blue badge holders free.

 Welcoming all visitors; Please see the access statement on the website for all details on how we can assist.

 Dogs welcome.

 Stay at Chatsworth; Holiday Cottages, Luxury Hotels & Beautiful Inns.

 Audio guides available in English, French, German, Spanish & Mandarin at a cost of £3 per person.

 The house taster tour lasts 45 mins & costs £4 per adult & £2 per child. Buggy & walking tours in Garden.

 Bursting with history, art & a farmyard, to enrich your students' curriculum - For all stages of learning.

 Plenty of places to stop for a treat – offering light bites, hearty meals or indulgent afternoon teas.

 The Cavendish restaurant, The Flying Childers restaurant & The Carriage House (self-service.)

 Farm Shop; open 9am-6pm Mon-Sat &11am-5pm on Suns. Also the Orangery shop & the Stables shop.

 Offering all you need for team building days; product launches, exhibitions, meetings & conferences.

 Organising celebrations, from award ceremonies & banquets, to christenings & bar mitzvahs.

Offering a range of wedding packages to create a special day, whatever your style and budget.

35,000-acre Estate in Derbyshire offers a wide range of beautiful locations for TV, film & stills.

CONTACT
Owner: Chatsworth House Trust **Contact:** The Booking Office
Tel: 01264 565300 **Email:** Info@chatsworth.org

LOCATION
Bakewell, Derbyshire DE45 1PP
Map Ref: 6:P2 - **Car:** From London 3 hours M1/J29, signposted via Chesterfield. 3 miles East of Bakewell, off B6012,10 miles West of Chesterfield. **Rail:** Chesterfield Station, 11 miles. **Bus:** Chesterfield - Baslow 1½ miles.

OPENING TIMES
Chatsworth House, Garden & Farmyard: 24 Mar-6 Jan
The Farmyard: 17-25 Feb & 24 Mar-6 Jan
Visit www.chatsworth.org for opening times during the main, seasonal and Christmas seasons.

ADMISSION
Visit www.chatsworth.org for all ticket options.
Groups: 15+ Discounted bookings.

Melbourne Hall & Gardens

www.melbournehall.com

This beautiful house of history, in its picturesque poolside setting, was once the home of Victorian Prime Minister William Lamb. The fine gardens, in the French formal style, contain Robert Bakewell's intricate wrought iron arbour and a fascinating yew tunnel. Upstairs rooms available to view by appointment.

KEY FACTS

 No photography in house.

 Toilet facilities are available in the Visitors Centre.

 There is limited parking in Church Square and Castle Square. No coach parking.

 Partial. WC's.

Dogs are allowed around Melbourne Pool on a lead. Assistance dogs in the hall & gardens only.

 Obligatory in house Tue-Thurs.

 Melbourne Hall Tea Room.

 Hospice shop, gift shop, wine merchants, beauty clinic, violin shop, furniture restorer & antiques.

 Selection for sale at garden entrance.

 Please see the 'Events' page for all upcoming events or contact to book an event.

CONTACT
Owner: Lord & Lady Ralph Kerr
Contact: Melbourne Hall Estate Office
Tel: 01332 862502 **Email:** melbhall@globalnet.co.uk

LOCATION
Melbourne, Derbyshire DE73 8EN
Map Ref: 7:A5 - 8m South of Derby. From London, exit M1/J24.

OPENING TIMES
Every day, Aug only (not first 3 Mons) 2pm-5pm. Last admission 4.15pm. Gardens: 1 Apr-30 Sep, Weds, Sats, Suns, BH Mons, 1.30pm-5.30pm. Additional days in Aug when the Hall is open.

ADMISSION
Website www.melbournehall.com or ring 01332 862502 for up to date admission charges.

Renishaw Hall & Gardens

www.renishaw-hall.co.uk

Renishaw Hall and Gardens have been home to the Sitwell family for over 400 years. Its present owner, Alexandra, welcomes you. Renishaw Hall is set in 8 acres of Italianate gardens, designed by Sir George Sitwell featuring statues, yew hedges, beautiful herbaceous borders and ornamental ponds. Mature woodlands and lakes offer wonderful walks. The hall offers an intriguing insight into the Sitwell family's history, with a fascinating collection of paintings including work by John Piper. The hall and gardens are open for group and public tours, see website for details.

CONTACT
Owner: Mrs Hayward **Contact:** The Hall & Visitor Manager
Tel: 01246 432310 **Email:** enquiries@renishaw-hall.co.uk

LOCATION
Renishaw, Nr Sheffield, Derbyshire S21 3WB
Map Ref: 7:A2 - On A6135, 3 miles from M1/J30, located between Sheffield and Chesterfield.

OPENING TIMES
21 Mar-30 Sep. Gardens open Wed-Sun & BH Mons, 10.30am-4.30pm. Hall open to public on Fridays throughout season 1pm/2.30pm & weekends in Aug.

ADMISSION
HHA /RHS members: Free entry to Gardens. Guided Hall Tours £6.50. Discounts for coach/group bookings over 20 people.
Non-member Gardens - Adults: £6.50, Concs: £5.50, Child: £3.25, Under 5's: Free, Family: (1+3) £10 / (2+3) £15.
Non-member Hall & Gardens - Adults: £13, Concs: £12, Child: £8.

KEY FACTS

 Toilet facilities inlcuding disabled WC's available during garden opening.

 Baby changing facilities available.

 Parking £1 per car for the day.

 Partial. Please see the full access statement on the website for further details.

 Dog welcome on leads.

 Pre-booking advisable. Hall, garden & vineyard tours throughout year. Private & coach tours, by appointment.

 Educational visits by arrangement.

 Licensed café open during garden opening times and situated in the stables.

 Gift Shop open during garden opening times and situated in the stables.

 Plant sales by Handley Rose Nursery available at the visitor centre.

 Please contact for corporate functions.

Please see the 'What's On' section of the website for all upcoming events.

Chatsworth House

Stanford Hall

www.stanfordhall.co.uk

Stanford has been the home of the Cave family, ancestors of the present owner since 1430. In the 1690s, Sir Roger Cave commissioned the Smiths of Warwick to pull down the old Manor House and build the present Hall. Throughout the house are portraits of the family and examples of furniture and objects which they collected over the centuries. There is also a collection of Royal Stuart portraits. The Hall and Stables are set in an attractive Park on the banks of Shakespeare's Avon. There is a walled Rose Garden and an early ha-ha.

CONTACT
Owner: Mr & Mrs N Fothergill
Contact: Nick Fothergill
Tel: 01788 860250
Email: enquiries@stanfordhall.co.uk

LOCATION
Lutterworth, Leicestershire LE17 6DH
Map Ref: 7:B7 - M1/J18 6m. M1/J20, 6m.
M6 exit/access at J1, 4m. Historic House signs.

OPENING TIMES
Special 3 week Easter: Mon 19 Mar-Fri 6 Apr 2018.
Open other days in conjunction with park events and Bank Holidays. See website or call for details.

Pre-booked groups Mon-Fri only by appointment only.

ADMISSION
House & Grounds
Adult: £8, Child (5-15 yrs): £2.50.
Private group tours (20+)
Adult: £8, Child: £2.50.
Special admission prices will apply on event days.

KEY FACTS

 Parkland, helicopter landing area & lecture room.

 Toilet facilities available.

 1,000 cars and 6-8 coaches. Coach parking on gravel in front of house.

 Partial. WC's.

 Dogs on leads only.

 Accommodation available for Group bookings only. Caravan Site 01788 860387.

 Tour time: ¾ hour in groups of approximately 25 people.

 Educational visits available.

 Stables Tea Room.

 On site Gift shop selling Antiques, Confectionery and Stanford Hall memorabilia.

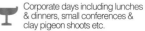 Corporate days including lunches & dinners, small conferences & clay pigeon shoots etc.

 For all upcoming events please see 'Public Events' on the website.

 Offering civil ceremonies and wedding receptions.

 Filming opportunities available.

Burghley House

Burghley House

www.burghley.co.uk

Burghley House, home of the Cecil family for over 400 years is one of England's Greatest Elizabethan Houses.

Burghley was built between 1555 and 1587 by William Cecil, later Lord Burghley, principal adviser and Lord High Treasurer to Queen Elizabeth I. During the 17th and 18th Centuries, the House was transformed by John 5th Earl of Exeter and Brownlow, the 9th Earl; travelling to the cultural centres of Europe and employing many of the foremost craftsmen of their day.

Burghley contains one of the largest private collections of Italian art, unique examples of Chinese and Japanese porcelain and superb items of 18th Century furniture. Principal artists and craftsmen of the period are to be found at Burghley: Antonio Verrio, Grinling Gibbons and Louis Laguerre all made major contributions to the beautiful interiors.

Park and Gardens

The house is set in a 300-acre deer park landscaped by 'Capability' Brown and is one of the finest examples of his work. A lake was created by him and delightful avenues of mature trees feature largely in his design. Brown also carried out alterations to the architecture of the House and added a summerhouse in the South Gardens. The park is home to a large herd of Fallow deer, established in the 16th Century.

The Garden of Surprises is a modern oasis of flowing water and fountains, statues, and obelisks. The contemporary Sculpture Garden was reclaimed from 'Capability' Brown's lost lower gardens in 1994 and is dedicated to exhibiting innovative sculptures. The private gardens around the house are open from mid-March to mid-April for the display of spring bulbs.

OWNER
Burghley House Preservation Trust Ltd

CONTACT
Contact: House Manager
Tel: 01780 752451
Fax: 01780 480125
Email: burghley@burghley.co.uk

LOCATION
Stamford, Lincolnshire PE9 3JY
Map Ref: 7:E7
Burghley House is 1m SE of Stamford. From London, A1 2hrs. Visitors entrance is on B1443.

Rail: London - Peterborough 1hr (East Coast mainline). Stamford Station 12mins, regular service from Peterborough.

Taxi: Direct line 01780 481481

OPENING TIMES
House & Gardens
17 Mar-28th Oct (closed 30 Aug-2 Sep).
Open Daily, (House closed on Fridays) 11am-5pm (Last admission 4.30pm).

ADMISSION
Please see our website for all details on admission prices and the ticket options available.

REGULAR EVENTS
Please see 'The Burghley Events Diary' on the 'What's on' page of the website for all upcoming special events.

KEY FACTS

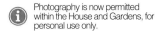 Photography is now permitted within the House and Gardens, for personal use only.

 Toilet facilities available.

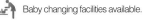 Baby changing facilities available.

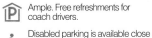 Ample. Free refreshments for coach drivers.

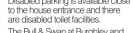 Disabled parking is available close to the house entrance and there are disabled toilet facilities.

 The Bull & Swan at Burghley and the William Cecil Hotel are places to stay near Burghley.

 By arrangement.

 Welcome. Guide provided.

 Licensed. The Garden Café is open daily from 11am-5pm.

 The Orangery Restaurant is open daily from 11am -5pm. Closes occasionally for private events.

 Courtyard shop is open daily from 11am-5pm.

 The Garden Shop is open daily from 11am-5pm.

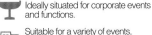 Ideally situated for corporate events and functions.

 Suitable for a variety of events, large park, golf course, helicopter landing area, cricket pitch.

 Civil wedding licence.

Grimsthorpe Castle, Park & Gardens

www.grimsthorpe.co.uk

Building styles from 13th Century. North Front is Vanbrugh's last major work. State Rooms and picture galleries including tapestries, furniture and paintings. Interesting collection of thrones, fabrics and objects from the old House of Lords, associated with the family's hereditary Office of Lord Great Chamberlain. 3,000 acre park with lakes, ancient woods, walking and cycle trail, cycle hire shop. Extensive gardens including unusual ornamental kitchen garden. Groups can explore the park in their own coach by booking a one-hour, escorted park tour. Tailor-made group visits available on request including Head Gardener tour. Full and half day bespoke visits for groups of 15+.

KEY FACTS

 No photography in house.

 Two sets of lavatories, both with facilities for disabled people.

 Baby changing facilities available.

 Ample parking available. Reserved parking available for disabled people.

 Please see the access for all section of the website for full details.

 Cycling is a great way to explore the hidden delights of the park. Cycling & cycle hire available.

 Dogs on leads only. Please avoid formal gardens & adventure playground.

 Properties available for let on the estate. Local accommodation available. Please see website.

 Obligatory except Suns and Bank Holiday Mons.

 Educational visits by arrangement.

 Morning coffee from 11am, light lunches 12pm-2.30pm. Afternoon tea service. Closes 5pm.

 Locally produced food and drink plus other gifts and souvenirs.

 Please contact for all corporate event enquiries.

Please see events section of the website for all upcoming events.

CONTACT
Owner: Grimsthorpe & Drummond Castle Trust Ltd.
A Charity registered in England, Wales & Scotland SCO39364.
Contact: Ray Biggs
Tel: 01778 591205 **Email:** ray@grimsthorpe.co.uk

LOCATION
Grimsthorpe, Bourne, Lincolnshire PE10 0LZ
Map Ref: 7:D5 - 4 miles North West of Bourne on A151,
8 miles East of Colsterworth Junction of A1.

OPENING TIMES
Castle: Apr & May, Sun, Thu & Bank Holiday Mons.
Jun-Sep, Sun-Thu inclusive. 12-4pm (last admission 3pm).
Park & Gardens: same days as Castle,
10.30am-6pm (last admission 5pm).
Groups: Apr-Sep: by arrangement. Closed Fridays & Sats.

ADMISSION
Castle, Park & Garden
Adult: £13, Child: £5.50, Concession: £12, Family (2+3): £31.50, Groups: 15+.
Park & Gardens
Adult: £7, Child: £6, Concession: £3, Family (2+3): £17.

Lincoln Castle

www.lincolncastle.com

Discover Lincoln Castle, home to one of the four surviving Magna Carta's; the attraction has undergone a £22m refurbishment. Bringing 1,000 years of history to life – right where it happened.

KEY FACTS

 Photography permitted in Castle for private use, but strictly prohibited in the Magna Carta Vault.

 Wheelchair accessible toilets are located on the ground floor of the prison or at the East Gate entrance.

 Baby changing facilities available.

 Closed 24-26 Dec & 31 Dec-1 Jan.

 Public car parking outside the Castle grounds.

 Partial. Please see the access statement on the website for full details.

 Audio tour included in admission price. Available in German and French.

 In summer at 11am, 12pm, 1.30pm, 2.30pm and in winter 11am, 1.30 pm.

 Please contact us for education visits. The programme is designed to bring history to life.

 Set within the prison and licensed. Offering a range of coffees, teas, sandwiches, snacks & cakes.

 Set within the prison with a range to suit all pockets.

 Tailor made packages. A unique place to hold events; the perfect setting for you to entertain.

 Events through the year. Some events will have separate admission prices.

 Wedding packages available.

CONTACT
Owner: Lincolnshire County Council
Tel: 01522 554559
Email: lincoln_castle@lincolnshire.gov.uk

LOCATION
Castle Hill, Lincoln LN1 3AA - **Map Ref:** 7:D2
Set next to Lincoln Cathedral in the Historic Quarter of the city.
Follow signs from A1 Newark or A15 North and South.

TYPICALLY OPEN
Apr-Sep 10am- 5pm (grounds close at 5:30pm)
Oct-Mar 10am-4pm (grounds close at 4.30pm)

ADMISSION
Adult: £13.50 (10% discount with online purchase. All-Inclusive only)
Child 5 & over: £7.20 (Under 5's free), Concessions: £11, Family: £34.20, Groups: +16.
Walk, Prison & Vault included. Entry to Castle grounds, shop & café are free. Please note, prices may change in April 2018.

Aubourn Hall
aubournhall.co.uk

The garden and lawns surround this mellow brick manor house dating from the early 17th Century and still lived in by the Nevile family. In recent years, the Rose Garden and Prairie gardens have become fully established giving a new emphasis to the shape of the gardens which continue to delight with their sweeping lawns, ponds and woodland walk.

KEY FACTS

 National Gardens Scheme - gardens open for charity.

 Limited for coaches.

 Partial. WC's.

 Guide dogs only.

 By arrangement.

 Homemade refreshments available.

 Available as a wedding reception venue. Please contact to find out more.

CONTACT
Owner:
Mr & Mrs Christopher Nevile
Contact:
Paula Dawson, Estate Office
Tel: 01522 788224
Fax: 01522 788199
Email: estate.office@ aubournhall.co.uk

LOCATION
Lincoln LN5 9DZ
Map Ref: 7:D3 - 6m SW of Lincoln. 2m SE of A46.

OPENING TIMES
Garden open for events. Groups and Garden visits from May-Sep. Contact or go to the website for details.
ADMISSION
Adult: £5, Child: Free.

Fulbeck Manor

Fulbeck Manor was built in c1580s; Tudor times, but is now largely Georgian in character. The house stands 3 storeys high including garrets, with a 5 bay front. The interiors feature portraits of the Fane family, who have lived here for over 400 years. The most impressive feature is a 17th Century staircase with spiral balusters.

CONTACT
Owner/Contact:
Mr Julian Francis Fane

Tel: 01400 272231
E-mail: fane@fulbeck.co.uk

LOCATION
Fulbeck, Grantham, Lincolnshire NG32 3JN

Map Ref: 7:D3

11 miles North of Grantham. 15 miles South of Lincoln on A607. Brown signs to Craft Centre & Tearooms and Stables.

OPENING TIMES
By written appointment.

ADMISSION
Adult: £7
Groups (10+): £6

KEY FACTS

 No photography.

 Open all year by written appointment.

 Ample for cars. Limited for coaches.

 Partial. WC's.

 Obligatory. Guided tours by owner approximately 1¼ hours.

 Tea Rooms at Craft Centre, 100 yards, for light lunches and teas.

Doddington Hall & Gardens
www.doddingtonhall.com

Romantic Smythson house standing today as it was built in 1595. Still a family home. Georgian interior with fascinating collection of porcelain, paintings and textiles. Five acres of wild and walled formal gardens plus kitchen garden provide colour and interest year-round. Award-winning Farm Shop, Café and Restaurant. Country Clothing, Farrow and Ball and Home Stores.

KEY FACTS

 Giant Lincoln Bike Shop on site; hire bikes to explore the estate plus cycle path connecting to Lincoln.

Four Holiday Cottages and 4 additional double rooms on the estate.

 Private guided tours available for group Visits (20+ people) Apr-Oct and Christmas.

 Award-winning Café and Restaurant, serving breakfast, lunch and Fri-Sat evenings.

Farm Shop supplies good quality, seasonal, local food and kitchen garden produce.

 Four special licensed sites in stunning surroundings.

CONTACT
Owner: Mr & Mrs J J C Birch
Contact: The Estate Office
Tel: 01522 694308
Email: info@doddingtonhall.com

LOCATION
Lincoln LN6 4RU
Map Ref: 7:D2 - 5m W of Lincoln on the B1190.

OPENING TIMES
Gardens only
11 Feb–1 Apr & Oct,
Sun only. 11am-4.30pm
House & Gardens
1 Apr–30 Sep, Wed, Fri, Sun & Bank Holiday Mon. 12pm-4.30pm (Gardens from 11am)
ADMISSION
Gardens only
Adult: £7, Child: £3.50, Family: £18
House & Gardens
Adult: £11, Child: £5.50, Family: £29, Groups: £12pp.

Grimsthorpe Castle

Althorp

www.spencerofalthorp.com

Althorp House was built in 1508, by the Spencers, for the Spencers, and that is how it has remained for over 500 years. Today, Althorp contains one of the finest private collections of art, furniture and ceramics in the world, including numerous paintings by Rubens, Reynolds, Lely, Gainsborough and Van Dyck.

Visitors can enjoy the House in the company of Althorp's expert tour guides, discovering the fascinating history of one of England's most beautiful, private, historic houses. Wander around the Gardens, the current Exhibitions and visit the Café and Gift Shop in the Stables.

CONTACT
Owner: The Rt Hon The 9th Earl Spencer
Contact: Althorp
Tel: 01604 770107
Email: mail@althorp.com

LOCATION
Northampton NN7 4HQ
Map Ref: 7:C9 - From the M1, 7m from J16 and 10m from J18. Situated on A428 Northampton - Rugby. Rail: 5m from Northampton station and 14m from Rugby station. Sat Nav Postcode: NN7 4HQ.

OPENING TIMES
Please visit website for current opening dates & times.

ADMISSION
Prices on application for adults, concessions and young children. HHA members are free entry.

Please call 01604 770107 or email groups@althorp.com to pre-book coach parties and group visits.

KEY FACTS

 No indoor photography with still or video cameras.

 Toilet facilities available.

 Baby changing facilities available.

 Free parking with a 5/10 minute walk to the house. Disabled parking available.

 House and estate accessible to wheelchairs, except the first floor of the House.

 The house is available for overnight private hire.

 Althorp interior is available to view with our expert tour guides, from the front of the house.

 The Stables Café serves a selection of drinks, cakes, sandwiches and snacks.

 Catering for private hire.

 The gift shop offers an array of bespoke goods, exclusively designed and manufactured for Althorp.

 Offering lunch parties, corporate functions and activity days etc. To enquire email admin@althorp.com

 Please see the 'News' page on the website for all upcoming events and exhibitions.

 Holding civil ceremonies and receptions with exclusive hire of the house day and night.

Featuring in photographic & film shoots: Tatler, Harper's Bazaar, Ralph Lauren and Vanity Fair.

Cottesbrooke Hall & Gardens

www.cottesbrooke.co.uk

Dating from 1702 the Hall's beauty is matched by the magnificence of the gardens and the excellence of the picture, furniture and porcelain collections. The Woolavington collection of sporting pictures is possibly the finest of its type in Europe and includes paintings by Stubbs, Ben Marshall and artists renowned for works of this genre. Portraits, bronzes, 18th Century English and French furniture and fine porcelain are among the treasures.

The formal gardens are continually being updated and developed by influential designers. The Wild Gardens, a short walk across the Park, are planted along the course of a stream.

CONTACT
Owner: Mr & Mrs A R Macdonald-Buchanan
Contact: The Administrator
Tel: 01604 505808
Email: welcome@cottesbrooke.co.uk

LOCATION
Cottesbrooke, Northamptonshire NN6 8PF
Map Ref: 7:B8
10m N of Northampton near Creaton on A5199 (formerly A50). Signed from Junction 1 on the A14.

OPENING TIMES
May-end of Sep. May & Jun: Wed & Thu, 2pm-5.30pm.
Jul-Sep: Thu, 2pm-5.30pm.
Open BH Mons (May-Sep), 2pm-5.30pm.
The first open day is Wed 2 May 2018.

ADMISSION
House & Gardens
Adult: £9, Child: £5, Conc: £8.50.
Gardens only
Adult: £7, Child: £4, Conc: £6.50.
Group & private bookings by arrangement.

KEY FACTS

 No large bags or photography in house. Filming and outside events.

 Toilet and disabled WC facilities available.

 Baby changing facilities available.

 Car and coach parking is included in the admission fee.

 Partial. Please contact prior to visit for full access details.

 Hall guided tours obligatory. Approx. 45 minutes and max of 18 people per tour.

 Educational visits by prior arrangement.

 Homemade cakes & drinks available in The Old Laundry between 2:30pm & 5pm on open days.

 For intimate and exclusive events. Contact the Estate Office on 01604 505717 for prices & availability.

 Special events.

East Midlands

Holdenby House

www.holdenby.com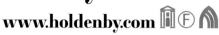

Once the largest private house in England and subsequently the palace of James I and prison of Charles I, Holdenby has appeared in the BBC's acclaimed adaptation of 'Great Expectations'. Sitting on a hill overlooking thousands of acres of rolling countryside, its suite of elegant state rooms open onto beautiful Grade I listed gardens making it an enchanting and ever popular venue for weddings. Its combination of grandeur and intimacy make it a magnificent location for corporate dinners and meetings, while the spacious grounds have accommodated many large events from Civil War battles to Formula One parties. Day visitors enjoy Sunday garden openings and other special events days with Icarus Falconry located in the walled garden.

KEY FACTS

 Children's play area. No photography in the house.

 Limited for coaches.

 Accessible. Please contact for further details.

 Dogs welcome in the gardens but must be kept on leads at all times.

 Private guided tours, by arrangement.

 Facilities for educational visits. 7 times Sanford Award Winner.

 Victorian Kitchen Teas on special event days; Refreshments available on Sun garden openings May-Aug.

 Gift shop.

 Conference venue for meetings, conferences, launches, dinners and parties.

 Please see the 'Events/News' section of the website for all upcoming events.

 The perfect and exclusive venue for your special day. Licensed for civil ceremonies & civil partnerships.

 Its historic interiors & exteriors make a very striking Location for Film, TV and Commercials.

CONTACT
Owner: James Lowther
Contact: Commercial Manager
Tel: 01604 770074
Email: office@holdenby.com

LOCATION
Northampton NN6 8DJ **Map Ref:** 7:B8 **OS Ref:** SP693 681 M1/J15a. 7m NW of Northampton off A428 & A5199.

OPENING TIMES
Gardens: Apr-Sep. See website for details.

ADMISSION
Adult: £5, Child: £3.50, Concessions: £4.50, Family (2+2): £15. Prices will vary on special event days. Please see our website for details.

Cottesbrooke Hall

Haddonstone Show Gardens

www.haddonstone.com

See Haddonstone's classic garden ornaments and architectural stonework in the beautiful walled manor gardens including: planters, fountains, statues, bird baths, sundials and balustrades - even an orangery, gothic grotto and other follies. As featured on BBC TV.

New features include replicas of Soane Museum designs and the acclaimed new busts of Lancelot 'Capability' Brown and Humphry Repton. Gastro pub nearby.

CONTACT
Owner: Haddonstone Ltd
Contact: Simon Scott, Marketing Director
Tel: 01604 770711
Email: info@haddonstone.co.uk

LOCATION
The Forge House, Church Lane, East Haddon, Northampton NN6 8DB **Map Ref:** 7:B8
7m NW of Northampton off A428. Located in village centre opposite school. Signposted.

OPENING TIMES
Mon-Fri, 9am-5.30pm. Closed weekends, Bank Holidays and the Christmas period. Check Haddonstone website for details of NGS weekend opening and Sat openings in Summer.

ADMISSION
Free (except NGS). Groups by appt only. No coach parties.

KEY FACTS

 No photography without permission.

 Accepts Euros.

 Open all year apart from weekends, bank holidays and the Christmas period.

 Almost all areas of garden accessible.

 By arrangement.

 Haddonstone designs can be ordered for delivery to addresses worldwide.

Limited.

Please see website for all upcoming events.

Lamport Hall & Gardens

www.lamporthall.co.uk

Lamport Hall was the home of the Isham family from 1560 until 1976, and is an architectural gem. It still houses the fine collection of furniture and paintings accumulated by the family, including many beautiful items acquired on the Grand Tour in the 1670s. Surrounded by parkland, the delightful 10-acre gardens are famous as the home of the world's oldest garden gnome, and there are fascinating examples of changes in garden design across the centuries. Added attractions include a large exhibition in the Edwardian stable block and the quirky Museum of Rural Life. Group visits to the Hall and gardens are very welcome, and a range of themed tours are available for groups.

CONTACT
Owner: Lamport Hall Preservation Trust
Contact: Executive Director
Tel: 01604 686272 **Fax:** 01604 686224
Email: admin@lamporthall.co.uk

LOCATION
Northamptonshire NN6 9HD
Map Ref: 7:C8 - Entrance on A508. Midway between Northampton and Market Harborough, 3m S of A14 J2.

OPENING TIMES
Apr-Oct, every Wed & Thu (guided house tours at 2.15pm & 3pm; free-flow around gardens). Also open most BH Sun/Mon. Private tours at other times by arrangement.
Please check website for opening times & prices.

ADMISSION
House & Garden
Adult: £9, Senior: £8.50, Groups: £8.50.
Garden Only
Adult: £6, Senior: £5.50, Groups: £5.50. Min charges apply.

KEY FACTS

 No photography in house.

 Lavatory facilities available.

 Open all year for pre-arranged groups only.

 Limited for coaches. Free parking is available in the stable yard.

 Partial please see website for full details. Disabled lavatory block at the front of the Hall.

 Guide dogs only in the Hall, but all dogs welcome on leads in the gardens.

 Tours last approximately 75 mins. There are 2 tours per afternoon leaving at 2.15pm & 3.00pm.

 Teas are served during opening hours in the Victorian Dining Room, access is for ticket holders only.

 Available for hire on an exclusive basis for small conferences, meetings & corporate hospitality etc.

 Please see the events section of the website for all upcoming events.

Provides a secluded & atmospheric location for your special day.

 Available for filming.

NOTTINGHAMSHIRE

Papplewick Hall

papplewickhall.co.uk

A beautiful classic Georgian house, built of Mansfield stone, set in parkland, with woodland garden laid out in the 18th Century. The house is notable for its very fine plasterwork, and elegant staircase. Grade I listed.

KEY FACTS

 No photography.

 Open all year by appointment.

 Limited for coaches. Free parking on NGS open days.

 Obligatory.

 Garden NGS open days 27 May, 2-5pm (Adult: £3.50 & Child: Free) The Village Fête on 16 Jun, 2-5pm.

CONTACT
Owner/Contact:
Mr J R Godwin-Austen
Tel: 0115 9632623
E-mail:
mail@papplewickhall.co.uk

LOCATION
Papplewick, Nottinghamshire NG15 8FE **Map Ref:** 7:B4 Halfway between Nottingham & Mansfield, 3m E of M1/ J27. The Hall is 1/2 mile north of Papplewick village, off Blidworth Waye (B683).

OPENING TIMES
1, 3 & 5 Wed in each month 2pm-5pm, & by appointment.
ADMISSION
Adult: £5, Groups (10+): £4

Clumber Park ©National Trust/Images

Clumber Park ©National Trust/Images

BOLSOVER CASTLE ⌗
Castle Street, Bolsover, Derbyshire S44 6PR
Tel: 01246 822844 **Email:** customers@english-heritage.org.uk

CALKE ABBEY ⚘
Ticknall, Derbyshire DE73 7LE
Tel: 01332 863822 **Email:** calkeabbey@nationaltrust.org.uk

Catton Hall 🏛ⓔ

Catton, Walton-On-Trent, South Derbyshire DE12 8LN
Catton, built in 1745, has been in the hands of the same family since 1405 and is still lived in by the Neilsons as their private home. Acres of flat and undulating parkland ideal for public and sporting events.
Location: 1 mile from A38 at Alrewas, between Birmingham and Derby.
Map Ref: 6:P5 **Tel:** 01283 716311 **Email:** estateoffice@catton-hall.com
Website: www.catton-hall.com **Open:** Prebooked groups all year round.

ELVASTON CASTLE & COUNTRY PARK
Borrowash Road, Elvaston, Derby, Derbyshire DE72 3EP
Tel: 01629 533870 **Email:** countrysideservice@derbyshire.gov.uk

EYAM HALL ⚘
Eyam, Hope Valley, Derbyshire S32 5QW
Tel: 01433 631976 **Email:** nicolawright@eyamhall.co.uk

HADDON HALL 🏛ⓔ
Estate Office, Hadd on Hall, Bakewell, Derbyshire DE45 1LA
Tel: 01629 812855 **Email:** info@haddonhall.co.uk

HARDWICK ESTATE ⚘
Doe Lea, Chesterfield, Derbyshire S44 5QJ
Tel: 01246 850430 **Email:** hardwickhall@nationaltrust.org.uk

HARDWICK OLD HALL ⌗
Doe Lea, Nr Chesterfield, Derbyshire S44 5QJ
Tel: 01246 850431 **Email:** customers@english-heritage.org.uk

HOPTON HALL 🏛ⓔ
Hopton, Wirksworth, Matlock, Derbyshire DE4 4DF
Tel: 01629 540923 **Email:** bookings@hoptonhall.co.uk

KEDLESTON HALL ⚘
Derbyshire DE22 5JH
Tel: 01332 842191 **Email:** kedlestonhall@nationaltrust.org.uk

Ogston Hall & Gardens

Ogston New Road, Brackenfield, Derbyshire DE55 6AP
Part Jacobean, Georgian house extensively remodelled by T.C Hine 1850-64. Beautiful terraced gardens with views over mature parkland.
Map Ref: 7:A3 - 6 miles E of Matlock, 1 mile N.E of Brackenfield, by Ogston Reservoir. Entrance opposite Ogston Lodge, Brackenfield.
Tel: 01773 520970 / 07796 130677 **Open:** 1-28 Aug, 2pm-5pm.
By appointment only. **Admission:** £10 per head.

THE PAVILION GARDENS
St John's Road, Buxton, Derbyshire SK17 6XN
Tel: 01298 23114 **Email:** terry.crawford@highpeak.gov.uk

PEVERIL CASTLE ⌗
Market Place, Castleton, Hope Valley S33 8WQ
Tel: 01433 620613 **Email:** customers@english-heritage.org.uk

SUDBURY HALL & MUSEUM OF CHILDHOOD ⚘
Ashbourne, Derbyshire DE6 5HT
Tel: 01283 585337 **Email:** sudburyhall@nationaltrust.org.uk

SUTTON SCARSDALE HALL ⌗
Hall Drive, Sutton Scarsdale, Chesterfield, Derbyshire S44 5UR
Tel: 01246 822844 **Email:** bolsover.castle@english-heritage.org.uk

TISSINGTON HALL 🏛ⓔ
Ashbourne, Derbyshire DE6 1RA
Tel: 01335 352200 **Email:** events@tissingtonhall.co.uk

WELBECK ABBEY 🏛
Welbeck, Worksop, Nottinghamshire S80 3LL
Tel: 01909 501700 **Email:** info@harleygallery.co.uk

WINGFIELD MANOR ⌗
South Wingfield, Derbyshire DE55 7NH
Tel: 0870 333 1181 **Email:** customers@english-heritage.org.uk

THE 1620 HOUSE & GARDEN
Manor Road, Coalville, Leicestershire LE67 2FW
Tel: 01455 290429 **Email:** dlhmanorhouse@leics.gov.uk

ASHBY DE LA ZOUCH CASTLE ⌗
South Street, Ashby De La Zouch LE65 1BR
Tel: 01530 413343 **Email:** customers@english-heritage.org.uk

BELVOIR CASTLE 🏛ⓔ
Belvoir, Grantham, Leicestershire NG32 1PE
Tel: 01476 871001

KIRBY MUXLOE CASTLE ⌗
Kirby Muxloe, Leicestershire LE9 2DH
Tel: 01162 386886 **Email:** customers@english-heritage.org.uk

LYDDINGTON BEDE HOUSE ⌗
Blue Coat Lane, Lyddington, Leicester LE15 9LZ
Tel: 0157 282 2438 **Email:** customers@english-heritage.org.uk

OAKHAM CASTLE
Castle Lane (Off Market Place), Oakham, Rutland LE15 6DF
Tel: 01572 758440

STAUNTON HAROLD HALL 🏛
Staunton Harold, Ashby de la Zouch, Leicestershire LE65 1RT
Tel: 01332 862599 **Email:** rowan@stauntonharoldhall.co.uk

STONEYWELL ⚘
Ulverscroft, Markfield, Leicestershire LE67 9QE
Tel: 01530 248040 **Email:** emily.wolfe@nationaltrust.org.uk

WHATTON HOUSE & GARDENS ◇
Loughborough, Leicestershire LE12 5BG
Tel: 01509 842268 **Email:** enquiries@whattonhouseandgardens.co.uk

Arabella Aufrere Temple

Brocklesby Park, Grimsby, Lincolnshire DN41 8PN
Garden Temple of ashlar and red brick with coupled Doric columns.
Map Ref: 11:E12 - Off A18 in Great Limber Village.
Tel: 01469 560214
Email: office@brocklesby.co.uk
Open: 1 Apr–31 Aug: viewable from permissive paths through Mausoleum Woods at all reasonable times. **Admission:** None.

AYSCOUGHFEE HALL MUSEUM & GARDENS
Churchgate, Spalding, Lincolnshire PE11 2RA
Tel: 01775 764555 **Email:** museum@sholland.gov.uk

BELTON HOUSE 🌿
Grantham, Lincolnshire NG32 2LS
Tel: 01476 566116 **Email:** belton@nationaltrust.org.uk

BOLINGBROKE CASTLE ⚜
Moat Lane, Old Bolingbroke, Spilsby, Lincolnshire PE23 4HH
Tel: 01529 461499 **Email:** customers@english-heritage.org.uk

Brocklesby Mausoleum

Brocklesby Park, Grimsby, Lincolnshire DN41 8PN
Family Mausoleum designed by James Wyatt and built between 1787 and 1794. **Map Ref:** 11:E12 - Off A18 in Great Limber Village.
Tel: 01469 560214
Email: office@brocklesby.co.uk
Open: By prior arrangement with Estate Office.
Admission: Modest admission charge for interior.

EASTON WALLED GARDENS 🏛ⓕ◇
Easton, Grantham, Lincolnshire NG33 5AP
Tel: 01476 530063 **Email:** info@eastonwalledgardens.co.uk

ELLYS MANOR HOUSE 🏛
Great Ponton, Nr Grantham, Lincolnshire NG33 5DP
Tel: 01476 530023 **Email:** ellysmanor@btinternet.com

ELSHAM HALL GARDENS & COUNTRY PARK 🏛ⓕ
Elsham Hall, Brigg, Lincolnshire DN20 0QZ
Tel: 01652 688698 **Email:** enquiries@elshamhall.co.uk

GAINSBOROUGH OLD HALL
Parnell Street, Gainsborough, Lincolnshire DN21 2NB
Tel: 01427 677348 **Email:** gainsborougholdhall@lincolnshire.gov.uk

GUNBY HALL 🌿
Spilsby, Lincolnshire PE23 5SL
Tel: 01754 890102 **Email:** gunbyhall@nationaltrust.org.uk

Leadenham House

Lincolnshire, LN5 0PU
Late 18th Century house in park setting. **Map Ref:** 7:D3 - Entrance on A17 Leadenham bypass (between Newark and Sleaford).
Tel: 01400 272680 **Email:** leadenhamhouse@googlemail.com
Open: 9-13, 16-20 & 30 Apr; 1-4, 14-18, 21-25 & 29 May; Spring & Aug Bank Holidays. **Admission:** £5. Please ring door bell. Groups by prior arrangement only.

LINCOLN MEDIEVAL BISHOPS' PALACE ⚜
Minster Yard, Lincoln, Lincolnshire LN2 1PU
Tel: 01522 527468 **Email:** customers@english-heritage.org.uk

MARSTON HALL 🏛
Marston, Grantham NG32 2HQ
Tel: 07812 356237 **Email:** johnthorold@aol.com

NORMANBY HALL COUNTRY PARK
Normanby, Scunthorpe DN15 9HU
Tel: 01724 720588 **Email:** normanby.hall@northlincs.gov.uk

SCAWBY HALL 🏛
Vicarage Lane, Scawby, Brigg, Lincolnshire DN20 9LX
Tel: 01652 654272 **Email:** info@scawbyhall.com

SCRIVELSBY WALLED GARDEN
The New Midge Barns, Hatton, Lincs LN8 5QL
Tel: 07435 009876 **Email:** info@keymarque.co.uk

TATTERSHALL CASTLE 🌿
Sleaford Road, Tattershall, Lincolnshire LN4 4LR
Tel: 01526 342543 **Email:** tattershallcastle@nationaltrust.org.uk

WOOLSTHORPE MANOR 🌿
Water Lane, Woolsthorpe by Colsterworth NG33 5PD
Tel: 01476 862823 **Email:** woolsthorpemanor@nationaltrust.org.uk

78 DERNGATE: THE CHARLES RENNIE MACKINTOSH HOUSE & GALLERIES
82 Derngate, Northampton, UK, NN1 1UH
Tel: 01604 603407 **Email:** info@78derngate.org.uk

APETHORPE PALACE ⚜
Hunting Way, Apethorpe, Peterborough, Northamptonshire PE8 5AQ
Tel: 0370 333 1181 **Email:** customers@english-heritage.org.uk

BOUGHTON HOUSE 🏛ⓕ
Kettering, Northamptonshire NN14 1BJ
Tel: 01536 515731 **Email:** blht@boughtonhouse.co.uk

CANONS ASHBY 🌿
Daventry, Bolsover, Northamptonshire NN11 3SD
Tel: 01327 861900 **Email:** canonsashby@nationaltrust.org.uk

COTON MANOR GARDEN
Nr Guilsborough, Northamptonshire NN6 8RQ
Tel: 01604 740219 **Email:** pasleytyler@cotonmanor.co.uk

Deene Park 🏛ⓕ

Corby, Northamptonshire NN17 3EW
Home of the Brudenell family since 1514, this 16th Century house incorporates a medieval manor with important Georgian additions.
Location: 6m NE of Corby off A43. **Map Ref:** 7:D7 **Tel:** 01780 450278
Email: admin@deenepark.com **Website:** www.deenepark.com
Open: Please see website for 2018 opening dates, times & prices.
Admission: House & Gardens - Adult: £12, Conc: £10, Child: £6

DELAPRE ABBEY
Abbey Cottage, Delapré Abbey, London Road, Northampton NN4 8AW
Tel: 01604 760817 **Email:** info@delapreabbey.org

KELMARSH HALL & GARDENS 🏛ⓕ
Kelmarsh, Northampton NN6 9LY
Tel: 01604 686543 **Email:** enquiries@kelmarsh.com

KIRBY HALL ⚜
Deene, Corby, Northamptonshire NN17 5EN
Tel: 01536 203230 **Email:** customers@english-heritage.org.uk

LYVEDEN 🌿
Nr Oundle, Northamptonshire PE8 5AT
Tel: 01832 205158 **Email:** lyveden@nationaltrust.org.uk

ROCKINGHAM CASTLE 🏛ⓕ
Rockingham, Market Harborough, Leicestershire LE16 8TH
Tel: 01536 770240 **Email:** estateoffice@rockinghamcastle.com

RUSHTON TRIANGULAR LODGE ⚜
Rushton, Kettering, Northamptonshire NN14 1RP
Tel: 01536 710761

SOUTHWICK HALL 🏛ⓕ
Southwick, Nr Oundle, Peterborough, Northamptonshire PE8 5BL
Tel: 01832 274064 **Email:** southwickhall@hotmail.co.uk

STOKE PARK PAVILIONS

Stoke Bruerne, Towcester, Northamptonshire NN12 7RZ
Tel: 07768 230325

Wakefield Lodge

Potterspury, Northamptonshire NN12 7QX
Georgian hunting lodge with deer park.
Location: 4m S of Towcester on A5. Take signs to farm shop for directions. **Map Ref:** 7:C10 **Tel:** 01327 811395
Open: House 16 Apr-29 May: Mon-Fri (closed BHs), 12 noon-4pm. Appointments by telephone. Access walk open May & Jun.
Admission: £10

WESTON HALL

Towcester, Northamptonshire NN12 8PU
Tel: 07710 523879 **Email:** george@crossovercapital.co.uk

CARLTON HALL

Carlton-On-Trent, Nottingham, Nottinghamshire NG23 6LP
Tel: 07775 785344 **Email:** carltonhallnotts@gmail.com

CLUMBER PARK

Worksop, Nottinghamshire S80 3AZ
Tel: 01909 544917 **Email:** clumberpark@nationaltrust.org.uk

DH LAWRENCE BIRTHPLACE

8a Victoria Street, Eastwood, Nottinghamshire NG16 3AW
Tel: 01159 173824 **Email:** dhlawrence@liberty-leisure.org.uk

HODSOCK PRIORY GARDENS

Blyth, Nr Worksop S81 0TY
Tel: 01909 591204

HOLME PIERREPONT HALL

Holme Pierrepont, Nr Nottingham NG12 2LD
Tel: 0115 933 2371 **Email:** rplb@holmepierreponthall.com

KELHAM HALL

Newark, Nottinghamshire NG23 5QX
Tel: 01636 650000 **Email:** info@kelham-hall.com

MR STRAW'S HOUSE

5-7 Blyth Grove, Worksop S81 0JG
Tel: 01909 482380 **Email:** mrstrawshouse@nationaltrust.org.uk

NEWSTEAD ABBEY

Ravenshead, Nottingham, Nottinghamshire NG15 8GE
Tel: 01623 455900 **Email:** sallyl@newsteadabbey.org.uk

NOTTINGHAM CASTLE & ART GALLERY

Lenton Road, Nottingham NG1 6EZ
Tel: 0115 876 1400 **Email:** nottingham.castle@nottinghamcity.gov.uk

RUFFORD ABBEY

Rufford Abbey Country Park, Ollerton, Nottinghamshire NG22 9DF
Tel: 01623 821338 **Email:** customers@english-heritage.org.uk

THRUMPTON HALL

Nottingham, Nottinghamshire NG11 0AX
Tel: 07796 956556 **Email:** enquiries@thrumptonhall.com

WOLLATON HALL & PARK

Wollaton Park, Nottingham NG8 2AE
Tel: 0115 915 3900 **Email:** maria.narducci@nottinghamcity.gov.uk

Burghley House

HEART OF ENGLAND

HEREFORDSHIRE • SHROPSHIRE • STAFFORDSHIRE
WARWICKSHIRE • WEST MIDLANDS • WORCESTERSHIRE

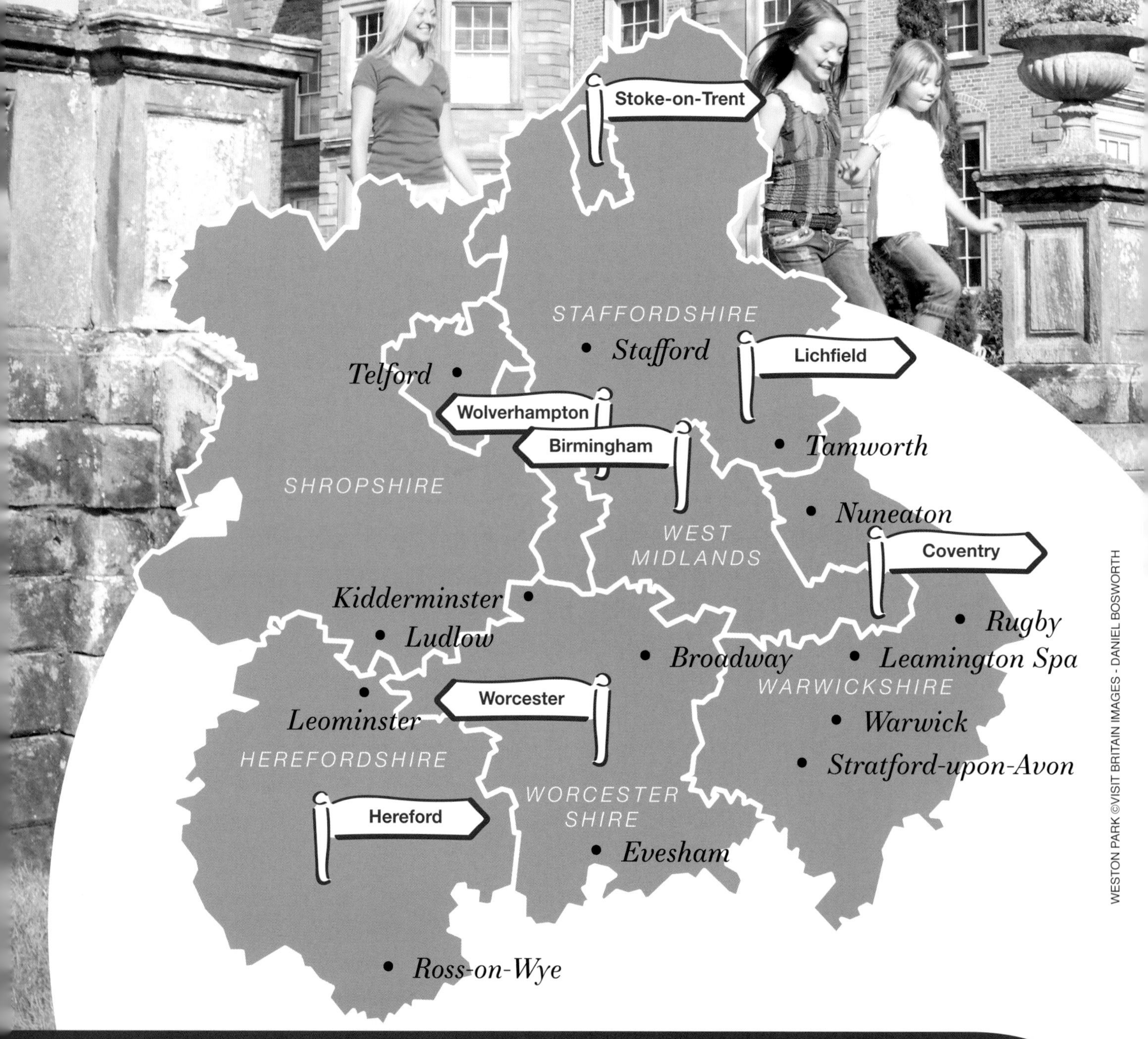
Stoke-on-Trent
STAFFORDSHIRE
Stafford
Lichfield
Telford
Wolverhampton
Birmingham
Tamworth
SHROPSHIRE
Nuneaton
WEST MIDLANDS
Coventry
Kidderminster
Ludlow
Rugby
Broadway
Leamington Spa
WARWICKSHIRE
Worcester
Leominster
Warwick
HEREFORDSHIRE
Stratford-upon-Avon
WORCESTER SHIRE
Hereford
Evesham
Ross-on-Wye

WESTON PARK ©VISIT BRITAIN IMAGES · DANIEL BOSWORTH

COUNTRYSIDE:

- Cotswolds
- Canals
- Offa's Dyke

HERITAGE:

- Shakespeare
- Gunpowder Plot
- Industrial Revolution

FOOD:

- Beer & cider
- Apples & pears
- Staffordshire oatcakes

DON'T MISS!

ARBURY HALL

It is 300 years since the birth of the remarkable Sir Roger Newdigate in 1719, who turned his home into a prodigy of Gothick revival. Outside the house is all pinnacles and points and inside the main rooms have soaring fan vaulted ceilings with plunging pendants and filigree tracery around the windows.

Highlights:

- Fan vaulted ceilings
- Arthur Devis' portrait of Sir Roger Newdigate
- Chelsea porcelain
- Chandelier in the Saloon

THE DINING ROOM, ARBURY HALL

SHAKESPEARE'S FAMILY HOMES

Through 5 houses you can explore the whole of William Shakespeare's personal history from the Tudor farm where his grandparents lived to an original interpretation of New Place, the now-lost house he bought to return to Stratford. Get to know the Bard.

Highlights:

- Shakespeare's ring
- Tudor medicine at Hall's Croft
- Ancient mulberry trees
- Gardens at Anne Hathaway's Cottage
- Specially commissioned artworks at New Place

SHAKESPEARE'S FATHER'S SHOP ©SHAKESPEARE BIRTHPLACE TRUST

MARK THE YEAR

300 YEARS
CHIPPENDALE

Celebrate our greatest furniture maker 300 years after his birth.
✔ *Weston Park*

ONE OF 12 CHIPPENDALE HALL CHAIRS AT WESTON PARK

200 YEARS
REPTON

Enjoy the gardens of Humphry Repton 200 years after his death.
✔ *Attingham Park*
✔ *Sufton Court*
✔ *Longner Hall*

REPTON GARDENS AT SUFTON COURT

MRS HUDSON'S HIDDEN GEM

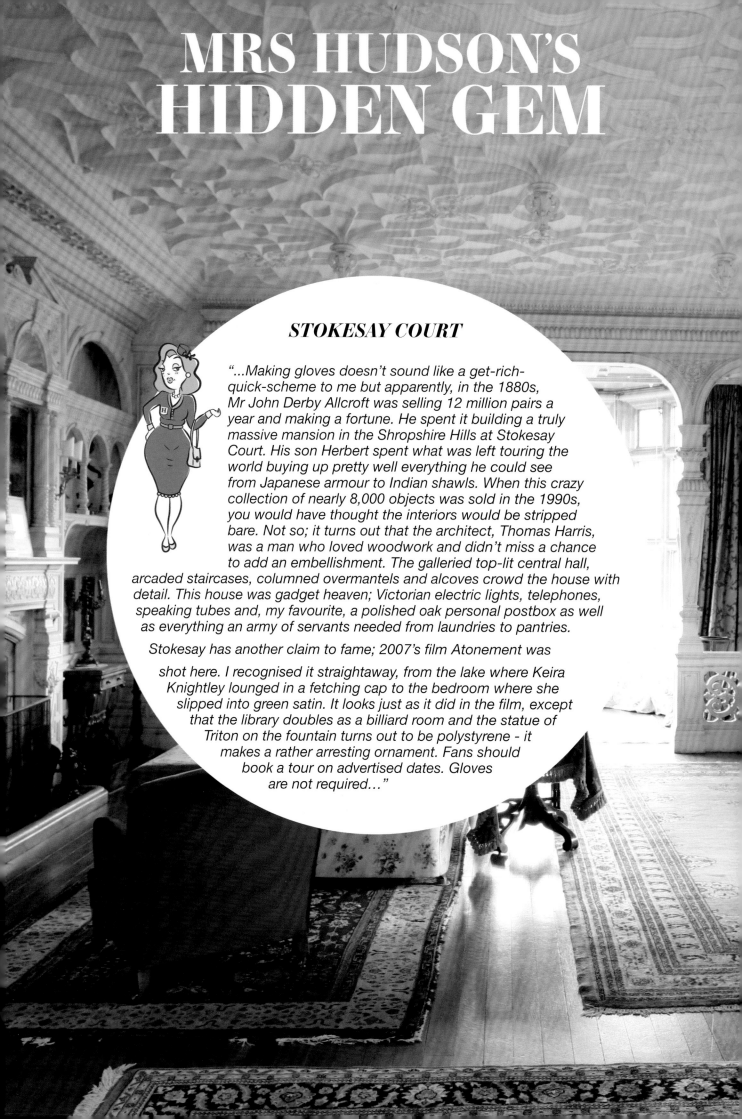

STOKESAY COURT

"...Making gloves doesn't sound like a get-rich-quick-scheme to me but apparently, in the 1880s, Mr John Derby Allcroft was selling 12 million pairs a year and making a fortune. He spent it building a truly massive mansion in the Shropshire Hills at Stokesay Court. His son Herbert spent what was left touring the world buying up pretty well everything he could see from Japanese armour to Indian shawls. When this crazy collection of nearly 8,000 objects was sold in the 1990s, you would have thought the interiors would be stripped bare. Not so; it turns out that the architect, Thomas Harris, was a man who loved woodwork and didn't miss a chance to add an embellishment. The galleried top-lit central hall, arcaded staircases, columned overmantels and alcoves crowd the house with detail. This house was gadget heaven; Victorian electric lights, telephones, speaking tubes and, my favourite, a polished oak personal postbox as well as everything an army of servants needed from laundries to pantries.

Stokesay has another claim to fame; 2007's film Atonement was shot here. I recognised it straightaway, from the lake where Keira Knightley lounged in a fetching cap to the bedroom where she slipped into green satin. It looks just as it did in the film, except that the library doubles as a billiard room and the statue of Triton on the fountain turns out to be polystyrene - it makes a rather arresting ornament. Fans should book a tour on advertised dates. Gloves are not required…"

DID YOU KNOW?

1 HARVINGTON HALL

No house in England has as many priest hides as Harvington Hall. The Catholic Pakington family could hide a priest in any of seven, lest they be caught flouting Elizabeth I's stringent recusancy laws.

HARVINGTON HALL

2 CROOME

Celebrity Irish beauty Maria Gunning came to live at Croome after her marriage to the 6th Earl of Coventry in 1752. Only eight years later, she was dead at 27 of lead poisoning caused by her face makeup.

3 LONGNER HALL

Protestant Edward Burton so hated the "mass-mongers" of his local church that, when he died in 1558 (on the same day as Catholic Mary I) he was buried in a tomb in his own grounds at Longner Hall.

4 ASTON HALL

In 1643 a Civil War cannonball smashed through the staircase at Aston Hall leaving a hole; the Royalist defenders had entertained King Charles I only the year before.

ASTON HALL

MARIA GUNNING FROM AN ENGRAVING AT BLICKLING HALL ©NATIONAL TRUST IMAGES - SUE JAMES

THROCKMORTON COAT ©NATIONAL TRUST IMAGES - JOHN HAMMOND

5 COUGHTON COURT

In 1811 Sir John Throckmorton of Coughton Court bet £1000 guineas that a coat could be made in a day. The sheep were shorn at sunrise, the thread spun, cloth woven, coat measured and stitched and Sir John wore it at dinner. It is still in the house.

6 KENILWORTH CASTLE

In 1575 Robert Dudley, Earl of Leicester spent £60,000 on new rooms and a perfumed garden at Kenilworth Castle to impress his Queen, Elizabeth I. She still didn't marry him.

3 REAL HERITAGE PLACES YOU CAN STAY IN

1.

WESTON PARK

Weston Park is a true stately home, an architecturally important 17th century country house with art and antiques collected by the Earls of Bradford over 300 years, set in Capability Brown parkland. The ultimate in luxurious stately home hire, the 28 bedrooms have en-suite or private bathrooms, antiques and five star service. The Temple of Diana, designed by James Paine in the 1760s, sleeps six and is one of four garden buildings converted for luxury self-catering.

WESTON PARK

2.

LUDLOW CASTLE

Staying in an authentic castle is to sleep close to history, at Ludlow the apartments in Castle House are within the outer bailey of this royal border fortress. Choose to remember the honeymoon here of Prince Arthur and Catherine of Aragon, the coloniser of Ireland Sir Henry Sidney or Comus, a masque performed here written by John Milton.

LUDLOW CASTLE

3.

UPTON CRESSETT HALL

Winner, Best Hidden Gem, 2011, Hudson's Heritage Awards

Apartments in the Elizabethan Gatehouse (choose the Rupert of the Rhine or Mrs Thatcher bedrooms) or the old coach house provide a flexible set of options, catered, self-catering or 'fridge-filler' menus. Decorative murals by Adam Dant combine the contemporary and traditional.

UPTON CRESSETT HALL

224

ENID MARX

1.

ENID MARX (1902-1998)
Wood engraver, textile designer & collector of folk art
at Compton Verney

2.

GEORGE ELIOT (1819 – 1880)
Novelist, poet, journalist &
translator at Arbury Hall.

3.

ELIZABETH WILBRAHAM (1632–1705)
Gentlewoman and architect
at Weston Park.

GEORGE ELIOT BY
SIR FREDERICK BURTON

ELIZABETH WILBRAHAM BY JOHN MICHAEL WRIGHT

SOULTON HALL, SHROPSHIRE

Handsome brick Tudor house built for Sir Rowland
Hill, Lord Mayor of London in the 1550s, now a guest
house run by the Ashton family. Choose from 8 rooms
in the main house or converted Carriage House or
Cedar Lodge. Bluebell woods and spacious grounds.

CASTLE HOUSE , HEREFORDSHIRE

Next to where the castle once stood is a handsome
Regency villa offering 24 individually designed
rooms. Menus feature produce from the local farm
of owner, David Watkins. Close to the wonders of
Hereford Cathedral including the Mappa Mundi.

LUNARTICKS

Birmingham is England's second city, the gateway to the Midlands and today a vibrant multi-racial, multi-cultural centre. Until the late 17th century, however, Birmingham was not much bigger or more important than other market towns like Warwick or Stratford. Its fortunes were founded as a merchant and trading centre for the agrarian economy in the hinterland.

The city's status really changed with rapid growth in the early 18th century so that by 1791 Birmingham could be called "the first manufacturing town in the world". The change was largely brought about by a group of remarkable men in what has become known as the 'Midlands Enlightenment'. The fulcrum of change was the establishment of the Lunar Society, a social get-together for some of the leading thinkers of the region. They called their club after the full moon nights on which they met, largely for the convenience of brighter moonlight to light their route home at the end of the evening. The founders of the group were friends, physician Erasmus Darwin of Litchfield and manufacturer, Matthew Boulton of Birmingham. These two dynamic men brought together chemists Joseph Priestley and James Keir, potter Josiah Wedgewood, steam engine innovator James Watt and writer Thomas Day to form a core group. Many more of the leading minds of the day were regular or occasional visitors or correspondents. In the early days, the group was held together by Scottish physician and mathematician William Small, but after his death in 1775, Matthew Boulton played a more prominent role and the meeting place for the Lunar Society moved from Litchfield to Boulton's home at Soho House in Birmingham.

226

Between them, these men were behind some of the key developments that would launch the Industrial Revolution. It was also no surprise that they had come to Birmingham in the first place. Innovation had already begun in the region. They were investors in Birmingham's burgeoning canal network and will have known both the Silk Mill in Derby founded in 1721, perhaps Britain's first factory, and the coke smelting technology developed by Abraham Darby in Coalbrookdale. When Matthew Boulton established the Soho Manufactory in 1765, he formalised a system of production under one roof that marked the beginning of a recognisable factory system and the end for cottage industry. His partnership with James Watt to manufacture steam engines brought a new reliable source of power that spread the Industrial Revolution nationwide. Josiah Wedgewood's technical innovations and disciplined production systems made Staffordshire the centre of pottery manufacture. They shared a wish for abolition, promulgated in the writings of anti-slavery campaigner, Thomas Day. Their discussions on full moon nights inspired a generation of progress that shifted the economy of Britain away from its agrarian roots into a new urban and industrial future.

The Lunar Society still meets in Birmingham and its members, then and now, are not averse to being labelled 'Lunarticks'. ■

THE GOLDEN BOYS, BOULTON, WATT AND WILLIAM MURDOCH, PIONEERS OF THE INDUSTRIAL REVOLUTION © OOSOOM, ENGLISH WIKIPEDIA

ERASMUS DARWIN HOUSE © ERASMUS DARWIN HOUSE MUSEUM

The Lunar Room at Soho House where the Lunar Society met.

Old Sufton

A 16th Century manor house which was altered and remodelled in the 18th and 19th Centuries and again in this Century. The original home of the Hereford family (see Sufton Court) who have held the manor since the 12th Century.

KEY FACTS

 Open all year by appointment.

 Parking is available.

 Partial.

 Obligatory.

 Small groups. No special facilities.

CONTACT
Owner: Trustees of Sufton Heritage Trust
Contact:
Mr & Mrs J N Hereford
Tel: 01432 870268 /
01432 850328
Email: james@sufton.co.uk

LOCATION
Mordiford, Hereford HR1 4EJ
Map Ref: 6:L10
Mordiford, off B4224 Mordiford - Dormington Road.

OPENING TIMES
By appointment to:
james@sufton.co.uk

Sufton Court

Sufton Court is a small Palladian mansion house. Built in 1788 by James Wyatt for James Hereford. The park was laid out by Humphry Repton whose 'red book' still survives.

The house stands above the rivers Wye and Lugg giving impressive views towards the mountains of Wales.

KEY FACTS

 Only small coaches.

 Accessible.

 In grounds, on leads.

 Obligatory.

 Small groups. No special facilities.

CONTACT
Owner: J N Hereford
Contact: Mr & Mrs J N Hereford
Tel: 01432 870268 /
01432 850328
Email: james@sufton.co.uk

LOCATION
Mordiford, Hereford HR1 4LU
Map Ref: 6:L10
Mordiford, off B4224 Mordiford - Dormington Road.

OPENING TIMES
15-28 May & 14-27 Aug;
2pm-5pm.
Guided tours: 2pm, 3pm & 4pm.

ADMISSION
Adult: £5, Child: 50p.

Sufton Court

Ludlow Castle

www.ludlowcastle.com

Ludlow Castle is one of the country's finest medieval ruins set in the glorious Shropshire countryside at the heart of the bustling black and white town of Ludlow. The castle was a Norman fortress extended over the centuries to become a fortified Royal Palace.

Castle House has been restored and now has Gift Shops, Tea Room and Terrace; three beautifully appointed self-catering apartments and is also a unique wedding venue.

KEY FACTS

 WC's, including disabled toilets.

 Baby changing facilities available.

 The Castle is closed for events set ups. Always check website before visiting for closures.

 The grounds are accessible but uneven in places. We provide WC's.

 Welcome throughout Castle, Tea Room & the Sir Henry Sidney Apartment.

 Three 4-5* self-catering apartments.

 £3 each.

By arrangement.

By arrangement.

Traditional Tea Rooms with waiting staff. Licensed.

3 gift shops; Castle Gift Shop, Castle Gallery & Picture Framing, The Cannon Gallery.

Please see website for special events.

Civil ceremonies & receptions in The Round Chapel, Castle House function rooms & marquee.

CONTACT
Owner: The Earl of Powis
Contact: Sonja Belchere (The Custodian)
Tel: 01584 874465
Email: info@ludlowcastle.com
Facebook: Ludlow Castle **Twitter:** @LudlowCastle1

LOCATION
Castle Square, Ludlow, Shropshire SY8 1AY
Map Ref: 6:L8
Ludlow is situated on the A49. From Birmingham, head west on the A456 through Kidderminster. Continue on the A456 through Tenbury Wells. Turn right onto the A49 & follow signs for Ludlow. From the M5 leave at Junction 3 & continue on the A456 through Kidderminster. Continue on the A456 through Tenbury Wells. Turn right onto the A49 & follow signs for Ludlow.

OPENING TIMES
Jan-Feb - Weekends only.
All week - Oct-Mar 10am-4pm. Apr-Sep 10am-5pm.

ADMISSION
Visit the website for up-to-date admission charges.

231

Weston Park

weston-park.com

The former home of the Earls of Bradford, the House, Park and Gardens is now owned and maintained by the Weston Park Foundation, an independent charitable trust. Built in 1671, by Lady Elizabeth Wilbraham, this warm and welcoming house is home to internationally important paintings including works by Van Dyck, Gainsborough and Stubbs; furniture and objets d'art, providing enjoyment for all visitors. Step outside to enjoy the 1,000 acres of glorious Parkland, take one of a variety of woodland and wildlife walks, all landscaped by the legendary 'Capability' Brown in the 18th Century.

CONTACT
Owner: The Weston Park Foundation
Contact: Andrea Webster **Tel:** 01952 852100
Email: enquiries@weston-park.com

LOCATION
Weston-Under-Lizard, Nr Shifnal, Shropshire TF11 8LE
Map Ref: 6:N6 - Birmingham 40 mins. Manchester 1 hr 30 mins. Motorway access M6/J12 or M54/J3 and via the M6 Toll road J12.

OPENING TIMES
Park & Gardens
Open daily from Sat 25 May-Sun 2 Sep 2018.
The House opening times vary and it is closed on Sats.
Please check weston-park.com before visiting.
Granary Grill & Deli & Art Gallery
Open all year round and free to enter.
Details are correct at the time of going to print.

ADMISSION
Park & Gardens
Adult: £7, Child (4-14 years): £4,
Family (2+3 / 1+4): £26, Senior £6.50.
Prices are correct at the time of going to print.

KEY FACTS

 Family friendly with the woodland adventure playground and play room.

 Toilet and baby changing facilities available.

 Ample free parking.

 Accessible. Please contact for further details.

 Dogs welcome in grounds, on leads.

 All of the 28 bedrooms are located within the House and have genuine appeal and character.

 Cultural tours by arrangement.

 Award-winning educational programme available. Private visits aligned with both National Curriculum & QCA.

 The Granary Deli & Café serves coffee, homemade cakes and light bites.

 Granary Grill. Licensed.

 Granary Deli & Café is open all year round. (Closed on Mons).

 Functions including incentives for staff, leadership away days and board meetings.

 Please see the 'Events Calendar' on the website for all the upcoming events.

 Civil wedding licence. Create your perfect day in a stately home more romantic than any castle or hotel.

Stokesay Court
www.stokesaycourt.com

Unspoilt and secluded, Stokesay Court is an imposing late Victorian mansion with Jacobean style façade, magnificent interiors and extensive grounds containing a grotto, woodland and interconnected pools. Set in the rolling green landscape of South Shropshire near Ludlow, the house and grounds featured as the Tallis Estate in award-winning film 'Atonement'. During WW1 Stokesay Court played an important role as a military hospital and displays bring this history to life.

CONTACT
Owner/Contact: Ms Caroline Magnus
Tel: 01584 856238
Email: info@stokesaycourt.com

LOCATION
Onibury, Craven Arms, Shropshire SY7 9BD
Map Ref: 6:K7 - A49 Between Ludlow and Craven Arms.

OPENING TIMES
Guided tours Apr-Oct for booked groups (20+).
Groups (up to 60) can be accommodated by arrangement.
Tours for individuals take place on dates advertised on website. Booking essential.

ADMISSION
Please check website for up-to-date admission prices.

KEY FACTS

 No stilettos. No photography in house.

 Toilet facilities available in the house.

 Apr-Oct on selected dates.

 Ample parking available.

 Partial. Accessible toilets.

 Dogs welcome on leads in the gardens only.

 Obligatory. Approx. 1 1/4 hours long and followed by morning coffee & cake.

 School and educational visits by arrangement.

 Tea and home baked refreshments included in ticket price.

 Offers an elegant and distinctive venue for business gatherings and entertaining.

 Enjoy a great family day out at an event, for up to date details see the 'What's on' section of the website.

 Stokesay Court is available as a location for both film and television productions.

Hodnet Hall Gardens
www.hodnethallgardens.org

Over 60 acres of brilliant coloured flowers, magnificent forest trees, sweeping lawns and a chain of ornamental pools which run tranquilly along the cultivated garden valley to provide a natural habitat for waterfowl and other wildlife. No matter what the season, visitors will always find something fresh and interesting to ensure an enjoyable outing.

CONTACT
Owner: Sir Algernon and the Hon Lady-Percy
Contact: Secretary
Tel: 01630 685786
Fax: 01630 685853
Email: secretary@hodnethall.com

LOCATION
Hodnet, Market Drayton
Shropshire TF9 3NN
Map Ref: 6:L5 - 12 miles North East of Shrewsbury on A53; M6/J15, M54/J3.

OPENING TIMES
Every Sun & BH Mon from Sun 1 Apr-Sun 30 Sep. Wed 16 May, 13 Jun & 18 Jul.

ADMISSION
Adult: £7, Child (aged 5-15): £1,Under 5's: Free.

KEY FACTS

 Facebook: /hodnethall Instagram: /Hodnethallgardens

 Parking available.

 Partial. WC's.

 Dogs welcome on leads.

 Serving delicious light lunches and afternoon teas during garden open days.

 Garden restaurant.

Please see website & Facebook page for upcoming special days and events.

Longner Hall

Designed by John Nash in 1803, Longner Hall is a Tudor Gothic style house set in a park landscaped by Humphry Repton. The home of one family for over 700 years. Longner's principal rooms are adorned with plaster fan vaulting and stained glass.

CONTACT
Owner: Mr R L Burton
Contact: Sara Watts
Tel: 07903 842235
Email: info@longner.co.uk

LOCATION
Uffington, Shrewsbury, Shropshire SY4 4TG
Map Ref: 6:L6 - 4 miles SE of Shrewsbury on Uffington road, ¼ mile off B4380, Atcham.

OPENING TIMES
Tours at 2pm & 3.30pm on weekdays from Mon 28 May - Fri 29 Jun & BH Mons: 2 Apr, 7 May & 27 Aug. Groups at any time by arrangement.

ADMISSION
Adult: £5, Child/OAP: £3.

KEY FACTS

 No photography in house.

 Limited for coaches.

 Partial.

 Guide dogs only.

 Obligatory.

 By arrangement.

Whitmore Hall

www.hha.org.uk

Whitmore Hall is a Grade I listed building, designated as a house of outstanding architectural and historical interest. Parts of the hall date back to a much earlier period and for 900 years has been the seat of the Cavenagh-Mainwarings, who are direct descendants of the original Norman owners. The hall has beautifully proportioned light rooms and is in excellent order. There are good family portraits to be seen with a continuous line dating from 1624 to the present day. The park encompasses a lime avenue leading from the hall to the parish church, an early Victorian summer house which was refurbished in 2017 and an outstanding, rare Elizabethan stable block.

KEY FACTS

 Ample parking available.

 Afternoon teas for small booked groups, May-Aug, on days open to the public.

Ground floor and grounds.

 Please contact us for information on Weddings at Whitmore.

CONTACT
Owner/Contact: Mr Guy Cavenagh-Mainwaring
Tel: 01782 680 478
Email: whitmore.hall@yahoo.com

LOCATION
Whitmore, Newcastle-Under-Lyme, Staffordshire ST5 5HW
Map Ref: 6:M4

On A53 Newcastle-Market Drayton Road, 3m from M6/J15.

OPENING TIMES
1 May-31 Aug: Tues and Weds, open 2pm-4.30pm with guided tours at 2.15pm, 3pm and 3.45pm.

ADMISSION
Adult: £5, Child: 50p.

Whitmore Hall ©Country Life

Chillington Hall

chillingtonhall.co.uk

Home of the Giffards since 1178, the present house dates from the 18th Century, firstly by the architect Francis Smith of Warwick in 1724 and completed by John Soane in 1786. Parkland laid out by 'Capability' Brown in the 1760s with additional work by James Paine. Chillington was the winner of the HHA/Sotheby's Restoration Award 2009 for work done on Soane's magnificent Saloon.

KEY FACTS

 Available for Weddings, Corporate Events, Filming, Hire of the Park and Private Parties.

 Parking available.

 WC's and car parking.

 In grounds.

 Guided tours will give you an in-depth history of this family house and its ancestors, and its contents.

CONTACT
Owner:
Mr & Mrs J W Giffard
Contact: Estate Office
Tel: 01902 850236
Email: office@chillingtonhall.co.uk
LOCATION
Codsall Wood, Wolverhampton, Staffordshire WV8 1RE
Map Ref: 6:N6 - 2 miles South of Brewood off A449. 4 miles North West of M54/J2.

OPENING TIMES
2pm-4pm (last entry 3.30pm)
1-5 Apr, 6, 7, 27 & 28 May, 4, 5, 6 Jun, 23-26, 30 & 31 Jul, 1, 2, 6 -9, 13-16 Aug.
Private groups at other times by prior arrangement.
ADMISSION
Adult: £8, Child: £4.
Grounds only: Half price.

Arbury Hall

www.arburyestate.co.uk

Arbury Hall, original Elizabethan mansion house, Gothicised in the 18th Century surrounded by stunning gardens and parkland.

Arbury Hall has been the seat of the Newdegate family for over 450 years and is the ancestral home of Viscount Daventry. This Tudor/Elizabethan House was Gothicised by Sir Roger Newdegate in the 18th Century and is regarded as the 'Gothic Gem' of the Midlands. The principal rooms, with their soaring fan vaulted ceilings and plunging pendants and filigree tracery, stand as a most breathtaking and complete example of early Gothic Revival architecture and provide a unique and fascinating venue for corporate entertaining, product launches, fashion shoots and activity days. Exclusive use of this historic Hall, its gardens and parkland is offered to clients. The Hall stands in the middle of beautiful parkland with landscaped gardens of rolling lawns, lakes and winding wooded walks. Spring flowers are profuse and in June rhododendrons, azaleas and giant wisteria provide a beautiful environment for the visitor. George Eliot, the novelist, was born on the estate and Arbury Hall and Sir Roger Newdegate were immortalised in her book 'Scenes of Clerical Life'.

KEY FACTS

 No cameras or video recorders indoors.

 Baby changing facilities available.

 200 cars & 3 coaches 250 yds from house. Follow tourist signs. Approach map available for coach drivers.

 Partial, WCs.

 Dogs on leads in garden. Guide dogs only in house.

 Obligatory. Tour time: 50mins.

 Stables Tea Rooms (on first floor) open from 1pm.

 Small selection of souvenir gifts.

 Exclusive lunches and dinners for corporate parties in dining room, max. 50, buffets 80.

 Available to host a wide variety of outside events throughout the spring & summer season.

 A marquee in the historic parkland with the Hall as a backdrop is available for Wedding receptions.

 As a film location, Arbury presents a variety of atmospheric settings for period and contemporary dramas.

CONTACT
Owner: The Viscount Daventry
Contact: Events Secretary
Tel: 01676 540529 **Email:** info@arburyestate.co.uk

LOCATION
Arbury Hall, Nuneaton, Warwickshire CV10 7PT
(for SATNAV use CV10 7NF)
Map Ref: 6:P7 - London, M1, M6/J3 (A444 to Nuneaton), 2m SW of Nuneaton. 1m W of A444. Nuneaton 5 mins. Birmingham City Centre 20 mins. London 2 hrs, Coventry 20 mins.

OPENING TIMES
Hall & Gardens: Bank Holiday weekends (Suns & Mons) from Easter-Aug Bank Holiday from 1pm-6pm. Last guided tour of the hall 4.30pm.
Groups: 25+ weekdays by prior arrangement from Apr-end Sep.

ADMISSION
Hall & Gardens
Adult: £8.50, Child (up to 14yrs): £4.50, Family (2+2): £20.
Garden only
Adult: £5.50, Child (up to 14 yrs): £4.

Shakespeare's Family Homes

www.shakespeare.org.uk ◇

Shakespeare's Birthplace - Where the story began

Explore the extraordinary story of William and the house he was born and grew up in. Our fascinating guides will captivate you with tales of his father's business ventures. Take centre stage with our costumed troupe, Shakespeare Aloud!

Mary Arden's Farm - A working Tudor farm

Visit the family farm where Shakespeare's mother grew up. Experience the sights, sounds and smells of a working Tudor farm and follow our resident Tudors as they work. Meet rare breed animals, enjoy archery and falconry, or explore the nature trails and playground. Don't miss our free events throughout the school holidays.

Anne Hathaway's Cottage - Love and marriage

Relive Shakespeare's Tudor love story in the place where he courted Anne his bride-to-be, and see original furniture including the Hathaway bed. Uncover 5 centuries of stories in the picturesque cottage and 13 generations of the family who lived there.

Shakespeare's New Place - His family home

The only home Shakespeare ever bought and where he lived for 19 years. Reopened in 2016 for the 400th anniversary of Shakespeare's death, come and walk in his footsteps and trace the footprint of his family home in a contemporary landscape setting. Enjoy specially commissioned sculptures and see a new side of Shakespeare with an exhibition of his world.

Hall's Croft - Daughter and Granddaughter

The luxurious Jacobean home of Shakespeare's daughter Susanna and her husband Doctor John Hall. Stroll round the walled garden planted with fragrant herbs used in his remedies. Browse in the gift shop or unwind in the Café .

CONTACT

Owner/Contact: The Shakespeare Birthplace Trust
General Enquiries Tel: 01789 204016
Group Visits Tel: 01789 201806
Email: info@shakespeare.org.uk / groups@shakespeare.org.uk

LOCATION

Henley Street, Stratford-upon-Avon CV37 6QW
Map Ref: 6:P9 **Car:** 2 hrs from London. 45 mins from Birmingham. 4m from M40/J15 & well signed from all approaches. (Free coach terminal for groups drop off & pick up at Birthplace. Max stay 15 mins).
Rail: Service from London (Marylebone).

OPENING TIMES

Daily throughout the year except Christmas Day & Boxing Day (Shakespeare's Birthplace is open on Boxing Day). Mary Arden's Farm closes for Winter from Nov-Mar. Opening times vary throughout the year. Please see website for up-to-date information.

ADMISSION

Visit the website for full details on ticket prices. You can enjoy 12 months' free admission with every ticket to Shakespeare's family homes. Tickets are valid for a year with unlimited entry. Pay for a day and take the whole year to explore!

KEY FACTS

 City Sightseeing bus tour connecting town houses with Anne Hathaway's Cottage & Mary Arden's Farm.

 Toilet facilities available.

 Baby changing facilities available.

 Please check for full details.

 Parking at Mary Arden's Farm. Pay & display parking at Anne Hathaway's Cottage.

 Partial. WC's.

 By special arrangement.

 Available for all houses. For information call 01789 201806.

 Mary Arden's Farm, Anne Hathaway's Cottage, Hall's Croft.

 Gifts available.

 Corporate functions available, telephone for details.

Please check website for details.

Birmingham Museums

www.birminghammuseums.org.uk

Birmingham Museum & Art Gallery - Free Entry

From Renaissance masterpieces to Egyptian mummies and the Staffordshire Hoard, the museum showcases a world class collection that offers fascinating glimpses into Birmingham's vibrant past.

Aston Hall

Experience the splendour of this 17th Century Jacobean mansion. Take a tour through majestic state rooms, including the imposing Long Gallery, and the beautiful Lady Holte's Garden.

Blakesley Hall

Visit one of Birmingham's finest timber-framed houses, built in 1590. With a herb garden and orchard within its grounds, Blakesley Hall is a peaceful haven set in an urban location.

Museum of the Jewellery Quarter

Enjoy a lively guided tour of the perfectly preserved Smith & Pepper jewellery factory, which reveals Birmingham's jewellery heritage and offers a unique glimpse of working life in the city's famous Jewellery Quarter.

Sarehole Mill

Discover the idyllic childhood haunt of J.R.R.Tolkien. One of only two surviving working watermills in Birmingham, gain a unique insight into the lives of the millers who once worked there. Today, the mill retains its tranquil atmosphere and the millpond provides a peaceful haven for kingfishers, moorhens and herons.

Soho House

Discover the elegant Georgian home of the pre-eminent industrialist and entrepreneur Matthew Boulton. Soho House was also the meeting place of the leading 18th Century intellectuals of the Lunar Society.

KEY FACTS

 Knowledgeable guides at all sites.

 Toilets at all sites.

 Baby changing facilities available at all sites.

 Parking available across sites. See Birmingham Museums website for full details.

 Wheelchair access across sites.

 Expert-led Heritage Tours are available across all heritage sites. See website for full details.

 School visits are welcome. See website for full details of our educational programme.

 Tea Rooms located at all sites.

 Gift shops located at all sites.

 Available for corporate hire and special events. See Birmingham Museums website for full details.

 Weddings and receptions available at some sites. See Birmingham Museums website for full details.

CONTACT
Birmingham Museums Trust
General Enquiries: 0121 348 8000
Group Bookings: 0121 348 8001
Email: enquiries@birminghammuseums.org.uk

LOCATION
Registered Address: Birmingham Museums Trust, Birmingham Museum & Art Gallery, Birmingham B3 3DH
Map Ref: 6:07

OPENING TIMES
Opening times vary throughout the year. See website for up-to-date information.

ADMISSION
Prices vary. See website for up-to-date information. Entry into grounds, gardens, visitor centres and Tea Rooms at our heritage sites is free.

ADDITIONAL INFORMATION
You can enjoy 12 months unlimited entry across all Birmingham Museums heritage sites, and exhibitions with an annual membership. With Membership Plus, you also get unlimited admission into Thinktank, Birmingham Science Museum. Journey to the stars in the Planetarium, discover Birmingham's Spitfire Story and uncover the Thinktank Ichthyosaur.

Birmingham Botanical Gardens

birminghambotanicalgardens.org.uk

15 acres of beautiful historic landscaped gardens with 7000 shrubs, plants and trees. Four glasshouses, Roses and Alpines, Woodland and Rhododendron Walks, Rock Pool, Herbaceous Borders, Japanese Garden. Children's playground, aviaries, gallery, and bandstand.

KEY FACTS

 Free car park for visitors. Please register your car on arrival for free parking all day.

 Excellent wheelchair access throughout the Gardens and Glasshouses.

 On application. Pre-booking for all school visits during term-time is essential.

 Pavilion Tea Room is the perfect place enjoy a refreshing drink and a bite to eat.

 Gift shop offers greetings cards, toys, stationery, gifts and garden tools .

 Purchase indoor and outdoor plants from the gift shop.

 An ideal venue for all kinds of events, both corporate and private, and a favourite for weddings.

Please visit the 'What's on' section for all family activities and events.

CONTACT
Owner:
Birmingham Botanical & Horticultural Society
Contact: Kim Hill
Tel: 0121 454 1860
Email: kim@birmingham botanicalgardens.org.uk

LOCATION
Westbourne Rd, Edgbaston, Birmingham B15 3TR
Map Ref: 6:O7 - 2m W of city centre. Follow signs to Edgbaston then brown tourist signs.

OPENING TIMES
Daily: 10am-dusk. Closed Christmas and Boxing Day. Refer to website for details.

ADMISSION
Adult: £7.50, Family: £22, Groups/Conc: £5.25, Child U5: Free.

Birmingham Botanical Gardens

Lady Holtes Garden & Aston Hall, Birmingham Museums

Harvington Hall

harvingtonhall.com

Tucked away in a peaceful corner of Worcestershire, Harvington Hall is a remarkable moated manor house with the largest surviving series of priest hides in the country and a rare collection of original Elizabethan wall paintings. The Hall is surrounded by beautiful walled gardens in a peaceful moatside setting. The Moatside Tea Room offers superb homemade cakes, scones and light lunches, and the Hall's gift shop offers a selection of Fairtrade and unusual gifts.

CONTACT
Contact: Hall Manager
Tel: 01562 777846
Email:
harvingtonhall@btconnect.com

LOCATION
Harvington, Kidderminster, Worcestershire DY10 4LR
Map Ref: 6:N8 - On minor road, ½m NE of A450/A448 crossroads at Mustow Green. 3m SE of Kidderminster.

OPENING TIMES
Mar-Oct, Wed-Sun, from 11.30am (closing times vary).

ADMISSION
Adult: £9, Child (5-16): £5, Senior: £8, Family (2+3): £25. Garden & Malt House Visitor Centre: £3.50.

KEY FACTS

 Limited for coaches.

 Partial. WC's.

 Pre-booked groups and schools also available.

 Tea Room offers a variety of light lunches & homemade cakes are available each time the hall is open.

Please see the *events library* on the website.

 Excellent facilities are available for wedding receptions and other occasions, for up to 50 guests.

The Tudor House Museum

tudorhousemuseum.org

Exhibits of Upton past and present, local pottery and "Staffordshire Blue".

CONTACT
Owner:
Tudor House Museum Trust
Contact: The Trustees
Tel: 01684 438820
Email:
lavendertudor@talktalk.net

LOCATION
16 Church Street, Upton-upon-Severn, Worcestershire WR8 0HT
Map Ref: 6:N10
OS Ref: SO852 406
Centre of Upton-upon-Severn, 7m SE of Malvern by B4211.

OPENING TIMES
Apr-Oct. Tue-Sun and BH afternoons. 1.30pm-4.30pm. Nov-Mar Suns 2pm-4pm.

ADMISSIONS
Adult: £3, Concs: £2, Child: Free (when accompanied by an adult).

KEY FACTS

 Toilet facilities available.

 Garden and ground floor only.

 Dogs welcome.

 Guided tours are available if pre-booked.

 Educational and school visits are available if pre-booked.

Little Malvern Court

littlemalverncourt.co.uk

Prior's Hall, associated rooms and cells, c1489. Former Benedictine Monastery. Oak-framed roof, five bays. Library, collection of religious vestments and relics. Embroideries and paintings. Gardens: 10 acres of former monastic grounds with spring bulbs, blossom, old fashioned roses and shrubs. Access to Hall only by flight of steps.

CONTACT
Owner: Trustees of the late T M Berington
Contact: Mrs T M Berington
Tel: 01684 892988
Email: littlemalverncourt@hotmail.com

LOCATION
Nr Malvern, Worcestershire, WR14 4JN **Map Ref:** 6:M9 3m S of Great Malvern on Upton-on-Severn Rd (A4104).

OPENING TIMES
18 Apr-19 Jul, Weds & Thus, afternoons 2.15pm-5pm, last admission 4pm. Open for NGS Mon 7 May, with Flower Festival in the Priory.

ADMISSION
House & Garden
Adult: £8, Child: £3.
Garden only
Adult: £7, Child: £2.
Groups by prior arrangement.

KEY FACTS

 There is a toilet facility available on site up a flight of stairs.

 Car parking is situated across the road from Little Malvern Court & Priory - clearly signposted .

 Partial. Garden is on a slope and access to the Prior's Hall is also up a flight of steps.

 Guided tours of house only.

 Tea, coffee and homemade cake is available in the Courtyard Tea Room from 2.30pm-5pm.

 Plant sales available.

 Please see the 'Events' page on the website for all special events.

Harvington Hall

BERRINGTON HALL ❧
Nr Leominster, Herefordshire HR6 0DW
Tel: 01568 615721 **Email:** berrington@nationaltrust.org.uk

BROCKHAMPTON ESTATE ❧
Bringsty, Nr Bromyard WR6 5TB
Tel: 01885 488099 **Email:** brockhampton@nationaltrust.org.uk

CROFT CASTLE ❧
Aymestrey, Nr Leominster, Herefordshire HR9 9PW
Tel: 01568 780246 **Email:** croftcastle@nationaltrust.org.uk

EASTNOR CASTLE 🏰Ⓔ ✦
Nr Ledbury, Herefordshire HR8 1RL
Tel: 01531 633160 **Email:** enquiries@eastnorcastle.com

GOODRICH CASTLE ⊞
Ross-On-Wye, Herefordshire HR9 6HY
Tel: 01600 890538 **Email:** customers@english-heritage.org.uk

HERGEST CROFT GARDENS 🏰Ⓔ
Kington, Herefordshire HR5 3EG
Tel: 01544 230160 **Email:** gardens@hergest.co.uk

KINNERSLEY CASTLE
Kinnersley, Herefordshire HR3 6QF
Tel: 01544 327407 **Email:** katherina@kinnersley.com

Langstone Court 🏰

Llangarron, Ross on Wye, Herefordshire HR9 6NR
Mostly late 17th Century house with older parts. Interesting staircases, panelling and ceilings. **Map Ref:** 6:L11- Ross on Wye 5m, Llangarron 1m.
Tel: 01989 770254 **Email:** richard.jones@langstone-court.org.uk
Website: www.langstone-court.org.uk
Open: Under discussion with HMRC. Please see www.langstone-court.org.uk for up-to-date information. **Admission:** Free

THE LASKETT GARDEN
Laskett Lane, Much Birch, Herefordshire HR2 8HZ
Tel: 07989 338217 **Email:** info@thelaskettgardens.co.uk

ACTON BURNELL CASTLE ⊞
Acton Burnell, Shrewsbury, Shropshire SY5 7PF
Tel: 0121 625 6832 **Email:** andrea.fox@english-heritage.org.uk

ATTINGHAM PARK ❧
Atcham, Shrewsbury, Shropshire SY4 4TP
Tel: 01743 708170/162 **Email:** attingham@nationaltrust.org.uk

BENTHALL HALL ❧
Broseley, Shropshire TF12 5RX
Tel: 01746 780838 **Email:** wendy.barton@nationaltrust.org.uk

COUND HALL
Cound, Shropshire SY5 6AH
Tel: 01743 761721

DUDMASTON ESTATE ❧
Quatt, Bridgnorth, Shropshire WV15 6QN
Tel: 01746 780866 **Email:** dudmaston@nationaltrust.org.uk

HAWKSTONE HALL & GARDENS
Marchamley, Shrewsbury, Shropshire SY4 5LG
Tel: 01630 685242 **Email:** hawkhall@aol.com

MAWLEY HALL
Cleobury Mortimer DY14 8PN
Tel: 0208 298 0429 **Email:** rsharp@mawley.com

MUCH WENLOCK PRIORY ⊞
Much Wenlock, Shropshire TF13 6HS
Tel: 01952 727466 **Email:** customers@english-heritage.org.uk

SOULTON HALL
Soulton, Nr. Wem, Shrewsbury, Shropshire SY4 5RS
Tel: 01939 232786 **Email:** enquiries@soultonhall.co.uk

STOKESAY CASTLE ⊞
Nr Craven Arms, Shropshire SY7 9AH
Tel: 01588 672544 **Email:** customers@english-heritage.org.uk

UPTON CRESSETT HALL & GATEHOUSE 🏰
Bridgnorth, Shropshire WV16 6UH
Tel: 01746 714616 **Email:** laura@uptoncressett.co.uk

Pitchford Hall & Tree House

Condover, Shrewsbury, Shropshire SY5 7DN
In the grounds of Britain's finest half-timbered house; Pitchford Hall. Perched in a lime tree is the world's oldest treehouse; standing since the late 1600s. **Map Ref:** 6:K6 - Sat Nav Postcode: SY5 7DN
Website: www.pitchfordestate.com
Open: Please book 90 minute guided tours in advance through www.InvitationtoView.co.uk **Admission:** £20

WALCOT HALL 🏰
Lydbury North, Shropshire SY7 8AZ
Tel: 01588 680570 **Email:** enquiries@walcothall.com

WENLOCK PRIORY ⊞
5 Sheinton Street, Much Wenlock, Shropshire TF13 6HS
Tel: 01952 727466 **Email:** customers@english-heritage.org.uk

BIDDULPH GRANGE GARDEN ❧
Grange Road, Biddulph, Staffordshire ST8 7SD
Tel: 01782 517999 **Email:** biddulphgrange@nationaltrust.org.uk

BOSCOBEL HOUSE & THE ROYAL OAK ⊞
Bishop's Wood, Brewood, Staffordshire ST19 9AR
Tel: 01902 850244 **Email:** customers@english-heritage.org.uk

CASTERNE HALL 🏰Ⓔ
Ilam, Nr Ashbourne, Derbyshire DE6 2BA
Tel: 01335 310489 **Email:** mail@casterne.co.uk

ERASMUS DARWIN HOUSE
Beacon Street, Lichfield, Staffordshire WS13 7AD
Tel: 01543 306260 **Email:** enquiries@erasmusdarwin.org

The Heath House

Tean, Stoke-On-Trent, Staffordshire ST10 4HA
Set in rolling parkland with fine formal gardens, Heath House is an early Victorian mansion built 1836-1840 in the Tudor style.
Map Ref: 6:O4 **Tel:** 01538 722212 **Email:** info@theheathhouse.co.uk
Website: www.theheathhouse.co.uk **Open:** 2pm-6pm. Last entries 4.30pm. Dates are subject to change due to refurbishment please phone in advance to confirm. **Admission:** £6.50pp. No concessions.

MOSELEY OLD HALL ❧
Moseley Old Hall Lane, Wolverhampton WV10 7HY
Tel: 01902 782808 **Email:** moseleyoldhall@nationaltrust.org.uk

SANDON HALL 🏛
Sandon, Staffordshire ST18 OBZ
Tel: 01889 508004 **Email:** info@sandonhall.co.uk

SHUGBOROUGH ESTATE 🍂
Milford, Stafford, Staffordshire ST17 0XB
Tel: 08454 598900 **Email:** shugborough@nationaltrust.org.uk

SINAI PARK HOUSE
Shobnall Road, Burton upon Trent, Staffordshire DE13 0QJ
Tel: 01889 598600 **Email:** kate@brookesandco.net

THE TRENTHAM ESTATE
Stone Road, Trentham, Staffordshire ST4 8AX
Tel: 01782 646646 **Email:** enquiry@trentham.co.uk

ASTLEY CASTLE
Nuneaton, Warwickshire CV10 7QS
Tel: 01628 825925 **Email:** bookings@landmarktrust.org.uk

BAGOTS CASTLE
Church Road, Baginton CV8 3AR
Tel: 07786 438711 **Email:** delia@bagotscastle.org.uk

CHARLECOTE PARK 🍂
Wellesbourne, Warwick, Warwickshire CV35 9ER
Tel: 01789 470277 **Email:** charlecotepark@nationaltrust.org.uk

COMPTON VERNEY ART GALLERY & PARK
Warwickshire CV35 9HZ
Tel: 01926 645500 **Email:** info@comptonverney.org.uk

COUGHTON COURT 🏛Ⓕ
Alcester, Warwickshire B49 5JA
Tel: 01789 400777 **Email:** office@throckmortons.co.uk

FARNBOROUGH HALL 🍂
Banbury OX17 1DU
Tel: 01295 690002 **Email:** farnboroughhall@nationaltrust.org.uk

HILL CLOSE GARDENS TRUST
Bread and Meat Close, Warwick, Warwickshire CV34 6HF
Tel: 01926 493339 **Email:** centremanager@hcgt.org.uk

HONINGTON HALL 🏛
Shipston-On-Stour, Warwickshire CV36 5AA
Tel: 01608 661434 **Email:** bhew@honingtonhall.plus.com

KENILWORTH CASTLE & GARDEN ⌗
Kenilworth, Warwickshire CV8 1NE
Tel: 01926 852078 **Email:** customers@english-heritage.org.uk

LORD LEYCESTER HOSPITAL
High Street, Warwick CV34 4BH
Tel: 01926 491422

PACKWOOD HOUSE 🍂
Packwood Lane, Lapworth, Warwickshire B94 6AT
Tel: 01564 783294 **Email:** packwood@nationaltrust.org.uk

STONELEIGH ABBEY
Kenilworth, Warwickshire CV8 2LF
Tel: 01926 858535 **Email:** enquire@stoneleighabbey.org

UPTON HOUSE & GARDENS 🍂
Upton, Near Banbury, Warwickshire OX15 6HT
Tel: 01295 670266 **Email:** uptonhouse@nationaltrust.org.uk

WARWICK CASTLE
Warwick CV34 4QU
Tel: 01926 495421 **Email:** customer.information@warwick-castle.com

BACK TO BACKS 🍂
55-63 Hurst Street, Birmingham, West Midlands B5 4TE
Email: backtobacks@nationaltrust.org.uk

BADDESLEY CLINTON 🍂
Rising Lane, Baddesley Clinton, Warwickshire B93 0DQ
Tel: 01564 783294 **Email:** baddesleyclinton@nationaltrust.org.uk

CASTLE BROMWICH HALL GARDENS TRUST
Chester Road, Castle Bromwich, Birmingham B36 9BT
Tel: 0121 749 4100 **Email:** admin@cbhgt.org.uk

HAGLEY HALL 🏛Ⓕ
Hall Lane, Hagley, Nr. Stourbridge, Worcestershire DY9 9LG
Tel: 01562 882408 **Email:** info@hagleyhall.com

KINVER EDGE & THE ROCK HOUSES 🍂
Compton Road, Kinver, Nr Stourbridge, Staffordshire DY7 6DL
Tel: 01384 872553 **Email:** kinveredge@nationaltrust.org.uk

WIGHTWICK MANOR & GARDENS 🍂
Wightwick Bank, Wolverhampton, West Midlands WV6 8EE
Tel: 01902 761400 **Email:** wightwickmanor@nationaltrust.org.uk

WINTERBOURNE HOUSE & GARDEN 🏛Ⓕ
58 Edgbaston Park Road, Birmingham B15 2RT
Tel: 0121 414 3003 **Email:** enquiries@winterbourne.org.uk

BEWDLEY MUSEUM
12 Load Street, Bewdley, Worcestershire DY12 2AE
Tel: 0845 603 5699 **Email:** Alison.bakr@wyreforestdc.gov.uk

BROADWAY TOWER
Middle Hill, Broadway, Worcestershire WR12 7LB
Tel: 01386 852390

CROOME 🍂
Near High Green, Worcestershire WR8 9DW
Tel: 01905 371006 **Email:** croome@nationaltrust.org.uk

HANBURY HALL 🍂
Droitwich, Worcestershire WR9 7EA
Tel: 01527 821214 **Email:** hanburyhall@nationaltrust.org.uk

MADRESFIELD COURT
Madresfield, Malvern WR13 5AJ
Tel: 01684 573614 **Email:** tours@madresfieldestate.co.uk

SPETCHLEY PARK GARDENS 🏛Ⓕ
Spetchley Park, Worcester WR5 1RS
Tel: 01453 810303 **Email:** hb@spetchleygardens.co.uk

WITLEY COURT & GARDENS ⌗
Great Witley, Worcestershire WR6 6JT
Tel: 01299 896636 **Email:** customers@english-heritage.org.uk

YORKSHIRE

EAST YORKSHIRE • NORTH YORKSHIRE
SOUTH YORKSHIRE • WEST YORKSHIRE

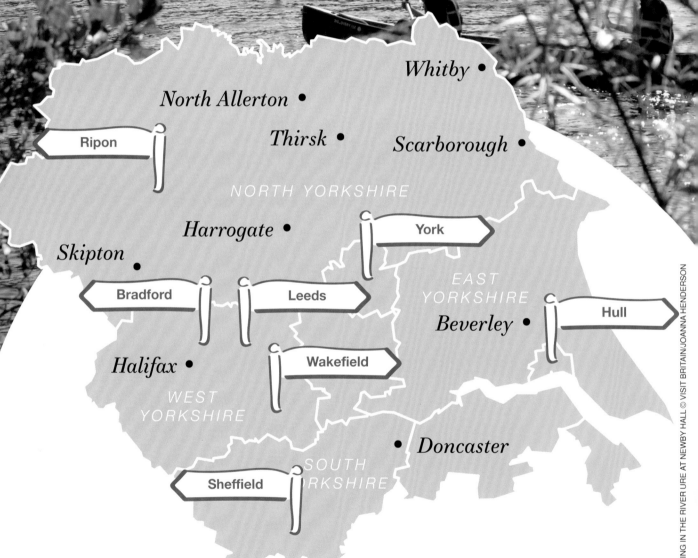

Whitby •

North Allerton •

Ripon

Thirsk •

Scarborough •

NORTH YORKSHIRE

Harrogate •

York

Skipton
•

EAST YORKSHIRE

Bradford

Leeds

Beverley •

Hull

Halifax •

Wakefield

WEST YORKSHIRE

Doncaster •

SOUTH YORKSHIRE

Sheffield

🌲 COUNTRYSIDE:

- Dales, Moors & Wolds
- Tour de Yorkshire
- Herriot Country

⏳ HERITAGE:

- Wars of the Roses
- Thomas Chippendale
- Abolition of slavery

🍴 FOOD:

- Yorkshire parkin
- Pontefract cakes
- Yorkshire pudding

THE GREAT HALL, CASTLE HOWARD

SKIPTON CASTLE

Skipton is home to one of the most complete and well preserved medieval castles in England. Skipton nearly didn't survive. The castle garrison withheld a long three year siege in 1645 during the English Civil War. On surrendering, the castle roof was removed but its new owner, Lady Anne Clifford, undertook an enlightened programme of restoration.

Highlights:

- The double towered gatehouse
- The medieval kitchens
- Tudor apartments in the Conduit Court
- Masons' marks carved into the stonework
- Yew tree planted by Lady Anne to mark the restoration in 1659
- 17th century shell grotto in the East Gatehouse Tower

TERRACE AND PARKLAND, HAREWOOD HOUSE © HAREWOOD HOUSE TRUST - LEE BEAL

DON'T MISS!

CASTLE HOWARD

The dome at Castle Howard was a first for a private house. Sir John Vanbrugh created this sublime example of English Baroque for the 3rd Earl of Carlisle, working with Nicholas Hawksmoor. Under the dome is the Great Hall, an astonishingly theatrical space with 70 foot columns drawing your eye to airy classical scenes by Antonio Pellegrini.

Highlights:

- The 3rd Earl's Italian landscapes & antique sculptures
- The 4th Earl's Old Masters & English portraiture
- Bedroom furniture by John Linnell
- Stained glass by Edward Burne Jones in the chapel
- The Temple of the Winds & Mausoleum in the Park
- The Atlas Fountain

THE GATEHOUSE, SKIPTON CASTLE

HAREWOOD HOUSE

A triumph of the best taste of the Georgian era, designed by John Carr of York, interiors by Robert Adam enhanced by the best makers of the day, Thomas Chippendale, Joseph Rose, Joshua Reynolds, Thomas Gainsborough and Capability Brown. A tradition of patronage has brought works by JMW Turner, Jacob Epstein, Carl Fabergé to the house as well as changing exhibitions of contemporary artists.

Highlights:

- Chinoiserie in the East Bedroom
- Chippendale's Diana & Minerva commode
- Adam by Jacob Epstein
- The Terrace Gallery
- Views from the Terrace Café

MRS HUDSON'S HIDDEN GEM

MARKENFIELD HALL

"…My first sight of Markenfield Hall, hiding between two stone barns, I felt a bit like Alice when she caught a glimpse through the door into the Queen's garden. Markenfield is, quite simply, like walking into a postcard. It's easy to think of 14th century folk living in hovels or castles but what about the gentry? They lived in houses like Markenfield, hidden behind a deep moat for defence, looking inwards to a courtyard for all the comings and goings, with living quarters and barns, kitchens and workshops all adjoining.

Thomas Markenfield and his uncle, Richard Norton, were among the leaders of The Rising of the North, not an episode of Game of Thrones but a significant rebellion by the catholic Earls of the North against protestant Elizabeth I in 1569. In the chapel hangs a copy of the banner which streamed behind white-haired Richard Norton as the rebels left the courtyard at Markenfield, headed for defeat, death and exile. The family fortunes crashed and Markenfield spent the following centuries as a forgotten farmhouse. Today it is once again loved, a hidden haven of quiet and beauty with rich rewards for those who venture off the track to find it…"

THE MEDIEVAL GREAT HALL, MARKENFIELD HALL

MARK THE YEAR

CHINESES CHIPPENDALE CHAIR, NOSTELL PRIORY © NATIONAL TRUST IMAGES

ROCOCO MIRROR BY THOMAS CHIPPENDALE, NOSTELL PRIORY © NATIONAL TRUST IMAGES/ANDREAS VON EINSIEDEL

300 YEARS
CHIPPENDALE

Celebrate our greatest furniture maker 300 years after his birth.
- Harewood House
- Newby Hall
- Temple Newsam
- Nostell Priory
- Sledmere
- Burton Constable Hall
- Fairfax House
- Burton Agnes Hall

200 YEARS
REPTON

Enjoy the gardens of Humphry Repton 200 years after his death.
- Harewood House
- Wentworth Woodhouse
- Rudding Park Hotel
- Oulton Hall Hotel

100 YEARS
WOMEN & SUFFERAGE

STATUE OF THE BRONTE SISTERS AT THE BRONTE PARSONAGE MUSEUM

1. THE BRONTË SISTERS, CHARLOTTE (1816-55), EMILY (1818-48), ANNE (1820-49)
Novelists and writers at The Brontë Parsonage Museum.

AVIATOR AMY JOHNSON WAVES TO THE CROWD AFTER LANDING AT BRISBANE, 1930

3. AMY JOHNSON (1903 -1941)
Pioneering aviator at Sewerby Hall.

ANNE LISTER BY JOSHUA HORNER

4. ANNE LISTER (1791–1840)
Sexually liberated landowner, diarist, traveller & mountaineer at Shibden Hall.

Lady Ann Clifford only Da and hair to George Earl of Cumberland She First Marrie to Richard Earl of Dorset after to Philip Herbert Earl of Pembroke

ÆTATE SVE 30
1620

2. LADY ANNE CLIFFORD (1590-1676)
Campaigner for women's legal rights, builder and restoration pioneer at Skipton Castle.

ST HILD FROM ST HILDA'S CHURCH, WHITBY

5. SAINT HILD OF WHITBY (614-80)
Saxon princess, abbess, adviser to Kings, host of the Synod of Whitby at Whitby Abbey.

ROSALIND HOWARD, COUNTESS OF CARLISLE

6. ROSALIND HOWARD, COUNTESS OF CARLISLE (1845-1921)
The Radical Countess, women's rights & temperance activist at Castle Howard.

DID YOU KNOW?

1 NEWBURGH PRIORY

In 1660, Oliver Cromwell's corpse was dug up and hanged as a regicide. His daughter Mary petitioned for his bones and buried them in a brick vault in an attic room at her home, Newburgh Priory. The vault has never been opened so Cromwell must still be there. His head ended up at Sidney Sussex College, Cambridge.

2 RIPLEY CASTLE

After the Battle of Marston Moor, fervent royalist Jane Ingleby of Ripley Castle kept a pistol trained on Oliver Cromwell in the Library all night to stop him searching for her brother, William, who was hiding in a priest's hole upstairs. Jane had fought in the battle and returned wounded just before Cromwell knocked on her door in 1644.

3 BURTON CONSTABLE HALL

At Burton Constable Hall is the skeleton of a 60 ft sperm whale, beached in 1825, displayed by Sir Clifford Constable and featured by Hermann Melville in Moby Dick.

LIBRARY AT RIPLEY CASTLE

SOUTH FRONT, NEWBURGH PRIORY

4 BURTON AGNES HALL

When Anne Griffiths died of injuries inflicted by brigands at Burton Agnes Hall, she asked to be buried in the unfinished house. Her wish was ignored and the house endured years of hauntings until her skull was buried in one of the walls. No one is sure which.

BURTON CONSTABLE WHALE

5 NORTON CONYERS

The story that Charlotte Brontë was inspired to write Jane Eyre by a visit to Norton Conyers in 1839 looks likely after a recent discovery. An unknown staircase leading to a forgotten attic chamber suggests that a family legend about Mad Mary is true. Charlotte was a governess when she came here, just like her heroine, Jane.

6 MERCHANT ADVENTURERS' HALL

On the wall of the medieval chapel at the Merchant Adventurers' Hall in York are flood marks from 1831, 1947 and 1952, all overtaken by the highest to date in 2015.

3 TOP SPOTS FOR FAMILIES

1.
BURTON CONSTABLE HALL

Explore the house and its cabinet of curiosities, new displays in the stable block, giant games on the Orangery lawn, Indoor Riding School play area, park and woodlands to explore, lots of picnic spots and 'Constable Moby' the sperm whale skeleton.

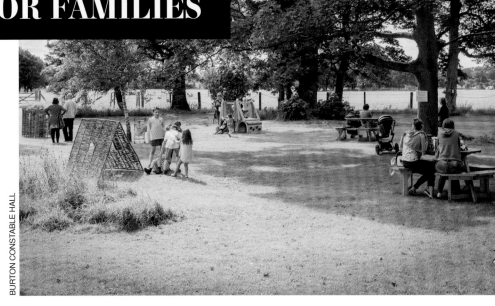

BURTON CONSTABLE HALL

FAIRY DAY AT NEWBY HALL & GARDENS

2.
NEWBY HALL & GARDENS

Winner, Best Family Day Out, Hudson's Heritage Awards 2016

Adventure Gardens,

Miniature Railway, Children's Tours, Zimbabwean Wood sculptures, under 14s Gift Shop, children's bushcraft courses, Pirate Days, Fairy Days, dolls house & teddy bear exhibitions.

STOCKELD PARK, ENCHANTED FOREST

3.
STOCKELD PARK

Winner, Best Family Day Out, Hudson's Heritage Awards 2012

Open for adventures in school holidays, particularly Christmas, enchanted forest, adventure playgrounds, roller skating, boats, scooters, go karts, maze, ice skating in winter.

THE FEVERSHAM ARMS

Originally a coaching inn, rebuilt in 1855 by the Earl of Feversham. Now the Verbena Spa (one of Tatler's 101 Spas of the World) offers guests more than just a change of horses.

THE TRADDOCK

The 1740s country house hotel was built in the medieval 'trading paddock'. Popular with geologists in the 1930s, today it is ideal for visitors to the Yorkshire Dales National Park's dramatic limestone scenery.

THE SPORTSMAN'S ARMS

A traditional inn with a warm welcome for walkers and anglers and a reputation for fine dining, particularly game and seafood. The adjacent packhorse bridge was on the medieval supply route for Fountains Abbey.

LASTINGHAM GRANGE

The old, stone-walled country house, built around a courtyard and set within 10 acres of attractive gardens, is owned and personally run by the Wood family. This charming hotel is situated on the edge of the Moors in the historic village of Lastingham, a peaceful backwater in the heart of the North York Moors National Park.

THE CONISTON HOTEL AND COUNTRY ESTATE

Nestled in the heart of the Yorkshire Dales, part of the 1400-acre Coniston Estate. Home to a shooting ground, falconry centre, Land Rover 4x4 experience, fly fishing on the 24-acre lake or River Aire and a great base to explore the Yorkshire Dales countryside.

CHIPPENDALE

By Dr Adam Bowett, Chairman of the Chippendale Society

Thomas Chippendale (1718-1778) is the most famous name in British furniture-making. Born in Yorkshire, Chippendale probably received a practical apprenticeship from his father and then training with Richard Wood, the leading furniture maker in York, before moving to London in the 1750s. In 1754 he published the first edition of The Gentleman and Cabinet Maker's Director, the first work of its kind solely devoted to the furniture and furnishing of the 18th century British interior. As a result, his influence was so pervasive, that the name of Chippendale is often applied indiscriminately to mid-18th century furniture and his designs were widely copied.

The furniture Thomas Chippendale supplied for his aristocratic patrons ranks among the finest ever made in Britain. He worked initially in the popular Rococo style, using a range of materials, from carved mahogany to gilded wood, japanned Chinoiserie and fine upholstery. From the 1760s onwards, he turned to the new neo-classical taste promoted by architects such as James Stuart, William Chambers and Robert Adam. Using fashionable and exotic materials such as satinwood, rosewood, purpleheart, ebony and ivory, Chippendale developed a unique and distinctive interpretation of the British neo-classical style. Many of Chippendale's pieces remain in the houses for which they were commissioned and have been cherished by generations of owners and visitors alike.

300

Chippendale's workshop was able to supply his clients with furnishings of every kind. In effect, he was an entrepreneur running a large business employing perhaps as many as 50 in-house craftsmen and any number of out-workers. He was the artistic director of the enterprise, supervising the workforce and its production, appeasing clients and always keeping one step ahead of new fashions. Ideally, he preferred long-running commissions to equip large country or town houses from attic to basement, with grand pieces for the reception rooms (including wallpapers and textiles), 'neat but substantially good' items for the family rooms, and utilitarian objects for the servants. Harewood House and Nostell Priory, for example, bear witness to this practice to this day.

THE GALLERY, HAREWOOD HOUSE © PAUL BARKER - HAREWOOD HOUSE TRUST

THE BLUE DRAWING ROOM, DUMFRIES HOUSE

Research to date has identified over seventy of Chippendale's clients, their patronage being documented in invoices, payments in account books and entries in bank ledgers. About 600 pieces of furniture can be attributed to his workshop. The development of his style can be traced from the Director-style rococo furniture made for Dumfries House (late 1750s), through the early Adam-inspired pieces for Sir Laurence Dundas at Aske Hall (early-mid 1760s), to the mature neo-Classicism of Harewood (early 1770s), leading to the super-refined elegance of Burton Constable (late 1770s).

Chippendale's eldest son, also called Thomas Chippendale (1749-1822) joined his father's firm and, after his father's death, developed his designs to keep pace with changing fashion. Among his patrons was Sir Richard Colt Hoare whose house and park at Stourhead, Wiltshire, is one of the greatest artistic achievements of the Georgian age. ■

To celebrate Chippendale 300, check each region to find the best places to enjoy Chippendale furniture. A major free entry exhibition will be held at Leeds City Museum.

THE GREAT DRAWING ROOM - BURTON CONSTABLE

DETAIL OF SETTEE AT BURTON CONSTABLE

© HAREWOOD HOUSE TRUST

© HAREWOOD HOUSE TRUST

Thomas Chippendale, Britain's greatest furniture maker was born 300 years ago in 1718. Some of his best interiors survive today remarkably unchanged.

THE FAMILY PARLOUR, DUMFRIES HOUSE

Wassand Hall

www.wassand.co.uk

Fine Regency house by Thomas Cundy the elder. Beautifully restored Walled Gardens, woodland walks, Parks and vistas over Hornsea Mere, part of the Estate since 1530. The Estate has been in the family since 1530 to the present day. Rupert Russell being the great nephew of the late Lady Strickland-Constable.

The House contains a fine collection of 18th/19th Century paintings, English and Continental silver, furniture and a very fine collection of Meissen porcelain. Wassand is very much a family home and retains a very friendly atmosphere. Homemade afternoon teas are served in the conservatory on open days.

CONTACT
Owner: Trustees of Wassand Will Trust
Contact: Shirley Power - 01964 537474
Office Tel: 01965 537047 / 01672 564352
Email: rupert@reorussell.co.uk

LOCATION
Seaton, Hull, East Yorkshire HU11 5RJ
Map Ref: 11:F9 - On the B1244 Seaton-Hornsea Road. Approximately 2 miles from Hornsea.

OPENING TIMES (2018)
May: Fri 25, Sat 26, Sun 27, Mon 28 - Vintage Cars.
Jun: Wed 13, Thu 14, Fri 15, Sat 16, Sun 17, Thu 28, Fri 29, Sat 30.
July: Sun 1, Mon 2, Wed 11, Thu 12, Fri 13, Sat 14, Sun 15 - Concert - Hall Closed.
Aug: Wed 1, Thu 2, Fri 3, Sat 4 - Hall & Garden Closed
Sun 5, Mon 6, Fri 24, Sat 25, Sun 26, Mon 27.

ADMISSION
Hall & Gardens - Adult: £6.50, OAP: £6,
Child (11-15yrs): £3.50, Child (Under 10): Free.
Hall or Garden Only
Adult: £4.50, OAP: £4, Child (11-15yrs): £2,
Child (Under 10): Free.

KEY FACTS

 Group Bookings - Guided Tours, Bird Hide inclusive ticket contact Shirley Power 01964 537474.

 Toilets (including disabled).

 Baby changing facilities available.

 Ample parking for cars, free. Limited space for coaches.

 Limited. Wheelchair access to ground floor of hall. Disabled parking close to the Walled Garden.

 Dogs welcome in grounds, on leads.

 By arrangement.

 Ideal place for outdoor school visits. National Curriculum can be met through fun & challenging activities.

 Refreshments available for ticket holders.

 See open days and events on the website for all up to date events. Vintage Car Rally & Plant Fair.

Burton Constable Hall

Burton Constable Hall & Grounds

burtonconstable.com

There's so much to discover inside and out at this fascinating stately home. Visit the Hall's many grand rooms crammed with fine and decorative art, furniture and country house paraphernalia. Explore the 'Capability Brown' parkland and visit the historic stables, where you can discover the iconic Burton Constable Whale mentioned in Moby-Dick! In 2018 Burton Constable is delighted to be taking part in Chippendale 300: a celebration of Britain's greatest furniture maker.

CONTACT
Owner:
Burton Constable Foundation
Contact:
Mrs Helen Dewson
Tel: 01964 562400
Email: enquiries@ burtonconstable.com

LOCATION
Skirlaugh, Hull,
East Yorks HU11 4LN

Map Ref: 11:E10

Beverley 14 miles, Hull 10 miles. Signed from Skirlaugh.

OPENING TIMES / ADMISSIONS
Please visit our website for opening times and prices.

KEY FACTS

 Ample free parking.

 Mostly accessible.

 On leads in grounds. Guide dogs only in hall.

 Stables Tea Room.

 Small gift shop.

Burton Agnes Hall

255

Castle Howard

www.castlehoward.co.uk

Designed by Sir John Vanbrugh in 1699 Castle Howard is undoubtedly one of Britain's finest private residences.

Built for Charles Howard the 3rd Earl of Carlisle and taking over 100 years to complete, today Castle Howard remains home to the Howard family. Discover the rich and varied history, dramatic interiors and sweeping parklands of this magnificent house.

Free flowing tours of the house allow you to explore at your leisure, with friendly and knowledgeable guides throughout happy to share stories. From decadent bedrooms and lavish drawing rooms to the stunning Great Hall and vast Long Gallery, there are architectural wonders and world renowned collections in every room.

The house façade bristles with carvings and the gold topped dome reaches skyward giving Castle Howard its iconic silhouette.

Spend a day exploring the beautiful gardens; with meandering woodland paths, lakeside terraces and sweeping vistas dotted with temples, statues and follies. The walled garden is the perfect place to relax with a stunning collection of roses, herbaceous borders and a formal potager. Seasonal highlights include daffodils, rhododendrons, bluebells, roses and striking autumnal hues.

Enjoy a changing programme of exhibitions and events, including Christmas opening when the house is decorated for the festive season. Plus free outdoor tours, illustrated children's trail, adventure playground and summer boat trips on the Great Lake (weather permitting). Treat yourself at a range of cafés and shops, including garden centre, farm shop and gift shops.

KEY FACTS

 Photography allowed.

 School parties welcome.

 Toilet facilities available.

 Choice of four cafés.

 Baby changing facilities available.

 Fitzroy restaurant.

 Gardens, shops and cafés open all year.

 Gift shops & farm shop.

Free parking.

Garden centre.

Access to all areas except High South, Exhibition Wing and Chapel.

Available for private events.

Dogs on leads welcome in gardens only. Assistance dogs welcome in house.

Full programme for all the family.

 Camping and caravanning.

Great Hall licensed for weddings.

 Guides in each room.

 'Lady L', 'Barry Lyndon', 'Brideshead Revisited' & BBC's 'Death Comes to Pemberley'.

OWNER
Castle Howard Estate Ltd

CONTACT
Visitor Services
Tel: 01653 648333
Email: house@castlehoward.co.uk
Twitter: @castlehowardest
Facebook: /castlehoward
Instagram: @castle_howard

LOCATION
Castle Howard, York, North Yorkshire YO60 7DA
Map Ref: 11:C8

Car: From the North: From the A1 take the A61 to Thirsk then the A170 to Helmsley. Before Helmsley turn right onto the B1257 and follow the brown signs. From the South: Take the A1M to Junction 44 and follow the A64 east to York. Continue past York and follow the brown signs.
Bus: Service from York.
Rail: London Kings Cross to York 1hr. 50 mins. York to Malton Station 30 mins.

OPENING TIMES
House & Grounds
Visit www.castlehoward.co.uk for details of opening times.

Grounds
Open all year except Christmas Day.

Stable Courtyard Shops, Café & Garden Centre
Visit website for details of opening times. For more information please contact Castle Howard Estate Office on 01653 648444.

ADMISSION
Visit www.castlehoward.co.uk for details of admission prices.

CONFERENCE/FUNCTIONS
Long Gallery with a maximum capacity of 200. Grecian Halll with a maximum capacity of 70.

Markenfield Hall

www.markenfield.com

From the first glimpse of the Hall from between the farm buildings, to the moment the Mediaeval Courtyard opens up as visitors pass beneath the Tudor Gatehouse, Markenfield never fails to astound.

The earliest part of the house was built circa 1230, with its Undercroft consisting of the three surviving vaulted ground floor rooms on the east side of the house.

This earlier house was enlarged by Canon John de Markenfield, who received the Licence to Crenellate the Hall on 28 February 1310 resulting in the distinctive outline that you see to this day.

The house was bought – and essentially saved – in 1761 by Fletcher Norton, the first Lord Grantley of Markenfield (a title still held by the family).

CONTACT
Owner: Mr Ian & Lady Deirdre Curteis
Contact: The Administrator
Tel: 01765 692303 **Fax:** 01765 607195
Email: info@markenfield.com

LOCATION
Nr Ripon, North Yorkshire HG4 3AD
Map Ref: 10:P8
Car: Access from West side of A61. 2½ miles South of the Ripon bypass. Entrance off the A61.
Bus: Stop 100m from end of drive & drive a mile long.

OPENING TIMES
29 Apr-13 May and 10-24 Jun, 2pm-5pm each day. Last entry 4:30pm. Group bookings can be accepted all year round by appointment.

ADMISSION
Adult: £6
Child: £3
Concessions: £5
Booked Groups: From £8 per person for a guided tour (min charge £120).

KEY FACTS

 For more information please visit the website or contact the hall.

 Parking during open days is in the one acre paddock.

 Partial. Wheelchair access to the ground floor only.

 Dogs welcome in grounds only.

 Tours last approx 1½ hrs, followed by time to wander around. Allow 2 hours in all for your visit.

 Educational visits by arrangement.

 Offering tea & cake for groups at a cost of £12 pp (including the tour).

 Small gift shop.

 Plant sales available.

 Corporate functions are available, please contact for further details.

 For all upcoming events please see the 'Events' section of the website.

 With its outline reflected in the encircling moat, provides a wonderfully intimate venue for a wedding.

Plumpton Rocks

www.plumptonrocks.com

A Grade 2* listed man-made lake and surrounding pleasure gardens against a backdrop of towering rocks eroded by the wind. It has been described by English Heritage to be of outstanding interest. The large picturesque garden was formed in the 1760s by creating a lake at the foot of an extensive range of weathered and contorted gritstone outcrops. The 30 acre park provides seemingly endless opportunities to explore, with tranquil lakeside walks, dramatic Millstone Grit rock formations, romantic woodland walks winding through bluebells and rhododendrons.

Painted by Turner and described by Queen Mary as 'Heaven on earth'. The lake, woodlands and dam have recently been restored to their 18th Century magnificence.

CONTACT
Owner/Contact: Robert de Plumpton Hunter
Tel: 01289 382322
Email: info@plumptonrocks.com

LOCATION
Plumpton, Knaresborough,
North Yorkshire HG5 8NA

Map Ref: 11:A9
Between Harrogate and Wetherby on A661, 1m SE of A661 junction with Harrogate southern bypass.

OPENING TIMES
Mar-Oct on Sats, Suns & Bank Holidays at 11am-6pm.

ADMISSION
Adult: £3.50
Concessions: £2.50
(Prices subject to change)

ADDITIONAL
Winners of the Hudson's Hidden Gem Award 2017.

KEY FACTS

 The rocks are steep, footpaths uneven & lake is deep. Stout walking shoes are essential.

 Limited for coaches.

 Unfortunately the garden is not suitable for disabled access.

 Dogs are welcome in the grounds on leads.

School & educational visits by arrangement.

Broughton Hall Estate

www.broughtonhall.co.uk

Broughton Hall on the edge of the stunning Yorkshire Dales National Park is available for private hire. With sixteen en suite bedrooms Broughton provides the ultimate destination for family reunions, house parties, corporate events or a base to explore the surrounding countryside. Guests can also exclusively hire Utopia, a contemporary space set in the Dan Pearson designed Walled Garden, and Eden, our party house, both perfect for Weddings and Events. Avalon, our wellbeing and retreat centre, is also available for our guests, pre-booking is required. There are also luxury holiday cottages on the Estate.

KEY FACTS

 Toilet facilities available.

 Must be booked in advance/prior appointment.

 Ample car parking.

 Accessible.

 Cycle routes on site.

 Dogs welcome.

 16 luxury bedrooms with en suite bathrooms. Further accommodation available on estate.

 By arrangement.

 Must be pre-booked.

 Utopia open Mon-Fri serving breakfast and lunch.

 Lunch and dinner - Licensed.

 Company retreats & board meetings at the Hall. Meetings & Events space available at Utopia.

 Please see out facebook page for events: facebook.com /broughtonestateyorkshire

 Chapel on site for Catholic services.

CONTACT
Owner: The Tempest Family
Contact: The Estate Office
Tel: 01756 799608
Email: info@broughtonhall.co.uk

LOCATION
Skipton, Yorkshire BD23 3AE
Map Ref: 10:N9
On A59, 2 miles West of Skipton.

OPENING TIMES
Utopia, set in the Dan Pearson designed walled garden at Broughton is open for breakfast and lunch, Mon-Fri. Viewings of other properties are by prior arrangement only.

ADMISSION
Please contact for prices.

Fairfax House

www.fairfaxhouse.co.uk

Come and unlock the splendour within one of the finest Georgian townhouses in England. A classical architectural masterpiece with superb period interiors, incomparable stucco ceilings and the outstanding Noel Terry collection of furniture, Fairfax House transports you to the grandeur of 18th Century city living. Don't miss a programme of special events and exhibitions.

KEY FACTS

 No photography or video filming is permitted within the house without special permission.

 Open all year. Closed 24-26 Dec and Jan.

 Parking in adjacent Clifford's Tower car park nearby.

 The 1st floor is accessible via a staircase therefore limited. Contact to discuss your requirements.

 Audio guides in French, German, Italian, Spanish, Polish, Japanese & Chinese

 A range of group tours bring this superb townhouse to life, exploring its fascinating history.

 Engaging learning opportunities available to all levels of education.

 Gift shop.

 Stunning venue for private dining & drinks receptions.

 Please see the 'What's On' section of the website for all the dates you need to keep free in your diary.

CONTACT
Owner: York Civic Trust **Contact:** Hannah Phillip, Director
Tel: 01904 655543 **Email:** info@fairfaxhouse.co.uk

LOCATION
Castlegate, York, North Yorkshire YO1 9RN
Map Ref: 11:B9 - Centrally located behind Fenwicks, close to Clifford's Tower & Jorvik Centre. Park & Ride 2 mins away.

OPENING TIMES
10 Feb-31 Dec (closed 24-26 Dec). Tue-Sat & BHs: 10am-5pm. Sun: 11am-4pm. Mon: Guided tours at 11am and 2pm.

ADMISSION
Adult: £7.50, Conc: £6, Child (6-16): £3 (Under 6: Free), Family (2+3): £17.50. Daytime & exclusive access evening group tours available, plus catering package options.

Hovingham Hall

www.hovingham.co.uk

Attractive Palladian family home, designed and built by Thomas Worsley. The childhood home of Katharine Worsley, Duchess of Kent. It is entered through a huge riding school and has beautiful rooms with collections of pictures and furniture. The house has attractive gardens with magnificent Yew hedges and cricket ground.

CONTACT
Owner: Sir William Worsley
Tel: 01653 628771
Email: office@hovingham.co.uk

LOCATION
Hovingham, York, North Yorkshire YO62 4LU
Map Ref: 11:C8
18 miles North of York on Malton/Helmsley Road (B1257)

OPENING TIMES
1-28 Jun inclusive
12.30pm-4.30pm
Guided Tours only
Last tour at 3.30pm

ADMISSION
Adult: £10.50, Child: £5,
Concs: £10, Family (2+3): £27
Garden Only: £5

KEY FACTS

No photography permitted in the Hall.

Limited. None for coaches.

Partial ground floor only.

Obligatory. Last tour at 3.30pm.

Tea Room open daily 12.30pm-4.30pm, in June.

Magnificent reception rooms providing a special setting for entertaining.

Skipton Castle

www.skiptoncastle.co.uk

For over 900 years Skipton Castle has stood firm through wars and sieges at the gateway to the Yorkshire Dales. Once home to the famous Clifford Lords, it is one of the best preserved and most complete medieval castles in England. Fully roofed, it is a fascinating and delightful place to explore in any season - from the atmospheric Dungeon to the great Watch Tower, from the Chapel to the beautiful Conduit Court.

CONTACT
Penny Cannon
Tel: 01756 792442
Email: info@skiptoncastle.co.uk

LOCATION
Skipton, North Yorkshire BD23 1AW
Map Ref: 10:O9 - In the centre of Skipton, at the North end of the High Street.

OPENING TIMES
All year Mon-Sat 10am-5pm
Sun 11am-5pm (Oct-Mar 4pm).
Closed 23-25 Dec.

ADMISSION
Adult: £8.30, Child: £5.20,
Conc: £7.30, Family: £26.60.

KEY FACTS

By arrangement.

Tour guides, educational rooms and teachers packs available.

Licensed. Open all year.

Specialist books, cards, gifts. Online shop.

Historical Re-enactments. Plays. Art Exhibitions. For further details on events please visit the website.

Civil wedding licence. Max 80 guests.

Newby Hall & Gardens

www.newbyhall.com

Designed under the guidance of Sir Christopher Wren, this graceful country house, home to the Compton family, epitomises the Georgian 'Age of Elegance'. Its beautifully restored interior presents Robert Adam at his best with rare Gobelins tapestries and one of the UK's largest private collections of classical statuary. The award-winning gardens created in the early 1920s, boast one of Europe's longest double herbaceous borders and are of interest to specialist and amateur gardeners alike.

CONTACT
Owner: Mr Richard Compton
Contact: Visitor Services
Tel: 01423 322583 opt 3
Email: info@newbyhall.com

LOCATION
Ripon, N Yorkshire HG4 5AE
Map Ref: 11:A8 - Midway between London & Edinburgh. 40 mins from York, 30 mins from Harrogate.

OPENING TIMES
Summer - House*: 30 Mar-30 Sep. Apr, May, Jun & Sep: Tue-Sun & BH Mons; Jul-Aug: Daily. Garden, dates as House, 11am-5.30pm. Last admission 5pm. Winter, Oct-end Mar closed.

ADMISSION
See website for 2018 prices.

KEY FACTS

*Areas of the House can be closed to the public from time to time, please check website for details.

Ample. Hard standing for coaches.

Suitable. WC's. Parking. Electric and manual wheelchairs available - booking essential.

Obligatory. See website for tour times.

Wedding receptions and special functions. House licensed for civil ceremonies.

Markenfield Hall

Harewood House & Gardens

www.harewood.org

Explore one of Yorkshire's most loved country houses with award-winning gardens and grounds.

Built 1759, Harewood House is the seat of the Earl and Countess of Harewood. The magnificent Georgian building has remained within the Lascelles family since its construction and has retained much of its original splendour. Designed by renowned Georgian architect John Carr, furnished by Thomas Chippendale and with interiors by Robert Adam, Harewood House offers visitors the chance to unearth striking, original features and experience the grandeur of one of Yorkshire's finest country houses.

In each room, friendly guides are on hand to offer insights into the history and detail of the house, including the extensive art collections. From El Greco, JMW Turner and Joshua Reynolds to Epstein, Sidney Nolan and Gaudier-Brzeska, there is a diverse range on offer, spanning centuries of patronage. Representing one of Capability Brown's most important designs, the Grade 1 listed parkland has remained unchanged since it was created in the late 18th Century. With a 32 acre lake, soft rolling hills and mature, established tree lines, you can experience the idyllic, picturesque views Brown imagined for Harewood. With over 100 acres of grounds and gardens to explore, from the informal Himalayan Garden which bursts into life in May, to the productive Walled Garden surrounded by warm red brick walls, visitors won't be disappointed.

Visitors can also enjoy contemporary art exhibitions, the rare Bird Garden, the Farm Experience, and a selection of popular cafés. Whether you want to visit the house and its awe-inspiring collections or enjoy the beautiful gardens, Harewood provides a wonderful day of discovery.

2018 sees Harewood celebrate England's finest cabinet maker, Thomas Chippendale. Harewood was Chippendale's largest commission and the interiors he realised were amongst the finest in Britain. Visitors will be able to see some of his greatest pieces highlighted in a series of exhibitions, displays and tours. To commemorate the end of WW1, we will be celebrating the resilience of the human spirit with a new exhibition, Seeds of Hope in the Walled Garden.

OWNER
The Earl and Countess of Harewood

CONTACT
Tel: 0113 218 1010
Email: info@harewood.org

LOCATION
Harewood House, Harewood, Leeds, West Yorkshire LS17 9LG

Map Ref: 10:P10

Car: A1 N or S to Wetherby. A659 via Collingham, Harewood is on A61 between Leeds and Harrogate. Easily reached from A1, M1, M62 and M18. 40 mins from York, 20 mins from centre of Leeds or Harrogate.

Bus: No. 36 from Leeds or Harrogate.

Rail: London Kings Cross to Leeds/Harrogate 2hrs 20 mins. Leeds/Harrogate Station 7m.

Air: Leeds Bradford Airport 9m.

OPENING TIMES
House, Gardens, Grounds, Bird Garden, Farm Experience, Courtyard,& Bookshop:
From 24 Mar-28 Oct 2018.

Please see website or call our team for details.

ADMISSION
Please see website up-to-date details.

THE TERRACE, HAREWOOD HOUSE ©LEE BEEL & HAREWOOD HOUSE TRUST

KEY FACTS

 Please see website for further information.

 Toilet facilities available.

 Baby changing facilities available.

 Free. Designated for blue badge holders.

 WCs. No access to State Rooms for electric wheelchairs. Courtesy wheelchair.

 On leads. Service dogs welcome except in Bird Garden and Farm Experience.

Guided tours by prior arrangement.

 Sandford Award for Education. School parties welcome.

 Terrace Café. Licensed.

 Courtyard Café - Licensed.

 Gifts, souvenirs, postcards and publications.

 Fine dining in house and private venue hire available.

Please see the 'What's on' page of the website for events, fairs & festivals etc.

 A popular location choice for both film & television, playing host to a number of well known productions.

Lotherton Hall

www.leeds.gov.uk/lothertonhall

A scenic country estate, Lotherton combines a grand Edwardian mansion with stunning grounds and a wealth of wildlife, including a deer park and new Wildlife World attraction. Explore intriguing stories of the former owners and servants who cared for this majestic home, as well as stunning collections of decorative arts from across the world. Discover changing exhibitions in the elegant Fashion Galleries or roam the nature trails and woodland play area.

KEY FACTS

 Welcoming group visits, please call to arrange your day out.

 Changing Places & disabled WC facilities available.

 Baby change is available in the Courtyard toilets and in the house.

 Admission to the estate includes car parking.

 Passenger lift in the House. Please see access statement on website for full details.

 Dogs are welcome to all areas except the house, Stables Café & bird garden.

 Groups can take advantage of special packages including house or garden tours and catering.

 1 to 4 hour cross-curricular workshops to choose from, or a tailored package for you & your students.

 Stables Café serves hot & cold snacks and light meals. Famous for their home-made cakes!

 Shop offers souvenirs & giftware, children's toys and some great bargain books.

 Accommodating for large corporate events in the Sir Alvary Room.

 Please see the 'Things to do and see' section of the website for all headlining events.

Providing a perfect setting for your wedding day; overlooking the beautiful Yorkshire countryside.

CONTACT
Owner: Leeds City Council
Contact: Visitor Services
Tel: 0113 378 2959
Email: lotherton.hall@leeds.gov.uk

LOCATION
Aberford, Leeds, West Yorkshire LS25 3EB
Map Ref: 11:B10
Situated off Collier Lane which is just off junction 47 of the M1. If you are using a route planner, please use postcode: LS25 3EB.

OPENING TIMES
Please check the website or call for seasonal opening dates.

ADMISSION
Please check the website for current admission prices.

Adventure Playground, Harewood House
©Harewood House Trust & John Steele

Temple Newsam
www.leeds.gov.uk/templenewsam

Discover 500 years of history in this beautiful Tudor-Jacobean mansion set within 1500 acres of parkland. Explore over 40 restored rooms filled with a wealth of fine and decorative art treasures, from paintings to Chippendale furniture, textiles, silver and ceramics. Uncover the secrets of past residents – from royal connections to servants' stories. Enjoy a changing programme of events, exhibitions and activities for families, as well as a child-friendly rare breeds farm, café and gift shop.

CONTACT
Owner: Leeds City Council
Contact: Visitor Services **Tel:** 0113 336 7461
Email: temple.newsam.house@leeds.gov.uk

LOCATION
Temple Newsam Road, Leeds LS15 OAE
Map Ref: 10:P10 - 4 miles East of city centre B6159 or 2 miles from M1 junction 46. 4 miles from city centre.

OPENING TIMES
Please check the website or call 0113 336 7461 for seasonal opening times.

ADMISSION
Please check the website or call 0113 336 7461 for admission prices.

KEY FACTS

 Welcoming group visits, please call to arrange your day out.

 Toilet & disabled WC facilities available.

 Baby change facilities in the house and courtyard toilets.

 Walking distance to the stable courtyard & home farm. Patrolled. Charge except blue badge holders.

 Passenger lift in the house. Please see access statement on website for full details.

 Assistance dogs permitted in the house and farm.

There are a range of tours available each week - check the website.

 A programme of cross-curricular schools workshops are available, & a range of adult talks & workshops.

 Tea Rooms open every day in the summer, closing on Mons in the winter. Serving snacks, hot & cold meals.

 Gift shop offers luxurious home fragrances, home accessories, stationary and food range.

 Offers a unique & flexible location for your meeting, training session or team away day.

 Please see website for all events.

Licensed to hold weddings & civil partnership ceremonies, provides both grandeur & intimacy.

York Gate Garden
www.yorkgate.org.uk

Inspirational one acre garden widely recognised as one of Britain's finest small gardens. A series of smaller gardens with different themes and in contrasting styles are linked by a succession of delightful vistas. Striking architectural features play a key role throughout the garden which is noted for its exquisite planting details and Arts and Crafts features.

CONTACT
Owner: Perennial Gardeners' Royal Benevolent Society
Contact: Garden Administrator
Tel: 0113 267 8240
Email: yorkgate@perennial.org.uk

LOCATION
Back Church Lane, Adel, Leeds LS16 8DW
Map Ref: 10:P10 - 2¼ miles SE of Bramhope, just off A660.

OPENING TIMES
1 Apr-28 Sep, Sun-Thu Including BHs 12:30pm-4:30pm.

ADMISSION
Standard: £5, Gift Aid: £5.50 Child (U16) & Carers: Free Annual Friends Membership £25 per annum. POA for groups.

KEY FACTS

 Parking by the church on Church Lane. A lovely 5 min walk through the Church yard to the entrance.

 Partial. Please contact for details.

 By arrangement and on most Sundays.

 Cheery Tea Room open for drinks, freshly made cakes & light bites.

 Wide selection of locally sourced items, garden gear, cards and gifts.

 Seasonal plants available.

Private catering available.

Lotherton Hall

BURTON AGNES HALL & GARDENS 🏠Ⓕ
Driffield, East Yorkshire YO25 4NB
Tel:01262 490324 **Email:** office@burtonagnes.com

SEWERBY HALL & GARDENS
Church Lane, Sewerby, Bridlington YO15 1EA
Tel: 01262 673769 **Email:** sewerby.hall@eastriding.gov.uk

SLEDMERE HOUSE 🏠Ⓕ
Sledmere, Driffield, East Yorkshire YO25 3XG
Tel: 01377 236637 **Email:** info@sledmerehouse.com

ALLERTON PARK
Knaresborough, North Yorkshire HG5 0SE
Tel: 01423 330927

Aske Hall 🏠

Richmond, North Yorkshire DL10 5HJ
A predominantly Georgian collection of paintings, furniture and porcelain
in house which has been the seat of the Dundas family since 1763.
Map Ref: 10:P6 - 4m SW of A1 at Scotch Corner, 2m from the A66, B6274.
Tel: 01748 822000 **Email:** mandy.blenkiron@aske.co.uk
Website: www.aske.co.uk **Open:** 13 & 14 Sep (Heritage Open Days)
Tours (15 people per tour) at 10, 11 & 12. Booking advisable. **Admission:** Free.

BARLEY HALL
2 Coffee Yard, Off Stonegate, York YO1 8AR
Tel: 01904 610275 **Email:** dscott@yorkat.co.uk

BENINGBROUGH HALL & GARDENS 🦋
Beningbrough, North Yorkshire YO30 1DD
Tel: 01904 472027 **Email:** beningbrough@nationaltrust.org.uk

BOLTON ABBEY
Skipton, North Yorkshire BD23 6EX
Tel: 01756 718009 **Email:** tourism@boltonabbey.com

BOLTON CASTLE 🏠Ⓕ
Nr Leyburn, North Yorkshire DL8 4ET
Tel: 01969 623981 **Email:** info@boltoncastle.co.uk

BROCKFIELD HALL 🏠Ⓕ
Warthill, York YO19 5XJ
Tel: 01904 489362 **Email:** simon@brockfieldhall.co.uk

CLIFFORD'S TOWER ⌗
Tower Street, York YO1 9SA
Tel: 01904 646940 **Email:** customers@english-heritage.org.uk

CONSTABLE BURTON HALL GARDENS 🏠Ⓕ
Leyburn, North Yorkshire YO62 5EB
Tel: 01677 450428 **Email:** gardens@constableburton.com

DUNCOMBE PARK 🏠Ⓕ
Helmsley, North Yorkshire YO25 4NB
Tel: 01439 770213 **Email:** info@duncombepark.com

THE FORBIDDEN CORNER LTD
Tupgill Park Estate, Coverham, Nr Middleham, North Yorkshire DL8 4TJ
Tel: 01969 640638 **Email:** forbiddencorner@gmail.com

FOUNTAINS ABBEY & STUDLEY ROYAL 🦋
Ripon, North Yorkshire HG4 3DY
Tel: 01765 608888 **Email:** fountainsabbey@nationaltrust.org.uk

THE GEORGIAN THEATRE ROYAL
Victoria Road, Richmond, North Yorkshire DL10 4DW
Tel: 01748 823710 **Email:** admin@georgiantheatreroyal.co.uk

HELMSLEY CASTLE ⌗
Castlegate, Helmsley, York YO62 5AB
Tel: 01904 601946 **Email:** www.english-heritage.org.uk

HELMSLEY WALLED GARDEN
Cleveland Way, Helmsley, North Yorkshire YO62 5AH
Tel: 01439 771427 **Email:** info@helmsleywalledgarden.org.uk

JERVAULX ABBEY
Ripon, North Yorkshire HG4 4PH
Tel: 01677 460226

KIPLIN HALL & GARDENS 🏠Ⓕ
Nr Scorton, Richmond, North Yorkshire DL10 6AT
Tel: 01748 818178 **Email:** info@kiplinhall.co.uk

MERCHANT ADVENTURERS' HALL
Fossgate, York YO1 9XD
Tel: 01904 654818 **Email:** enquiries@theyorkcompany.co.uk

MIDDLEHAM CASTLE ⌗
Castle Hill, Middleham, Leyburn, North Yorkshire DL8 4QR
Tel: 01969 623899

NEWBURGH PRIORY
Coxwold, York, North Yorkshire YO61 4AS
Tel: 01347 868372 **Email:** estateoffice@newburghpriory.co.uk

NORTON CONYERS 🏠
Wath, Nr Ripon, North Yorkshire HG4 5EQ
Tel: 01765 640333 **Email:** info@nortonconyers.org.uk

NUNNINGTON HALL 🦋
Nunnington, North Yorkshire YO62 5UY
Tel: 01439 748283 **Email:** nunningtonhall@nationaltrust.org.uk

ORMESBY HALL 🦋
Ladgate Lane, Ormesby, Middlesbrough TS7 9AS
Tel: 01642 324188 **Email:** ormesbyhall@nationaltrust.org.uk

PARCEVALL HALL GARDENS 🏠Ⓕ
Skyreholme, Nr Appletreewick, North Yorkshire BD23 6DE
Tel: 01756 720311 **Email:** parcevallhall@btconnect.com

RHS GARDEN HARLOW CARR
Crag Lane, Harrogate, North Yorkshire HG3 1QB
Tel: 01423 565418 **Email:** harlowcarr@rhs.org.uk

RICHMOND CASTLE ⌗
Richmond, North Yorkshire DL10 4QW
Tel: 01748 822493 **Email:** caroline.topps@english-heritage.org.uk

RIEVAULX TERRACE & TEMPLES 🦋
The National Trust, Rievaulx, North Yorkshire YO62 5LJ
Tel: 01723 870423 **Email:** nunningtonhall@nationaltrust.org.uk

RIPLEY CASTLE 🏠Ⓕ
Ripley, Harrogate, North Yorkshire HG3 3AY
Tel: 01423 770152 **Email:** enquiries@ripleycastle.co.uk

RIPON CATHEDRAL
Ripon, North Yorkshire HG4 1QR
Tel: 01765 602072

SCAMPSTON WALLED GARDEN 🏛Ⓔ
Scampston Hall, Malton, North Yorkshire YO17 8NG
Tel: 01944 759111 **Email:** info@scampston.co.uk

SCARBOROUGH CASTLE ⌗
Castle Road, Scarborough, North Yorkshire YO11 1HY
Tel: 01723 383636 **Email:** scarborough.castle@english-heritage.org.uk

SHANDY HALL
Coxwold, Thirsk, North Yorkshire YO61 4AD
Tel: 01347 868465 **Email:** shandyhall@dial.pipex.com

SION HILL HALL 🏛
Kirby Wiske, Thirsk, North Yorkshire YO7 4EU
Tel: 01845 587206 **Email:** sionhill@btconnect.com

STOCKELD PARK 🏛
Off the A661, Wetherby, North Yorkshire LS22 4AN
Tel: 01937 586101 **Email:** office@stockeldpark.co.uk

SUTTON PARK 🏛Ⓔ
Sutton-On-The-Forest, N. Yorkshire YO61 1DP
Tel: 01347 810249 **Email:** suttonpark@statelyhome.co.uk

THORP PERROW ARBORETUM
Bedale, North Yorkshire DL8 2PR
Tel: 01677 425323 **Email:** enquiries@thorpperrow.com

TREASURER'S HOUSE 🦋
Minster Yard, York, North Yorkshire YO1 7JL
Tel: 01904 624247

WHITBY ABBEY ⌗
Whitby, North Yorkshire YO22 4JT
Tel: 01947 603568 **Email:** customers@english-heritage.org.uk

BRODSWORTH HALL & GARDENS ⌗
Brodsworth, Nr Doncaster, Yorkshire DN5 7XJ
Tel: 01302 722598 **Email:** customers@english-heritage.org.uk

CANNON HALL MUSEUM, PARK & GARDENS
Cawthorne, Barnsley, South Yorkshire S75 4AT
Tel: 01226 790270 **Email:** cannonhall@barnsley.gov.uk

CONISBROUGH CASTLE ⌗
Castle Hill, Conisbrough, Doncaster DN12 3BU
Tel: 01709 863329 **Email:** enquiries@english-heritage.org.uk

CUSWORTH HALL, MUSEUM & PARK
Cusworth Lane, Doncaster DN5 7TU
Tel: 01302 782342 **Email:** museum@doncaster.gov.uk

WENTWORTH CASTLE GARDENS
Lowe Lane, Stainborough, Barnsley S75 3ET
Tel: 01226 776040 **Email:** heritagetrust@wentworthcastle.org

WENTWORTH WOODHOUSE 🏛
The Mansion, Wentworth, Rotherham S62 7TQ
Tel: 01226 351161 **Email:** tours@wentworthwoodhouse.co.uk

BRAMHAM PARK 🏛Ⓔ
The Estate Office, Bramham Park, Bramham LS23 6ND
Tel: 01937 846000 **Email:** enquiries@bramhampark.co.uk

BRONTE PARSONAGE MUSEUM
Church Street, Haworth BD22 8DR
Tel: 01535 642323 **Email:** lauren.livesey@bronte.org.uk

CLIFFE CASTLE MUSEUM
Spring Gardens Lane, Keighley BD20 6LH
Tel: 01535 618241 **Email:** daru.rooke@bradford.gov.uk

EAST RIDDLESDEN HALL 🦋
Bradford Road, Riddlesden, Keighley, West Yorkshire BD20 5EL
Tel: 01535 607075 **Email:** eastriddlesden@nationaltrust.org.uk

Ledston Hall 🏛

Hall Lane, Ledston, Castleford, West Yorkshire WF10 2BB
17th Century mansion with some earlier work, lawned grounds.
Location: 2m N of Castleford, off A656. **Map Ref:** 11:A11
Tel: 01423 707838 **Email:** victoria.walton@carterjonas.co.uk
Website: www.whelerfoundation.co.uk
Open: Exterior only: May-Aug: Mon-Fri, 9am-4pm. Other days by appointment. **Admission:** Free.

NOSTELL PRIORY & PARKLAND 🦋
Doncaster Road, Wakefield, West Yorkshire WF4 1QE
Tel: 01924 863892 **Email:** nostellpriory@nationaltrust.org.uk

OAKWELL HALL & RED HOUSE
Nutter Lane, Birstall WF17 9LG / Oxford Road, Gomersal BD19 4JP
Email: oakwell.hall@kirklees.gov.uk / red.house@kirklees.gov.uk

PONTEFRACT CASTLE
Castle Chain, Pontefract, West Yorkshire WF8 1QH
Tel: 01977 723 440 **Email:** castles@wakefield.gov.uk

SHIBDEN HALL
Lister's Road, Halifax, West Yorkshire HX3 6XG
Tel: 01422 352246 **Email:** shibden.hall@calderdale.gov.uk

Harewood House ©Harewood House Trust

NORTH WEST

CHESHIRE • CUMBRIA • LANCASHIRE
MANCHESTER • MERSEYSIDE

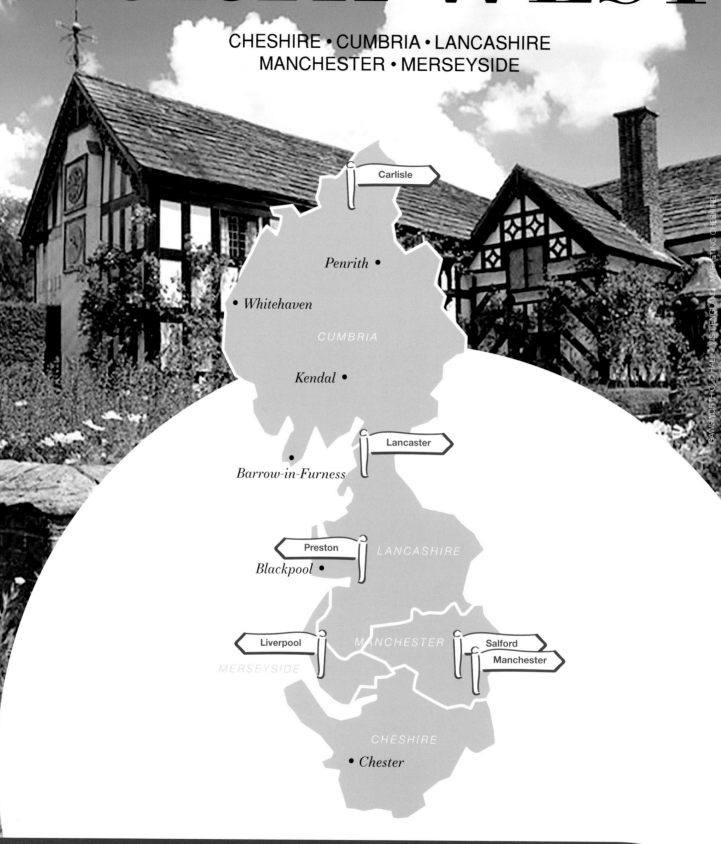

Carlisle

Penrith •

• Whitehaven

CUMBRIA

Kendal •

Lancaster

• Barrow-in-Furness

Preston

Blackpool •

LANCASHIRE

Liverpool

MANCHESTER

Salford

Manchester

MERSEYSIDE

CHESHIRE

• Chester

GAWSTHORPE HALL ©VISITENGLAND/MARKETING CHESHIRE

🌲 COUNTRYSIDE:

- Lake District
- Forest of Bowland
- Morecambe Bay

⏳ HERITAGE:

- Gillow of Lancaster
- Maritime heritage
- Textile heritage

🍴 FOOD:

- Black pudding
- Cumberland sausage
- Damson gin

CAPESTHORNE HALL

The Bromley-Davenports of Capesthorne have been here far longer than the house, an 1837 Jacobethan mansion of gables, towers and turrets given a touch more grandeur in the 1860s. You'll find a rich collection of portraits, heraldic glass, porcelain and sculptures.

Highlights:

- Staircase Hall
- Dorothy Davenport's needlework bedhangings
- The American Room

THE SCULPTURE GALLERY, CAPESTHORNE HALL

LEVENS HALL

A largely Elizabethan house with fine panelling and furnishings and many treasures from the earliest English pistols in Britain to the Duke of Wellington's campaign bed. Its glory is the topiary garden laid out by Guillaume Beaumont in the 1690s, the oldest topiary garden in the world.

Highlights:

- 1690s Topiary garden
- Napoleonic memorabilia
- Stuart furniture
- Bagot goats in the deer park

LEVENS HALL FROM THE TOPIARY GARDENS

MRS HUDSON'S HIDDEN GEM

ADLINGTON HALL

"…Sometimes in an old house, I just want to step through a wormhole. I get that feeling at Adlington Hall and I'd pick a day in 1742. Charles Legh's friend, the most famous composer in England, George Frederick Handel, has come to stay. Charles is about 45, Handel ten years older. After a day's hunting, Handel plays the superb old organ in the medieval Great Hall and sets Charles' hunting poem to music. Perhaps it deserved a toast or two! Charles is keen to show off his family home; he's changing much of the old black and white Tudor building, adding new entertaining rooms and a whole new wing in fashionable brick with stone dressings. Charles is proud of his long lineage; the magnificent canopy at the other end of the hall features coats of arms of all the leading local families. Perhaps after supper, they take a stroll and Charles describes how his Wilderness garden will look with bosky allees leading towards a statue of a classical river god.

So 1742 is a good date but the house is full of dates. Spot 1505 in the Great Hall; 1581 over the black & white porch; 1693 on the organ; 1757 over the classical portico that finished off Charles Legh's grand new mansion…"

THE GREAT ORGAN ADLINGTON HALL © JONATHAN SCOTT

300 YEARS
CHIPPENDALE
Celebrate our greatest furniture maker 300 years after his birth.
- ✔ *Holker Hall*
- ✔ *Tabley Hall*
- ✔ *Levens Hall*

THE DRAWING ROOM, HOLKER HALL

200 YEARS
REPTON
Enjoy the gardens of Humphry Repton 200 years after his death.
- ✔ *Rode Hall*
- ✔ *Tatton Park*

THE REPTON GARDENS AT RODE HALL

100 YEARS
WOMEN & SUFFRAGE

ELIZABETH RAFFALD FROM THE TITLE PAGE OF THE EXPERIENCED ENGLISH HOUSEKEEPER

ELIZABETH GASKELL'S HOUSE LIBRARY

2. **ELIZABETH GASKELL (1810-65)**
Novelist at
Elizabeth Gaskell's House.

BEATRIX POTTER AT HILL TOP, BEATRIX POTTER GALLERY
©NATIONAL TRUST IMAGES - ROBERT THRIFT

ELIZABETH RAFFALD.

1. **ELIZABETH RAFFALD (1733-81)**
Cookery writer, wedding cake inventor
at Arley Hall.

3. **BEATRIX POTTER (1866-1943)**
Children's author, conservationist
at Hill Top farm.

DID YOU KNOW?

1 LYME PARK

In 1415, Sir Piers Legh of Lyme Park was wounded fighting the French at Agincourt. His faithful mastiff stood over his fallen body and protected him until the battle was over. The family adopted the dog as their crest and the English breed is descended from Lyme Park Mastiffs.

2 PEOVER HALL

Elizabethan Peover Hall is an important survival but the Carolean stable block built in 1654 as a gift from mother to son, is much more so.

3 DALEMAIN

The 17th century recipe book compiled by Elizabeth Rainbow contains one of the earliest known recipes for marmalade which inspired a global event, The World's Original Marmalade Festival at Dalemain.

ELIZABETH RAINBOW FROM PORTRAIT AT DALEMAIN

LION, A LYME PARK MASTIFF BY JOHN TRIVETT NETTLESHIP © NATIONAL TRUST IMAGES

4 ARLEY HALL ▶

In 1830 the new gardens at Arley Hall had a radical innovation, one of the first herbaceous borders in Britain.

5 CAPESTHORNE HALL ▶

One of the carved roundels on the staircase at Capesthorne Hall depicts a man with a noose around his neck from the family crest. The family were firm Tories and the man they chose to depict is Liberal Prime Minister Gladstone.

6 COMBERMERE ABBEY ▶

During the funeral of the 2nd Viscount Combermere of Combermere Abbey in 1891, his sister took a picture of the library, only to see his ghost sitting in his chair.

THE LIBRARY AT COMBERMERE ABBEY

DOUBLE HERBCEOUS BORDER AT ARLEY HALL © VISIT BRITAIN IMAGES/JOE WAINWRIGHT

4 TOP LITERARY SPOTS

1.
DOVE COTTAGE
Home of poet William Wordsworth, his wife Mary and sister Dorothy, often visited by Coleridge and then owned by Thomas de Quincey. Little changed since Wordsworth's day.

2.
HILL TOP
Traditional Lakeland farm purchased by Beatrix Potter in 1906. Filled with scenes and furnishings featured in her books.

DOVE COTTAGE

THE ENTRANCE HALL AT HILL TOP©NATIONAL TRUST IMAGES - JAMES DOBSON

3.
MIREHOUSE

17th century house of the Spedding family, friends of poets Wordsworth, Tennyson, Southey as well as Thomas Carlyle & John Constable. Biennial Poetry Prize.

4.
BRANTWOOD

Home of John Ruskin, critic, commentator and patron of the Pre-Raphaelite brotherhood. Enjoy Ruskin's study; views over Coniston; reconstructed lithophone (stone xylophone).

SKETCHES OF ALFRED, LORD TENNYSON AND ARTHUR HALLAM AT MIREHOUSE

BRANTWOOD ©VISIT ENGLAND - VISIT CUMBRIA - DAVE WILLIS

PLACES TO STAY
HISTORIC HOTELS IN CUMBRIA
www.signpost.co.uk

AYNSOME MANOR HOTEL, CUMBRIA

Edwardian country house dating in parts to 1512 overlooking medieval Cartmel Priory with connections to its founder, William Marshall. Its sheltered situation offers a good base for the South Lakes.

HOLBECK GHYLL COUNTRY HOUSE HOTEL, CUMBRIA

Victorian hunting Lodge built for Lord Lonsdale, now a comfortable hotel, restaurant and spa. Stay in the Potter suite to echo actress Renee Zellweger. Views across Windermere.

LOVELADY SHIELD COUNTRY HOUSE HOTEL, CUMBRIA

Regency country house near England's highest market town of Alston in the Pennines. Good access to walking, Pennine Way and cross country cycling as well as South Tynedale narrow gauge railway.

GILPIN HOUSE HOTEL, CUMBRIA

There were not many decades of the 20th century when the Cunliffe family were absent from Gilpin House Hotel & Lake House; two luxury country houses in the beautiful Lake District.

CHESHIRE
Adlington Hall & Gardens
www.adlingtonhall.com

Adlington Hall, home of the Leghs from 1315 was built on the site of a Hunting Lodge in the Forest of Macclesfield in 1040. Two oaks, part of the original building, remain rooted in the ground supporting the east end of the Great Hall. Between the trees in the Great Hall stands an organ built by 'Father' Bernard Smith. Played on by Handel. The Gardens, laid out over many centuries, include a Lime walk planted in 1688 and a Regency rockery surrounding the Shell Cottage. The Wilderness area includes a Rococo styled landscape garden containing the chinoserie T'Ing House, a Pagoda bridge and the classical Temple to Diana. The 60 acres of gardens also include the stunning Rose Garden and Yew Tree Maze.

CONTACT
Contact: Philippa Reed
Tel: 01625 827595
Email: enquiries@adlingtonhall.com

LOCATION
Mill Lane, Adlington, Macclesfield, Cheshire SK10 4LF **Map Ref:** 6:N2
5 miles North of Macclesfield, A523,13 miles South of Manchester. London 178m.

OPENING TIMES (2018)
Apr: 8, 15, 22 & 29.
May: 6, 7, 13, 20 & 28.
Jun: 3, 10, 17 & 24.
Jul: 1, 8, 15, 22 & 29.
Aug: 5, 12, 19, 26 & 27.
Sep: 2, 9, 16, 23 & 30.
(Please always check website before travelling).

ADMISSION
Adult: £9, Student: £5, Child: £5,
Group Discount: 20+ £8.50pp.
Garden only
Adult: £6, Student/Child: Free.

276

KEY FACTS
 The highlight of any visit to the house is The Great Hall.
 WC's. Accessible toilets in both the Hall and The Hunting Lodge.
 Baby facilities available.
 Public open days on Sundays and Bank Holiday Mondays during Apr-Sep.
 There is ample free car parking in the grounds so there will be no problems reaching the hall.
 Lift in the Hunting Lodge. Wheelchair access is limited, contact for more information
 Well behaved dogs allowed in the grounds on leads.
 Groups of 20 or more by arrangement any time of the year.
 By arrangement.
 Tearoom open on Hall open days. Offering hot and cold drinks, homemade cakes & scones.
 Plant Hunters Fair.
 Corporate hospitality available - please call or check website for more detail.
 Please see the 'What's on' section of the website for special events.
 Beautiful venue for weddings and celebrations.

Capesthorne Hall

www.capesthorne.com

Capesthorne Hall, built between 1719 and 1732 and set in 100 acres of picturesque Cheshire parkland, has been touched by nearly 1,000 years of history. The Hall has a fascinating collection of fine art, marble sculptures, furniture and tapestries. In the grounds enjoy the family Chapel, the 18th Century Italian Milanese gates, the beautiful lakeside gardens and woodland walks.

The Hall and grounds can also be hired for Civil Wedding ceremonies and receptions, corporate events and family celebrations.

KEY FACTS

 Toilet & Baby changing facilities available.

 100 cars/20 coaches on hard-standing & unlimited in park.

 Partial. WC's and designated parking bays are available.

 Dogs allowed in certain areas of the grounds.

 Caravan Park 4* AA Rated, open Mar-Oct inclusive.

 Guided tours available for pre-booked parties (except Suns).

 Pre-booked educational visits available.

 The Butler's Pantry offers light refreshments including afternoon teas. Open 12 noon until 4:30pm.

 Available for corporate functions. Catering can be provided for groups (full menus on request).

 Available for festivals, activity days and garden parties.

 Licensed for civil weddings.

Provides a variety of film locations and creates the perfect backdrop for any shoot.

CONTACT
Owner: Sir William and Lady Bromley-Davenport
Contact: Christine Mountney
Tel: 01625 861221 **Email:** info@capesthorne.com

LOCATION
Siddington, Macclesfield, Cheshire SK11 9JY
Map Ref: 6:N2 **OS Ref:** SJ840 727
West of Macclesfield. 30 minutes South of Manchester on A34. Near M6, M60 and M62.

OPENING TIMES
Mar-Oct Suns/Mons & Bank Holidays.
Hall: 1.30pm-4pm. Last admission 3.30pm.
Gardens & Chapel: 12 noon-5pm.
Groups: Welcome by appointment with discounts.

ADMISSION
Suns & BHs - Hall, Gardens & Chapel:
Adult: £10, Child (5-16 yrs): £5,
Senior: £9, Family: £27.50.
Suns - Gardens & Chapel only:
Adult: £7, Child (5-16 yrs): £3, Senior: £6.
Mons Only - Park, Gardens & Chapel: £12 per car, Hall Entrance: £3 per person, Group discounts available.

CHESHIRE

Cholmondeley Castle Garden

www.cholmondeleycastle.com

Cholmondeley Castle Gardens are said by many to be amongst the most beautiful they have seen, being one of Cheshire's Gardens of Distinction and medal winners at RHS Chelsea and Tatton Park Flower Shows. Beautifully landscaped these extensive ornamental gardens are dominated by a romantic Castle built in 1801 of local sandstone. Visitors can enjoy the tranquil Temple Water Garden with its small lake, enclosed by fine specimen trees and varieties of shrubs which change dramatically with the seasons. The Rose Garden, extended in 2017, has been planted with 250 roses, and a new 100m long double mixed border has been created. The Folly Garden and orchid meadows have been extended and refurbished.

The Lily pond situated below the Castle allows access to the Silver Garden and Castle terraces with views across the Parkland, whilst Tower Hill offers visitors the opportunity to enjoy a woodland ramble amongst interesting shrubs and trees under planted with many wild flowers and bulbs. The Lakeside walk with picnic and children's play areas offers spectacular views of Cholmondeley Castle, whilst St. Nicholas's Chapel is notable for its stained glass altar window, ornate panelling and peaceful atmosphere. The Tea Room is situated in the heart of the gardens along with the children's adventure den. A visit to the Gardens is essential to enjoy these wonderful surroundings.

CONTACT
Owner: The Marquess of Cholmondeley
Contact: The Secretary **Tel:** 01829 720383
Email: dilys@cholmondeleycastle.co.uk
Twitter: @CholmondeleyCas
Facebook: /Cholmondeleycastlegardens
Instagram: /Cholmondeley_Castle_Gardens

LOCATION
Malpas, Cheshire SY14 8AH
Map Ref: 6:L3 - Off A41 Chester/Whitchurch Road & A49 Whitchurch/Tarporley Road. 7 miles North of Whitchurch. Sat Nav. SY14 8ET.

OPENING TIMES
30 Mar-30 Sep. Wed, Thurs, Suns & Bank Holidays 11am-5pm (last entry 4.30pm). Open Suns only in Oct for Autumn Tints.

GARDEN ADMISSION
Adult: £7, Child: £4 (Under 5's: Free).
Groups: 25+ (discounts for group admissions).
For special events and variations to opening dates please refer to the website.

KEY FACTS

 The Deer Park Mere and Nature Trail offers a wonderful walk for visitors to enjoy.

 Toilet and baby changing facilities available.

 Parking available.

 Partial access, disabled WC's and access to Tea Room.

 Dogs welcome on leads.

 Guided tour of gardens, for groups only by pre-arrangement.

 Tea Room is situated in the gardens serving a range of teas, homemade cakes, light lunches & ice cream etc.

 See the 'What's On' section of the website for all upcoming events.

Gawsworth Hall

www.gawsworthhall.com

Fully lived-in Tudor half-timbered manor house with Tilting Ground. Former home of Mary Fitton, Maid of Honour at the Court of Queen Elizabeth I, and the supposed 'Dark Lady' of Shakespeare's sonnets. Fine pictures, sculpture, furniture and beautiful grounds adjoining a medieval church. Garden Theatre performances take place in the Hall courtyard in July and August.

CONTACT
Owner: Richards Family
Contact: Jonathan Richards
Tel: 01260 223456 **Additional Tel:** 01260 223440
Email: jonny@gawsworthhall.com

LOCATION
Macclesfield, Cheshire SK11 9RN
Map Ref: 6:N2 - 3 miles South of Macclesfield on the A536 Congleton to Macclesfield Road.

OPENING TIMES
See www.gawsworthhall.com for up-to-date opening times.

ADMISSION
Adult: £7.50
Child: £3.50
Groups (20+): £6

KEY FACTS

 Garden theatre – covered all-seater audience auditorium.

 Attached to the Tea Room. Disabled WC available.

 Parking is available.

 Partial. WC's. Please see the Access Statement on the website for full details.

In grounds.

 Educational visits by arrangement.

 Orchard Tearoom. Licensed.

 Licensed.

 Please see 'Events' section of the website.

 The perfect bespoke wedding venue; few settings offer the romance of Gawsworth Hall.

Rode Hall

www.rodehall.co.uk

Rode Hall is a fine early 18th Century country house with a beautiful collection of English porcelain, set in a Repton landscape. Home to the Wilbraham family since 1669, the extensive gardens include a woodland garden, formal rose garden designed by Nesfield in 1860 and a stunning two acre walled kitchen garden which provides produce for the monthly farmers' market and delightful Tea Rooms. Rode Pool has its own heronry on Birthday Island and the icehouse in the park is well worth a visit.

CONTACT
Owner/Contact: Randle Baker Wilbraham
Tel: 01270 873237 **Email:** enquiries@rodehall.co.uk

LOCATION
Church Lane, Scholar Green, Cheshire ST7 3QP
Map Ref: 6:M3 - 5m SW of Congleton between the A34 & A50. Kidsgrove railway station 2 miles North West of Kidsgrove.

OPENING TIMES
4 Apr-26 Sep, Weds & BH Mons. Gardens 11am-5pm, House 12pm-4pm. Groups welcome by appointment. The gardens are also open alongside the monthly farmers' market on the first Sat of every month, (exc Jan) 9am-1pm. Snowdrop Walks 3 Feb-4 Mar, Daily except Mons, 11am-4pm. Bluebell Walks 28 Apr-6 May.

ADMISSION
House & Garden - Adult: £8, Concessions: £7, Child: £2.
Gardens - Adult: £5, Child: £2.

KEY FACTS

 Rode Hall Farmers Market: First Saturday of each month (except Jan).

 Toilet facilities available.

 Baby changing facilities available.

 Parking spaces available.

 Wheelchair users are most welcome but there is only partial access. Please call for details.

 Well behaved dogs on leads are most welcome.

 Special packages including food and a personal guided tour can be organised in advance.

 Light lunches and cream teas. Homemade cakes and refreshments.

 Gifts available to purchase.

 Plants and seasonal garden produce may also be purchased from the Tea Room.

 Please see the 'What's on' section of the website for all upcoming events.

 For media visits please contact Gemma Achary Gibb, on 07958 700818.

Tabley House

www.tableyhouse.co.uk

The finest Palladian House in the North West, Tabley a Grade I listing, was designed by John Carr of York for the Leicester family. It contains one of the first collections of English paintings, including works of art by Turner, Reynolds, Lawrence, Lely and Dobson. Furniture by Chippendale, Bullock and Gillow and fascinating family memorabilia adorn the rooms. Fine plasterwork by Thomas Oliver and carving by Daniel Shillito and Mathew Bertram. Interesting Tea Room and 17th Century Chapel adjoin, including Burne-Jones window.

KEY FACTS

 No photography in galleries. No stiletto heels. Heel guards can be provided.

 Parking is free for visitors please follow the burgundy signs.

 Call the office before arriving to arrange for lift entrance to be opened.

 By arrangement, also available outside normal opening hours, guides provided at no extra charge.

Suitable for post 16 students.

Serving light lunches, afternoon teas, refreshments & homemade cakes.

Postcards for sale in house.

 Suitable for drinks receptions & presentations for up to 100 people.

 Special events.

Civil wedding & partnerships licence. Naming ceremonies and renewal of vows.

CONTACT
Owner: The University of Manchester
Contact: The Administrator
Tel: 01565 750151
Email: tableyhouse@btconnect.com

LOCATION
Tabley Lane, Knutsford, Cheshire WA16 0HB **Map Ref:** 6:M2 M6/J19, A556 S on to A5033. 2 miles West of Knutsford.

OPENING TIMES
House: Apr-end Oct, Thu-Sun & Bank Holidays, 1pm-5pm. Last admission at 4.30pm.
Tea Room: From 12pm-5pm.

ADMISSION
Adult: £5, Child/Student: £1.50.
Groups by arrangement.

Peover Hall & Gardens

www.peoverhall.com

A Grade 2* listed Elizabethan family house dating from 1585. Situated within some 500 acres of landscaped 18th Century parkland with formal gardens designed between 1890-1900 that include a series of "garden rooms" filled with clipped box, lily ponds, Romanesque loggia, warm brick walls, unusual doors, secret passageways, beautiful topiary work and walled gardens. The grounds of the Hall house working stables, estate cottages and the parish church of St Laurence which, contains 2 Mainwaring Chapels. The architectural jewel Grade I listed Carolean stables built in 1654, with richly carved stalls and original Tuscan columns and strap work.

KEY FACTS

 Hall tours at 2.30pm and 3.30pm and other days and times by arrangement.

 Teas and cakes.

CONTACT
Owner: Mr R Brooks
Contact: The House Manager
Tel: 07553153383
Email: bookings@peoverhall.com

LOCATION
Over Peover, Knutsford WA16 9HW
Map Ref: 6:M2 - 4 miles South of Knutsford off A50 at Whipping Stocks Inn.

OPENING TIMES
May-Aug, Tue & Thu afternoons.
Stables & Gardens: 2-5pm.
Church: 2pm-4pm.

ADMISSION
Please see website for updated admission prices.

Adlington Hall

Askham Hall

www.askhamhall.co.uk

Meander through the beautiful gardens, visit the animals and enjoy lunch in the Kitchen Garden Café.
Askham Hall is Grade I listed, dating back to the late 1200s. It has recently been transformed from a stately family home into a stylish retreat also with a restaurant, 17 bedrooms and a wedding barn.

CONTACT
Owner: Charles Lowther **Contact:** Marie-Louisa Raeburn
Tel: 01931 712350 **E-mail:** enquiries@askhamhall.co.uk

LOCATION
Askham, Penrith, Cumbria CA10 2PF **Map Ref:** 10:L5
Askham Hall in Cumbria is situated in a quiet and picturesque village within easy access (about 10 mins' drive) from Penrith and junction 40 of the M6. Follow the brown tourist signs.

OPENING TIMES
Gardens & café: Every day except Sat. 10am-5pm in high season, reduced hours and times in low season.
Restaurant & accommodation:
Tue-Sat for dinner and overnight stays.

ADMISSION
Gardens & Animals
Adult: £5 Child: Free.

KEY FACTS

 Askham Spa & Pool is open Apr-Oct.

 A large ground floor toilet with separate area for a wheelchair is provided for public & disabled use.

 Free parking in courtyard and drop off points directly outside hotel entrance.

 Accessible. Please see the access statement on our website for further details.

 Permitted in café and events barn but not gardens.

 Beautiful rooms to choose from. Individual bookings can be made 5 months in advance or less.

Groups by arrangement.

 By arrangement.

 Enjoy something delicious in our Kitchen Garden Café. Free to enter.

 The Askham restaurant is open to both residents and non residents.

 Exclusive & personalise gift vouchers now available to purchase securely online.

 Please contact for corporate events and functions.

 Please visit the 'News' section of our website for upcoming events.

 2 stunning churches within 1/2 a mile & approved venue for civil ceremonies. Perfect for weddings.

Dalemain Mansion & Historic Gardens

www.dalemain.com

Home of the Hasell family since 1679, Dalemain boasts a fine mixture of Mediaeval, Tudor and early Georgian architecture. The Award winning historic gardens cover 5 acres of richly planted borders with intriguing and unusual flower combinations. Highlights are the Rose Walk with over 100 old-fashioned roses, ancient apple trees and Tudor Knot Garden. The famous blue Himalayan Poppies bloom in early Summer in the wild garden, and the International Marmalade Awards and Festival take place every March.

CONTACT
Owner: Robert Hasell-McCosh Esq
Contact: Florence Lindeman - Marketing
Tel: 017684 86450 **Fax:** 017684 86223
Email: marketing@dalemain.com

LOCATION
Dalemain Estates, Penrith, Cumbria CA11 0HB
Map Ref: 10:L5 - On A592 1m S of A66. 4m SW of Penrith.
London, M1, M6/J40. Edinburgh, A73, M74, M6/J40.

OPENING TIMES
18 Mar-26 Oct, Sun-Thu. House: 10.30am-3.30pm.
Gardens, Tearoom & Gift Shop: 10am-4.30pm (3pm in Oct).
Special Garden openings: 10am-4.30pm on Fridays in Jun, Jul & Aug. See website for further details.

ADMISSION
House & Gardens or Gardens Only. Please see website for details. Group Prices on application. Groups:12+ please book.

KEY FACTS

 No photography in house.

 Baby changing facilities available.

 50 yards. Free parking.

 Partial. WC's.

 1hr tours. German and French translations. Garden tours available. Guided tour details on website.

 Please contact for more information on educational visits.

 Medieval Hall Tea Room - licensed.

 Gift shop with antiques and a selection of the world's best marmalades.

 Plant sales.

 Please contact for more information on corporate events.

 Phone for event enquiries.

 Dalemain offers the film-maker a wide variety of versatile locations. (Jane Eyre, Songs of Praise etc.)

Holker Hall & Gardens

www.holker.co.uk  Ⓕ

Holker is the family home of the Cavendish family, set amongst beautiful countryside surrounding the Lake District. Steeped in history, this magnificent Victorian Mansion of neo-Elizabethan Gothic style was largely re-built in the 1870's following a fire, but origins date back to the 1600's. The glorious gardens, café, brasserie, food hall and gift shop complete the visitor experience.

KEY FACTS

 No photography in house.

 Disabled toilets are located within The Courtyard Café complex and are signposted.

 Baby changing facilities and milk warming available at The Courtyard Café.

 Parking available.

 Two manual wheelchairs which can be borrowed to use on site. Please request further information.

 Dogs are allowed in to the Parkland so long as they remain on a lead. Access all for Service Dogs.

 For groups, by arrangement. Tours can be tailor made, for the hearing & sight impaired & disabled visitors.

 Extensive learning opportunities for children, particularly Keystage 1 and 2 levels.

 Visit The Courtyard Café for a wide selection of main meals, snacks, afternoon teas, drinks and ices.

 The Ilex Bar & Brasserie is a fresh dining experience set in the opulent surroundings of Holker Hall.

 Food hall & gift shop. Displays a wide selection of gifts, souvenirs, local products and books.

 Garden items are available in the gift shop.

 Corporate venue available for a variety of functions.

 Holker Chilli Fest & Spring and Winter Markets, see website for further details.

 For enquiries please contact Ben Glover on 015395 53907 or email beng@campbellandrowley.co.uk

There is great potential for location filming and photography in the gardens and parkland.

CONTACT
Owner: Cavendish Family **Contact:** Jillian Rouse
Tel: 015395 58328 **Fax:** 015395 58378
Email: info@holker.co.uk

LOCATION
Cark-In-Cartmel, Grange-Over-Sands, Cumbria LA11 7PL
Map Ref: 10:K8 - From Motorway M6/J36, Signed Barrow A590.

OPENING TIMES
23 Mar-28 Oct, Wed-Sun & BH Mons (closed Mon & Tue).
Hall: 11am-4pm.
Gardens: 10.30am-5pm
Café, Food Hall & Gift Shop: 10.30am-5pm

ADMISSION
Hall & Gardens - Adult: £12.50, Child: Free.
Gardens only - Adult: £8.50, Child: Free.
Hall only - Adults: £8, Child: Free.
Groups - Hall & Gardens: Adult £8.50. **Gardens:** Adult: £6.

Kirklinton Hall & Gardens

www.kirklintonhall.co.uk  Ⓕ

Adjacent to the 12th Century de Boyville stronghold, Kirklinton Hall is said to have been built from its stone. Begun in the 1670's, extended in the 1870's and ruined in the 1970's, the Hall has been a Restoration Great House, an RAF base, a school, a gangsters' gambling den and worse. Walk in the footsteps of Norman Knights, Cavalier Commanders, Victorian Plutocrats and the Kray twins. Now, Kirklinton Hall and its Gardens are being restored by the Boyle family to its former glory, a painstaking and fascinating process. It is also the official home of SlowFood Cumbria and is available for weddings and events. 'Spectacularly sinister ruin' - Pevsners Buildings of England.

KEY FACTS

 Faerie Glen & Dragon's Lair.

 Toilet/disabled facilities available.

 Free car parking.

 Site accessible for wheelchairs in the Hall, Shop, Toilet & Terrace except most of the woodlands walks.

 If you are keen on pushing pedals, try Route 10 on Sustrans that heads past the hall.

 Dogs are welcome on the site as long as you keep them on a lead and clean up after them.

Yurt hire & camping. To book email: info@kirklintonhall.co.uk

 By arrangement for groups.

 Contact property.

 Tea, coffee, homemade cakes, sandwiches & scones, ice cream, soft & alcoholic drinks.

 Gifts, treats, postcards, jams & chutneys.

 Homegrown fruit, veg & plants, David Austin roses.

 Please see the 'Events' section of the website for all upcoming events.

Contact for information on holding special celebrations here. Exclusive use, flexible space & truly unique.

CONTACT
Owner: Mr & Mrs Christopher Boyle
Contact: Sarah Schofield
Tel: 01228 231045 **Email:** info@kirklintonhall.co.uk
Facebook: Kirklinton Hall **Twitter:** @kirklintonhall

LOCATION
Kirklinton, Carlisle CA6 6BB **Map Ref:** 10:K3
6 miles North East of M6 junction 44, follow A7 towards Longtown. Kirklinton 5 miles. Then follow brown signs.

OPENING TIMES
1 Apr-30 Sep, 12pm-5pm Weekdays and Suns. Sats for public or private events. Available for weddings and receptions.

ADMISSION
Adult: £4
Child (Under 16yrs): £1
Season Tickets: Single £10 & Family £22
Free to HHA and MyCumbria Card Holders.

Levens Hall

www.levenshall.co.uk 🏛 Ⓕ

Levens Hall is an Elizabethan mansion built around a 13th Century pele tower. The much loved home of the Bagot family, with fine panelling, plasterwork, Cordova leather wall coverings, paintings by Rubens, Lely and Cuyp, the earliest English patchwork and Wellingtoniana combine with other beautiful objects to form a fascinating collection. The world famous Topiary Gardens were laid out by Monsieur Beaumont from 1694 and his design has remained largely unchanged to this day. Over 90 individual pieces of topiary, some over nine metres high, massive beech hedges and colourful seasonal bedding provide a magnificent visual impact.

CONTACT
Owner: R. A. Bagot
Contact: The Administrator
Tel: 015395 60321
Email: houseopening@levenshall.co.uk

LOCATION
Kendal, Cumbria LA8 0PD **Map Ref:** 10:L7
5 miles South of Kendal on the A6. Exit M6/J36.

OPENING TIMES
Apr-Oct, Sun-Thu (closed Fri & Sat).
Garden, Tea Room, Gift Shop & Plant Centre: 10am-5pm.
House: 12 noon-4pm. Groups (20+) please book.
Please see website for full details.

ADMISSION
House & Gardens or Gardens Only. Please see website for full details, special offers & current events.
Groups: Rates on application.

KEY FACTS

 No indoor photography.

 Toilet & baby changing facilities available.

 Free on-site parking.

 Partial. WC's.

 See website for a map of the nearby cycling route that starts and finishes at Levens.

 By arrangement. Charges apply. Private garden tours & evening guided tours.

 Accommodating school groups - please call or email for details.

 Refreshments are available.

 Licensed.

 Browse through the many home-made products in the gift shop.

 Plant centre offers a selection of perennial plants many of which can be seen growing in the garden.

 A truly exceptional venue offering a number of flexible spaces for hire both inside and out.

 See the website for the events calendar and daily activities which take place Sun-Thur.

 The house, garden and parkland offer a wide range of locations for TV, film & photography purposes.

Dalemain Mansion

Hoghton Tower

www.hoghtontower.co.uk 🏠 Ⓕ

A Tudor fortified Manor House, the ancestral home of the de Hoghton family. Join a tour of the staterooms to learn about the history of the house. Stroll through the stunning walled gardens. Browse the gift shop and finish with an afternoon tea in our Vaio Tea Room.

Self-catering accommodation is available in your very own tower. Private and school tours welcome by pre-booking. Wedding Venue.

KEY FACTS

 Access to toilets in the house and disabled toilet facility in the outer courtyard.

 The car park accommodates up to 134 cars. Parking for coaches is also available if booked in advance.

 Access limited. Please see the access statement on the website for further details.

 Irishman's Tower is an idyllic rural self-catering retreat.

 House, gardens & dolls houses available.

 School Tours – 'History as they like it'. Pre-book only.

 Classic English tea room, using both local and seasonal products in all the dishes.

 Stables gift shop offers a selection of gift ideas, from traditional children's toys to tasteful homeware.

 Unique function rooms & grounds provide the ideal setting for launches, conferences & team building.

 Please see the 'Events' section for all upcoming events and farmers markets.

Offers majestic and inspirational surroundings; Exclusive use to celebrate your special day.

 An ideally flexible and well positioned location for film production & photography shoots.

CONTACT

Owner: Hoghton Tower Preservation Trust
Booking Enquiries: Kasia Palinska
Marketing Enquiries: Brandon Taylor
Business/Corporate Enquiries: Lisa Higson
Tel: 01254 852986 **Email:** mail@hoghtontower.co.uk

LOCATION

Hoghton, nr Preston, Lancashire PR5 0SH **Map Ref:** 10:L11
M65/J3. Midway between Preston & Blackburn on A675.

OPENING TIMES

May-Sep (Sun-Thu), BHs (except Christmas & New Year) and every 3rd Sun of the Month. Mon-Thu 11am-5pm, Sun 10am-5pm (First Tour 11:30am, last tour 3:30pm).
Tea Room Mon-Thu 11am-5pm, Sun 10am-5pm.
Group visits by appointment all year round.
Please see our website for variations.

ADMISSION

Please check website.

Leighton Hall

Leighton Hall

www.leightonhall.co.uk Ⓕ

Leighton Hall's setting can only be described as spectacular; the Hall is nestled in a lush parkland with the Lake District as its backdrop. This romantic Gothic house is the lived-in home of the famous Gillow furniture making family, with some unique pieces on display. Visits include: entertaining house tours with no roped off areas, birds of prey displays, charming tea rooms, children's play area, beautiful gardens with a woodland walk and maze to explore.

CONTACT
Owner: Mr & Mrs R Reynolds
Contact: Mrs Lucy Arthurs / Mrs Suzie Reynolds
Tel: 01524 734474 **Fax:** 01524 720357
Email: info@leightonhall.co.uk
Facebook: LeightonHallLancashire **Twitter:** @Leighton_Hall
Instagram: leightonhalllancashire

LOCATION
Carnforth, Lancashire LA5 9ST **Map Ref:** 10:L8
Located 10 minutes drive from the M6, junction 35. Follow brown tourism signs North along the A6, travel through the village of Yealand Conyers, turn right up Peter Lane until you arrive at the main entrance. Do not follow SATNAV.

OPENING TIMES
May-Sept, Tue-Fri (also BH Sun and Mon, Suns in Aug) 2pm-5pm. Pre-booked groups and coach parties (25+) all year by arrangement. Group rates.

ADMISSION
Adult: £9, OAP/Student: £7.95, Child (5-12 years): £5.50, Family (2 + 3): £28. Grounds only: £4.95.

KEY FACTS

 No photography in the hall.

 Toilet facilities available.

 Baby changing facilities available.

 Free and ample parking - with disabled parking located closer to the Hall.

 Partial. WC's. Regrettably the halls first floor is inaccessible for wheelchair users.

 On leads, in the parkland only.

 Enthusiastic guides, bring Leighton's history to life. Informal and relaxed tours.

 3 themed packages available for Key Stage 1 & 2. Child friendly guides.

 Enjoy a relaxing cuppa, sandwich, home made cakes or scones, located in the Old Kitchens.

 Gift shop with a range of charming reasonably priced items.

 Plants for sale, located by the gift shop.

 Offering functions for corporate events i.e. brand awareness and product launches.

 Please see the 'Special Events' section of the website for all upcoming events.

The House & Gardens are exclusive for your wedding.

Hoghton Tower Woodland

Browsholme Hall

browsholme.com

Browsholme Hall has been the ancestral home of the Parkers, Bowbearers of the Forest of Bowland since the time Tudor times. Today it is still the family's home and Robert and Amanda Parker invite visitors to enjoy its magnificent architecture, fabulous interiors, antique furnishings and lovely gardens set in the beautiful landscape of the Forest of Bowland. Superb oak chests, Gillow furniture, portraits, porcelain, Civil War arms and many unique relics.

CONTACT
Owner:
Robert & Amanda Parker
Contact: Catherine Turner
Tel: 01254 827160
Email: info@browsholme.com

LOCATION
Clitheroe, Lancashire BB7 3DE
Map Ref: 10:M10
5m NW of Clitheroe off B6243.
What3Words: rumble.crunchy.roost

OPENING TIMES
Gardens & Tea Room:
11.30am–4pm.
Hall Tours: from 12pm.
May-end Sep, every Wed.
See website for Bank Holiday and Christmas openings.

ADMISSION
See website for full details.

KEY FACTS

 Booked parties & groups welcome at other times.

 A car park is situated by the Tithe Barn and 300 metres from the Hall entrance.

 Accessible. WC. There is a drop-off and pick up point for the disabled at the front of the Hall.

 Visit the Tithe Barn Café and Bar for light meals.

 See a calendar of events on the 'What's on' section of the website.

Giving the bride and groom as much choice and assistance as possible in planning their wedding.

Meols Hall

www.meolshall.com

17th Century house with subsequent additions. Interesting collection of pictures and furniture.

Tithe Barn available for wedding ceremonies and receptions all year.

KEY FACTS

 Parking available.

 Accessible.

 Assistance dogs only.

 One month of the year visitors to Meols Hall have the unique opportunity to take a tour of the house.

 Hosting challenging outdoor activities, product launches, staff motivation & incentive schemes.

 Please see the 'Events' page on the website for all upcoming events.

 Wedding ceremonies and receptions available in the Tithe Barn.

CONTACT
Owner: The Hesketh Family
Contact: Pamela Whelan
Tel: 01704 228326
Email: events@meolshall.com

LOCATION
Churchtown, Southport, Merseyside PR9 7LZ
Map Ref: 10:K11 - 3m NE of Southport town centre in Churchtown. SE of A565.

OPENING TIMES
May BH Mon: 7 & 28 May, 20 Aug-14 Sep, 1.30-5.30pm
ADMISSION
Adult: £4, Child: £1. Groups welcome. Afternoon Tea is only available for bookings of 25+.

Speke Hall ©National Trust/Images

Manchester Cathedral

ARLEY HALL & GARDENS 🏛ⓕ
Northwich, Cheshire CW9 6NA
Tel: 01565 777353 **Email:** helen.begent@arleyhallandgardens.com

BEESTON CASTLE ⌗
Chapel Lane, Beeston, Tarporley, Cheshire CW6 9TX
Tel: 01829 260464

COMBERMERE ABBEY 🏛✦
Whitchurch, Shropshire SY13 4AJ
Tel: 01948 662880 **Email:** estate@combermereabbey.co.uk

DORFOLD HALL 🏛ⓕ
Acton, Nr Nantwich, Cheshire CW5 8LD
Tel: 01270 625245 **Email:** info@dorfold.com

DUNHAM MASSEY 🌿
Altrincham, Cheshire WA14 4SJ
Tel: 0161 941 1025 **Email:** dunhammassey@nationaltrust.org.uk

LITTLE MORETON HALL 🌿
Congleton, Cheshire CW12 4SD
Tel: 01260 272018 **Email:** littlemoretonhall@nationaltrust.org.uk

LYME 🌿
Disley, Stockport, Cheshire SK12 2NX
Tel: 01663 762023 **Email:** lyme@nationaltrust.org.uk

NESS BOTANIC GARDENS
Neston Road, Ness, Cheshire CH64 4AY
Tel: 0845 030 4063 **Email:** nessgdns@liv.ac.uk

TATTON PARK 🌿
Knutsford, Cheshire WA16 6QN
Tel: 01625 374400/01625 374435 **Email:** tatton@cheshireeast.gov.uk

ABBOT HALL ART GALLERY
Abbot Hall, Kendal, Cumbria LA9 5AL
Tel: 01539 722464 **Email:** info@abbothall.org.uk

ALLAN BANK 🌿
Grasmere, Cumbria LA22 9QZ
Tel: 015394 35143 **Email:** allanbank@nationaltrust.org.uk

BLACKWELL, THE ARTS & CRAFTS HOUSE ✦
Bowness-on-Windermere, Cumbria LA23 3JT
Tel: 015394 46139 **Email:** info@blackwell.org.uk

BRANTWOOD 🏛
Coniston, Cumbria LA21 8AD
Tel: 01539 441396 **Email:** enquiries@brantwood.org.uk

BROUGHAM CASTLE ⌗
Penrith, Penrith CA10 2AA
Tel: 01768 862488 **Email:** customers@english-heritage.org.uk

CARLISLE CASTLE ⌗
Carlisle, Cumbria CA3 8UR
Tel: 01228 591922 **Email:** customers@english-heritage.org.uk

CARLISLE CATHEDRAL
Carlisle, Cumbria CA3 8TZ
Tel: 01228 548151

DOVE COTTAGE & WORDSWORTH MUSEUM
Grasmere, Cumbria LA22 9SH
Tel: 01539 435544 **Email:** enquiries@wordsworth.org.uk

HALECAT GARDEN NURSERY & GARDENS 🏛ⓕ
Witherslack, Grange-over-Sands, Cumbria LA11 6RT
Tel: 015395 520963 **Email:** matthewbardgett@hotmail.com

Capesthorne Hall

HILL TOP 🦋

Near Sawrey, Hawkshead, Ambleside, Cumbria LA22 0LF
Tel: 01539 436269 **Email:** hilltop@nationaltrust.org.uk

HOLEHIRD GARDENS

Patterdale Road, Windermere, Cumbria LA23 1NP
Tel: 01539 446008 **Email:** maggie.mees@btinternet.com

HUTTON-IN-THE-FOREST 🏠ⓕ

Penrith, Cumbria CA11 9TH
Tel: 01768 484449 **Email:** info@hutton-in-the-forest.co.uk

LANERCOST PRIORY ⌗

Lanercost, Brampton, Cumbria CA8 2HQ
Tel: 01697 73030 **Email:** customers@english-heritage.org.uk

LOWTHER CASTLE & GARDENS TRUST ◇✦

Penrith, Cumbria CA10 2HG
Tel: 01931 712192

MIREHOUSE 🏠ⓕ

Keswick, Cumbria CA12 4QE
Tel: 0117687 72287 **Email:** info@mirehouse.com

MUNCASTER CASTLE GARDENS 🏠ⓕ

Muncaster Castle, Ravenglass, Cumbria CA18 1RQ
Tel: 01229 717614 **Email:** info@muncaster.co.uk

NAWORTH CASTLE

Brampton, Cumbria CA8 2HF
Tel: 016977 3229 **Email:** office@naworth.co.uk

RYDAL MOUNT & GARDENS

Rydal, Cumbria LA22 9LU
Tel: 01539 433002 **Email:** info@rydalmount.co.uk

SIZERGH CASTLE & GARDEN 🦋

Sizergh, Kendal, Cumbria LA8 8AE
Tel: 0115395 60951 **Email:** sizergh@nationaltrust.org.uk

SWARTHMOOR HALL

Swarthmoor Hall Lane, Ulverston, Cumbria LA12 0JQ
Tel: 01229 583204 **Email:** info@swarthmoorhall.co.uk

TOWNEND 🦋

Troutbeck, Windermere, Cumbria LA23 1LB
Tel: 015394 32628 **Email:** townend@nationaltrust.org.uk

TULLIE HOUSE MUSEUM & ART GALLERY

Castle Street, Carlisle, Cumbria CA3 8TP
Tel: 01228 618718 **Email:** enquiries@tulliehouse.org

WINDERWATH GARDENS

Winderwath, Temple Sowerby, Penrith, Cumbria CA10 2AG
Tel: 01768 88250

WORDSWORTH HOUSE & GARDEN 🦋

Main Street, Cockermouth, Cumbria CA13 9RX
Tel: 01900 820884 **Email:** wordsworthhouse@nationaltrust.org.uk

WRAY CASTLE 🦋

Low Wray, Ambleside, Cumbria LA22 0JA
Tel: 015394 33250 **Email:** wraycastle@nationaltrust.org.uk

Astley Hall Museum & Art Gallery 🏛

Astley Park, Off Hallgate, Chorley PR7 1XA
A Grade 1 listed building set within the beautiful surroundings of Astley Park, with historic woodland, lake & Victorian walled garden.
Map Ref: 10:L11 **Tel:** 01257 515151 **Email:** astley.hall@chorley.gov.uk
Website: www.chorley.gov.uk/astleyhall **Open:** Mar-Dec, Sats, Suns & Bank Holidays. During the school holidays, Sat-Wed, 12pm-4:30pm
Admission: Donations welcome.

THE BEATLES CHILDHOOD HOMES 🦋

Woolton and Allerton, Liverpool L18 9TN
Tel: 0151 427 7231 **Email:** thebeatleshomes@nationaltrust.org.uk

GAWTHORPE HALL 🦋

Padiham, Nr Burnley, Lancashire BB12 8UA
Tel: 01282 771004 **Email:** gawthorpehall@nationaltrust.org.uk

LANCASTER CASTLE

Shire Hall, Castle Parade, Lancaster, Lancashire LA1 1YJ
Tel: 01524 64998 **Email:** lancastercastle@lancashire.gov.uk

LYTHAM HALL

Ballam Road, Lytham FY8 4JX
Tel: 01253 736652 **Email:** lytham.hall@htnw.co.uk

ORDSALL HALL

322 Ordsall Lane, Ordsall, Salford M5 3AN
Tel: 0161 872 0251 **Email:** ordsall.hall@scll.co.uk

RUFFORD OLD HALL 🦋

Rufford, Nr Ormskirk, Lancashire L40 1SG
Tel: 01704 821254 **Email:** ruffordoldhall@nationaltrust.org.uk

SAMLESBURY HALL 🏠ⓕ

Preston New Road, Samlesbury, Preston PR5 0UP
Tel: 01254 812010 **Email:** info@samlesburyhall.co.uk

SMITHILLS HALL

Smithills Dean Road, Bolton BL7 7NP
Tel: 01204 332377 **Email:** historichalls@bolton.gov.uk

TOWNELEY HALL ART GALLERY & MUSEUMS 🏠ⓕ

Burnley BB11 3RQ
Tel: 01282 447130

ELIZABETH GASKELL'S HOUSE

84 Plymouth Grove, Manchester M13 9LW
Tel: 0161 273 2215

HEATON HALL

Heaton Park, Prestwich, Manchester M25 9WL
Tel: 0161 235 8815

Manchester Cathedral

Victoria Street, Manchester M3 1SX
Manchester Cathedral Grade I listed masterpiece.
Map Ref: 6:N1 **Tel:** 0161 833 2220 **Fax:** 0161 839 6218
Email: office@manchestercathedral.org
Website: www.manchestercathedral.org
Open: Every day. Times vary, please check website for up-to-date information. **Admission:** Donations welcome.

SPEKE HALL GARDEN & ESTATE 🦋

The Walk, Speke, Liverpool L24 1XD
Tel: 0151 427 7231

Capesthorne Hall

NORTH EAST

COUNTY DURHAM • NORTHUMBERLAND
TYNE & WEAR

Berwick
-upon-
Tweed

Alnwick •

Rothbury •

NORTHUMBERLAND

Morpeth •

Newcastle upon Tyne

Sunderland

Hexham •

TYNE & WEAR

Durham

COUNTY DURHAM

Hartlepool •

Bishop Auckland •

Darlington •

BAMBURGH CASTLE ©VISIT BRITAIN IMAGES - JEFF PAUL

🌲 COUNTRYSIDE:

- Heather moorlands
- Sandy beaches
- Dark skies

⧖ HERITAGE:

- Hadrian's Wall
- Border castles
- Mining & railway heritage

🍴 FOOD:

- Pease pudding
- Craster kippers
- Singing Hinnies

DON'T MISS!

ALNWICK CASTLE

The second largest inhabited castle in England and stronghold of the Dukes of Northumberland since the 1250s. Home of celebrated knight Harry Hotspur and location for Harry Potter and Downton Abbey. State rooms designed by Anthony Salvin in the 1850s and exceptional art collection.

Highlights:

- Versailles cabinets
- Old Master paintings
- Porcelain collection
- Broomstick training

THE STATE DINING ROOM, ALNWICK CASTLE

CHILLINGHAM CASTLE

A medieval and Tudor castle rescued from near ruin, once an important border fortress with eclectic displays of armour and works of art displayed in a refreshingly accessible style. The State rooms were visited by James I in 1603 and there are regular reports of ghosts.

Highlights:

- James I room
- Torture Chambers
- Italian Garden
- Wild Chillingham Cattle

JAMES I ROOM, CHILLINGHAM CASTLE

AUCKLAND CASTLE

Watch the transformation of Auckland Castle, the gothick palace of the powerful Prince-Bishops of Durham over the next 3 years. Start at the Welcome Centre opening early 2018; major new attractions the Spanish Art Gallery, Faith Museum & Walled Garden open in 2019 and Postchaise Hotel in 2020.

Highlights:

- Welcome Centre
- Mining Art Gallery
- Behind the Scenes restoration tours
- Auckland Park Deer House (English Heritage)

THE LONG DINING ROOM, AUCKLAND CASTLE ©AUCKLAND CASTLE - COLIN DAVISON

MRS HUDSON'S HIDDEN GEM

LADY WATERFORD HALL

Winner, Best Hidden Gem, Hudson's Heritage Awards 2015

"…Imagine my delight when walking with Walpole in the furthest North of England when I stumbled on an unassuming village hall in the neat little village of Ford at the gates of a looming Victorian castle. All is not as it seems. The castle is let for children's activity holidays (everyone you talk to here has a fun memory of Ford). The village hall, it turns out, was a schoolroom founded in 1860 by Scots beauty Louisa, Marchioness of Waterford. She was a painter schooled by Ruskin and part of the Pre-Raphaelite circle; the village hall is her masterwork. She adorned it with vast religious murals using the local kids as models. She was certainly less appreciated than her talent deserves, though she hangs in the Tate today. Fellow Pre-Raphaelite painter Dante Gabriel Rossetti said she "… would have been really great if she had not been such a swell and a stunner…". Huh!

There's lots to do in the villages around, a working watermill and a light railway connects to Etal's ruined English Heritage castle where James IV of Scotland stopped en route to the nearby battlefield of Flodden. The Peppermint Tearooms' Singing Hinnies are famous and Walpole loves the wide open spaces…"

MARK THE YEAR

100 YEARS
WOMEN & SUFFRAGE

PAULINE, LADY TREVELYAN BY WILLIAM BELL SCOTT
©NATIONAL TRUST IMAGES - DERRICK E WITTY

MARY ELEANOR BOWES, BY JC DILLMAN

1. MARY ELEANOR BOWES, COUNTESS OF STRATHMORE & KINGHORNE (1749-1800)
The Unhappy Countess
Heiress, pioneer of the pre-nup, notorious divorcee, botanist at Gibside.

2. PAULINE, LADY TREVELYAN (1916-1866)
Painter, patron of Pre-Raphaelites
at Wallington.

3. GRACE DARLING (1818-42)
Rescuer of HMS Forfarshire, Victorian celebrity
at Bamburgh.

GRACE DARLING'S DARING RESCUE, ONE OF THE MURAL PANELS BY WILLIAM BELL SCOTT AT WALLINGTON ©NATIONAL TRUST IMAGES

DID YOU KNOW?

1 ALNWICK CASTLE

Henry Percy, the Wizard Earl of Northumberland may have regretted appointing his relative Thomas Percy to run Alnwick Castle while he was in the South. Thomas was caught up in the 1605 Gunpowder Plot and killed in the pursuit that followed its exposure. The Earl spent the next 17 years imprisoned in the Tower.

2 SEATON DELAVAL HALL

Early owners of architect Sir John Vanbrugh's majestic Seaton Delaval Hall met tragic ends. Admiral George Delaval was killed in a fall from a horse in 1723, Captain Francis Blake Delaval died falling down the Portico steps in 1752, then his great-nephew John Delaval died at 19 in 1775 after having apparently been kicked by a laundry maid he was trying to seduce.

3 RABY CASTLE

Christopher, 1st Lord Barnard was so enraged by the marriage of his son Gilbert to "scandalous" Mary Randyll in 1712 that he engaged 200 workmen to destroy Raby Castle, so Gilbert could not inherit it. Gilbert retaliated by suing his father and finally succeeded in 1723. He had to partly rebuild his home and replant the woodlands.

SEATON DELAVAL HALL ©NATIONAL TRUST IMAGES - JOHN HAMMOND

THE BARONS' HALL, RABY CASTLE

HENRY PERCY, THE 9TH "WIZARD" EARL OF NORTHUMBERLAND, AFTER ANTHONY VAN DYCK ©SYON PARK

4 BOWES MUSEUM

John Bowes, who founded the Bowes Museum and built the French chateau that houses it in 1874, nearly missed inheriting the fortune of his father, the 10th Earl of Strathmore. The Earl only married John's mother, his mistress of 16 years, 16 hours before his death.

THE BOWES MUSEUM

5 CRAGSIDE

Cragside, home of the hydraulics pioneer and engineer William, Lord Armstrong, was the first house in the world to be powered by hydroelectricity when it was built in 1869. You can still see early labour saving devices and light fittings (1880) as well the hydro-electric generators.

6 THE ALNWICK GARDEN

The award-winning restaurant, café and rope walkway at these extraordinary gardens are in the largest treehouse in Europe.

EARLY ELECTRIC LAMPS AT CRAGSIDE ©NATIONAL TRUST IMAGES - JAMES DOBSON

TREEHOUSE RESTAURANT, THE ALNWICK GARDEN

HADRIAN'S WALL ©VISIT ENGLAND - HADRIAN'S WALL COUNTRY - ROGER CLEGG

TOP SPOTS WHERE HISTORY HAPPENED

1.

HADRIAN'S WALL

Built in AD122, 73 miles (80 Roman miles) of wall stretch across England marking the Northern boundary of the Roman Empire, the largest surviving Roman artefact anywhere. It was garrisoned by around 9,000 soldiers from all over the Empire, Gaul, Belgium, Spain, Romania, Syria and North Africa. Regular milecastles were supported by larger forts at Housesteads, Chesters, Vindolanda, Birdoswald & Segedunum.

2.

ALNWICK CASTLE

One of England's great heroes, Harry 'Hotspur' Percy was born at Alnwick Castle in 1364. Made famous by Shakespeare, he was already a legend, fighting his first battle at 12. Hotspur held the North against the Scots for Richard II before switching sides to support the rebellion of Henry IV. By 1402, he'd fallen out with Henry and met a dramatic death at the Battle of Shrewsbury when he raised his visor to take a look and an arrow pierced his brain. Henry IV is said to have wept at his death.

HARRY HOTSPUR AT ALNWICK CASTLE © ALNWICK CASTLE - SEAN ELLIOTT

3.
CHILLINGHAM CASTLE

Chillingham Castle was the base for Edward I's campaign against William Wallace in Scotland's Wars of Independence in 1298. A year earlier, Wallace had beaten the English at Stirling Bridge and launched a series of brutal raids into Northumberland. He burned around 700 villages before retreating North. Edward invaded on 3 July and, on the 22 July, defeated Wallace at Falkirk. Wallace was not captured until 1305 and hung, drawn and quartered. The Edward I Room at Chillingham recalls these events.

EDWARD I ROOM, CHILLINGHAM CASTLE

RABY CASTLE

4.
RABY CASTLE

In 1569, no less than 700 Catholic knights gathered in the Barons' Hall at Raby Castle to launch The Rising of the North against their protestant Queen, Elizabeth I. When the rebellion failed, Charles Neville, Earl of Westmorland forfeited Raby Castle and most of the knights were exiled or executed.

PLACES TO STAY
SIGNPOST GUIDES
HISTORIC PLACES TO STAY IN NORTH EAST
www.signpost.co.uk

WARREN HOUSE, NORTHUMBERLAND

A small Georgian country house once owned by the Jacobite Lord Derwentwater, executed in 1715. The house overlooks Budle Bay and Lindisfarne through woodlands and is in easy reach of castles at Bamburgh, Dunstanburgh, Alnwick and Warkworth.

THE BANQUETING HOUSE, TYNE & WEAR

A decorative Gothic folly converted by the Landmark Trust, on the edge of the National Trust's Gibside estate, built for intimate parties by coal magnate George Bowes in 1746. Sleeps up to 4.

www.landmark.org.uk

THE ESTATE HOUSE, NORTHUMBERLAND

The Estate House, an elegant Edwardian home, is located in the centre of Ford Village, in the heart of Northumberland's "Secret Kingdom", Coastal attractions at Holy Island or Bamburgh and the Border towns are all very accessible.

Raby Castle

www.rabycastle.com

Raby Castle is surrounded by a large deer park, with two lakes and a beautiful walled garden with formal lawns, yew hedges and an ornamental pond. It was built by the mighty Nevill family in the 14th Century, and has been home to Lord Barnard's family since 1626. Highlights include the vast Barons' Hall, where it is reputed 700 knights gathered to plot the doomed 'Rising of the North' rebellion, and the stunning Octagon Drawing Room. With Meissen porcelain, fine furniture and paintings by Munnings, Reynolds, Van Dyck, Batoni, Teniers, Amigoni and Vernet. Also in the grounds is the 18th Century Stable block with impressive horse-drawn carriage collection, and a delightfully converted Gift Shop and Tea Rooms, and woodland play area.

© RIGHTCLICKSTUDIOS.COM

CONTACT
Owner: Lord & Lady Barnard
Contact: Castle Admin Office
Tel: 01833 660202
Email: admin@rabycastle.com

LOCATION
Staindrop, Darlington, Co. Durham DL2 3AH

Map Ref: 10:O5

On A688, 1 mile North of Staindrop. 8 miles North East of Barnard Castle, 12 miles West North West of Darlington.

OPENING TIMES (2018)
Open seasonally from Apr-Oct.
Check Raby Castle website for exact opening times.

ADMISSION
Please check website for admission prices.

KEY FACTS

 No photography or video filming is permitted inside. Colour guidebook on sale.

 Toilet facilities located in the coach yard, also accessible toilets available.

 Baby changing facilities located in the accessible toilets.

 Ample car parking mainly on grass and coach parking on hard standing & designated access parking.

 Limited access to castle interior. Free wheelchair loan.

 Well behaved dogs on leads, not allowed inside buildings or walled gardens unless assistance dogs.

 Guided tours on weekdays during term time, every half an hour throughout the afternoon.

 For school visits please call for further information.

 Tearooms in coach yard serving homemade scones, cakes, lunches, hot & cold drinks & ice cream.

 Gift shop on site in coach yard.

 Regular events programme throughout the summer.

 Victoria (ITV, Series 1, 2016), Elizabeth (1998).

©GRAEME PEACOCK

The Auckland Project

aucklandproject.org

The Auckland Project is a visitor destination located in the market town of Bishop Auckland. Comprising Auckland Castle, a walled garden, deer park, Auckland Tower an information centre with 15m high viewing platform, museum and galleries. Auckland Castle is the former palace for the Prince Bishops of Durham, dating back 900 years. It houses Jacob and his Twelve Sons a rare cycle of paintings by Spanish master painter Francisco de Zurbarán. The Castle is undergoing major restoration work to restore it to its former Georgian Gothic opulence, it will reopen to visitors in May 2018. Moving from the Castle grounds into the Market Place you will find the Mining Art Gallery featuring work of acclaimed local artists.

KEY FACTS

 Free shuttle bus runs every 15 mins from 10am-5pm from North Bondgate car park to the Castle.

 Toilet facilities available.

 Baby changing facilities available.

 No parking on site. Park at North Bondgate car park.

 Accessible for the vast majority of visitors, but please contact prior to your visit for further details.

 Guide dogs only. Dog walkers welcome in deer park.

Please see website for local accommodation.

 Please see the website for tours and events.

 An active education programme; working with many schools across County Durham.

 Auckland Castle café will serve light lunches and a range of hot and cold beverages.

 A range of locally sourced gifts will be stocked in our shop.

 Available for private hire.

 Please see the 'Your Visit' page on the website for 'What's on'.

Offering a limited number of Chapel weddings in St Peter's Chapel.

CONTACT
Owner: The Auckland Project
Contact: Visitor Services
For openings, admissions & group bookings etc.
Tel: 01388 743 750
Email: enquiries@aucklandproject.org
Facebook: /aucklandproject
Twitter: @aucklandproject

LOCATION
Market Place, Bishop Auckland, County Durham DL14 7NR
Map Ref: 10:P5 - From the A1 motorway take the A688 (J61) to Bishop Auckland. Follow signs to N Bondgate car park DL14 7PG.

OPENING TIMES
Please see the website.

Durham Cathedral

www.durhamcathedral.co.uk

One of the finest examples of Romanesque architecture in Europe, located at the heart of a UNESCO World Heritage Site. Burial place of St Cuthbert and the Venerable Bede.

Explore Open Treasure, a new world-class visitor experience, and discover 2,000 years of history as the remarkable story of Durham Cathedral and its incredible collections is revealed.

KEY FACTS

 Photography is not permitted within the Cathedral.

 Toilets available, including accessible toilets.

 Open all year.

 Limited disabled, public parking nearby.

 Partial. Guides of Cathedral with wheelchair access routes are available.

 Adults: £0-£5, Conc: £0-£5, Children: Free (U16).

 For school visits email: education@durhamcathedral.co.uk

 Locally-sourced food and drink served daily, 10am-4.30pm.

 The Undercroft restaurant available for hire. Offers meals in a beautiful medieval space.

 Locally-sourced, bespoke gifts. Open daily, Mon.-Sat. 9am-5.30pm Sun. 12pm-5pm.

 For corporate events please email: events@durhamcathedral.co.uk

See the 'What's On' section of the website for all upcoming events.

CONTACT
Contact: The Cathedral Office
Tel: 0191 3864266
Email: enquiries@durhamcathedral.co.uk

LOCATION
Durham DH1 3EH
Map Ref: 10:P4 - Durham City Centre.

OPENING TIMES
Daily 7.30am-6pm (8pm Summer), with services 3 times daily.

ADMISSION
Free, donations welcome.
Admission applies to guided tours and open treasure.
Groups: Contact visits@durhamcathedral.co.uk

Alnwick
Castle
www.alnwickcastle.com

Home to the Duke of Northumberland's family, the Percy's, for over 700 years; Alnwick Castle offers history on a grand scale.

Alnwick Castle's remarkable history is brimming with drama, intrigue, and extraordinary people; from a gunpowder plotter and visionary collectors, to decadent hosts and medieval England's most celebrated knight: Harry Hotspur.

Combining magnificent medieval architecture with sumptuous Italianate State Rooms, Alnwick Castle is one of the UK's most significant heritage destinations. In recent years it has also taken starring roles in a number of film and television productions, featuring as a location for ITV's Downton Abbey and as Hogwarts School of Witchcraft and Wizardry in the Harry Potter films. With a history beginning in the Norman Age, Alnwick Castle was originally built as a border defence, before eventually being transformed from a fortification into a family home for the first Duke and Duchess of Northumberland in the 1760s. The castle's State Rooms were later recreated by the 4th Duke in the lavish Italian Renaissance style that we see today, now boasting one of the country's finest private collections of art and furniture.

This remarkable collection includes works by Canaletto, Titian, Van Dyck, Turner, and Dobson; an extensive gallery of Meissen, Chelsea, and Paris porcelain; and the priceless Cucci cabinets, originally created for Louis XIV of France. Alnwick Castle aims to create a vibrant and engaging heritage experience for families, with opportunities aplenty for children to get hands-on with history in the Knight's Quest arena, with dressing up, swordplay, medieval crafts and games.

OWNER
His Grace The Duke of Northumberland

CONTACT
Tel: 01665 511100
Group bookings: 01665 511184
Media & Filming: 01665 511794
Corporate: 01665 511086
Email: info@alnwickcastle.com

LOCATION
Alnwick, Northumberland NE66 1NQ
Map Ref: 14:M11
Well signposted less than a mile off A1; 35 miles north of Newcastle and 80 miles south of Edinburgh.

TRANSPORT ROUTES
Car | Bus | Train | Aeroplane | Ferry

OPENING TIMES
House: 29 Mar-29 Oct, 10am-5.30pm (last admission 3.45pm).
State Rooms: 10.45am-4.30pm (last admission 4pm, Chapel closes at 2.30pm).
Check website for up-to-date opening dates & times.

ADMISSION
Adult: £15.50
Concession: £12.75
Child (5-16yrs): £8
Family (2+up to 4): £42
Group Discount: 14+
Prices are subject to change, please check the website.

Additional: Tickets can be validated for unlimited free visits for 12 months, at no extra cost. (See website for T&Cs).

REGULAR EVENTS
Daily: Guided tours of the State Rooms & grounds. Knight's Quest activities, and broomstick training.
Seasonal: Knights tournaments, falconry displays, jester performances, and visits from skilled artisans.

KEY FACTS

 Storage available for suitcases. Photography not permitted in the state rooms.

 Toilet facilities available.

 Baby changing facilities available.

 Coach parking also available.

 Accessible WC's. Free wheelchair/ mobility scooter hire. Limited access in areas.

Free daily tours of the state rooms and grounds.

 9 bedroom county lodge available for rental.

 Workshops, activities and discounted admission available. Call 01665 511184.

 Courtyard Café. Licensed.

 Stables Fryery and Courtyard Barbeque.

 Gift shop open daily.

 Guest Hall - capacity 300 & Hulne Abbey - capacity 500. Team-building, banqueting, dinner & dances.

See website for details.

 Wedding ceremonies and receptions. Call 01665 511086.

Chillingham Castle

www.chillingham-castle.com

This remarkable and very private castle has been continuously owned by just one family line since the 1200's. A visit from Edward I in 1298 was followed by many other Royal visits right down through this century. See Chillingham's alarming dungeons as well as active restoration in the Great Halls and State Rooms which are gradually brought back to life with tapestries, arms and armour. We even have a very real torture chamber.

The 1100s stronghold became a fortified castle in 1344, see the original Royal Licence to Crenellate on view. Wrapped in the nation's history Chillingham also occupied a strategic position during Northumberland's bloody border feuds being a resting place to many royal visitors. Tudor days saw additions but the underlying medievalism remains. 18th and 19th Centuries saw decorative extravagances including 'Capability' Brown lakes and grounds with gardens laid out by Sir Jeffrey Wyatville, fresh from his triumphs at Windsor Castle. Prehistoric Wild Cattle roam the park beyond more rare than mountain gorilla (a separate tour) and never miss the family tomb in the church.

Gardens

With romantic grounds, the castle commands breathtaking views of the surrounding countryside. As you walk to the lake you will see, according to season, drifts of snowdrops, daffodils or bluebells and an astonishing display of rhododendrons. This emphasises the restrained formality of the Elizabethan topiary garden, with its intricately clipped hedges of box and yew. Lawns, the formal gardens and woodland walks are all fully open to the public.

CONTACT
Owner: Sir Humphry Wakefield Bt
Contact: The Administrator
Tel: 01668 215359
Email: enquiries@chillingham-castle.com

LOCATION
Northumberland NE66 5NJ
Map Ref: 14:L11
45 miles North of Newcastle between A697 & A1.
2 miles South of B6348 at Chatton. 6 miles South East of Wooler.
Rail: Alnmouth or Berwick.

OPENING TIMES (2018)
Summer Castle, Garden & Tea Room
30 Mar-28 Oct, 12 noon-5pm.
Winter Castle, Garden & Tea Room
Groups & Coach Tours any time by appointment.
All function activities available.

ADMISSION
Adult: £9.50, Child: £5.50, Conc: £8.50.
Family Ticket: £23 (2 adults & 3 children under 15).

KEY FACTS

 Sir Humphry has produced a room by room guide which can be purchased on arrival for £2.50.

 Toilet facilities available.

 Avoid Lilburn route, coach parties welcome by prior arrangement. Limited for coaches.

 Self-catering apartments to hire all year round.

 Private guided castle tours can be specially arranged, call for details.

 By arrangement, please call for details on educational visits.

 Medieval castle Tea Room serves delicious home made lunches & treats. Access free of charge.

 Gift shop.

 Corporate entertainment, lunches, drinks & dinners.

 Please see the 'Events' page on the website for all upcoming tours and events.

 Wedding ceremonies and receptions.

 "Elizabeth" staged many historic scenes here. "The Making of Harry Potter" was based here.

Lady Waterford Hall & Gallery

ford-and-etal.co.uk/lady-waterford-hall

At the heart of Ford and Etal Estates this 'must see venue' is the hidden gem of North Northumberland. Built as a school in 1860, the building houses a unique collection of magnificent watercolour murals (1861-1883) and smaller original paintings and sketches by Louisa Waterford, one of the most gifted female artists of the 19th Century. The fascinating story of Louisa's life and work is depicted through interpretation and film. Quizzes and games available for children to enjoy. Small gift shop.

CONTACT
Owner: Ford & Etal Estates / Lady Waterford Hall Trust
Tel: 01890 820338 / 07790 457850
E-mail: ladywaterfordhall@gmail.com

LOCATION
Ford, Berwick-Upon-Tweed, Northumberland TD15 2QA
Map Ref: 14:K10 - From A1 Berwick-upon-Tweed or northbound after Belford follow brown signs to Ford & Etal. From A697 northbound after Wooler/southbound after Cornhill-on-Tweed follow brown signs to Ford & Etal.

OPENING TIMES
Late Mar-end Oct. 11am-5pm daily (times may vary slightly early & late season), last entry 30 minutes before closing.

ADMISSION
Adult: £3, Concs/Child: £2.70 (Under 5's: Free), Family: £8. Joint tickets with Heatherslaw Cornmill are available offering a 20% discount on normal admission.

KEY FACTS

 Occasionally closed for private functions - please phone beforehand. Closes at 4pm in low season.

 Toilets available.

 Baby changing facilities available. Very child friendly.

 Free on street parking immediately outside building.

 Level access. Please see access statement on the website.

B&B, Self-Catering & Camping nearby, please see 'Where to Stay' section of the website.

 Min 11 people per group, discounts offered to pre-booked groups.

 Contact tourism@ford-and-etal.co.uk for information. Excellent educational experience on offer.

Tea Rooms nearby.

Small gift shop.

Hall available for private hire including wedding receptions (not civil ceremonies).

Please see the 'Events Calendar' for all the upcoming events.

Alnwick Castle © Sean Elliott Photography

BARNARD CASTLE ⊞
Nr Galgate, Barnard Castle, Durham DL12 8PR
Tel: 01833 638212 **Email:** barnard.castle@english-heritage.org.uk

BEAMISH, THE LIVING MUSEUM
Beamish Museum, Beamish, County Durham DH9 0RG
Tel: 0191 370 4000 **Email:** museum@beamish.org.uk

BOWES CASTLE ⊞
Bowes, Barnard Castle, County Durham DL12 9HP
Tel: 01912 691215 **Email:** grace.dunne@english-heritage.org.uk

THE BOWES MUSEUM
Barnard Castle, County Durham DL12 8NP
Tel: 01833 690606 **Email:** info@thebowesmuseum.org.uk

CROOK HALL & GARDENS
Sidegate, Durham DH1 5SZ
Tel: 0191 3848028

DURHAM CASTLE
Palace Green, Durham DH1 3RW
Tel: 0191 3343800

ROKEBY PARK 🏠ⓕ
Barnard Castle, County Durham DL12 9RZ
Tel: 01609 748612 **Email:** admin@rokebypark.com

THE ALNWICK GARDEN
Denwick Lane, Alnwick, Northumberland NE66 1YU
Tel: 01665 511350 **Email:** info@alnwickgarden.com

AYDON CASTLE ⊞
Corbridge, Northumberland NE45 5PJ
Tel: 01434 632450 **Email:** customers@english-heritage.org.uk

BAMBURGH CASTLE 🏠ⓕ
Bamburgh, Northumberland NE69 7DF
Tel: 01668 214208 **Email:** administrator@bamburghcastle.com

BELSAY HALL, CASTLE & GARDENS ⊞
Belsay, Nr Morpeth, Northumberland NE20 0DX
Tel: 01661 881636

BRINKBURN PRIORY ⊞
Long Framlington, Morpeth, Northumberland NE65 8AR
Tel: 01665 570628 **Email:** customers@english-heritage.org.uk

CHERRYBURN 🌿
Station Bank, Mickley, Stocksfield, Northumberland NE43 7DD
Tel: 01661 843276 **Email:** cherryburn@nationaltrust.org.uk

CHESTERS ROMAN FORT ⊞
Chollerford, Hexham, Northumberland NE46 4EU
Tel: 01434 681379 **Email:** customers@english-heritage.org.uk

Chipchase Castle 🏠ⓕ

Wark, Hexham, Northumberland NE48 3NT
Jacobean castle set in formal and informal gardens.
Map Ref: 10:N2 - 10m NW of Hexham via A6079 to Chollerton. 2m
SE of Wark **Tel:** 01434 230203 **Email:** info@chipchasecastle.com
Website: www.chipchasecastle.com **Open:** Castle: 1-28 Jun,
2pm-5pm daily. Gardens & Nursery: Easter-31 Aug, Thu-Sun Incl.
and BH Mon, 10am-5pm. **Admission:** Castle £6, Garden £4.

Kitchen, Raby Castle

CORBRIDGE ROMAN TOWN
Corchester Lane, Corbridge, Northumberland NE45 5NT
Tel: 01434 632349 **Email:** customers@english-heritage.org.uk

CRAGSIDE
Rothbury, Morpeth, Northumberland NE65 7PX
Tel: 01669 620333 **Email:** cragside@nationaltrust.org.uk

DUNSTANBURGH CASTLE
Dunstanburgh Road, Craster, Northumberland NE66 3TT
Tel: 01665 576231

EDLINGHAM CASTLE
Edlingham, Alnwick NE66 2BW
Tel: 0191 269 1200

ETAL CASTLE
Cornhill-On-Tweed, Northumberland TD12 4TN
Tel: 01890 820332 **Email:** customers@english-heritage.org.uk

GEORGE STEPHENSON'S BIRTHPLACE
Wylam, Northumberland NE41 8BP
Tel: 01661 853457 **Email:** georgestephensons@nationaltrust.org.uk

HERTERTON HOUSE GARDENS
Hartington, Cambo, Morpeth, Northumberland NE61 4BN
Tel: 01670 774278

HOUSESTEADS ROMAN FORT
Haydon Bridge, Hexham, Northumberland NE47 6NN
Tel: 01434 344363 **Email:** customers@english-heritage.org.uk

HOWICK HALL GARDENS & ARBORETUM
Alnwick, Northumberland NE66 3LB
Tel: 01665 577285 **Email:** estateoffice@howickuk.com

LINDISFARNE CASTLE
Holy Island, Berwick-Upon-Tweed, Northumberland TD15 2SH
Tel: 01289 389244 **Email:** lindisfarne@nationaltrust.org.uk

LINDISFARNE PRIORY
Holy Island, Berwick-Upon-Tweed, Northumberland TD15 2RX
Tel: 01289 389200 **Email:** lindisfarne.priory@english-heritage.org.uk

MELDON PARK KITCHEN GARDEN
Morpeth, Northumberland NE61 3SW
Tel: 01670 772341 **Email:** michelle@flyingfox.co.uk/james@flying-fox.co.uk

NORHAM CASTLE
Norham, Northumberland TD15 2JY
Tel: 01289 304493 **Email:** customers@english-heritage.org.uk

Preston Tower

Chathill, Northumberland NE67 5DH
Built by Sir Robert Harbottle in 1392.
Location: Follow Historic Property signs on A1 7m N of Alnwick.
Map Ref: 14:M11 **Tel:** 01665 589227 / 07966 150216
Website: www.prestontower.co.uk
Open: All year daily, 10am-6pm, or dusk, whichever is earlier.
Admission: Adult £2, Child 50p, Concessions £1.50. Groups £1.50.

PRUDHOE CASTLE
Prudhoe, Northumberland NE42 6NA
Tel: 01661 833459 **Email:** customers@english-heritage.org.uk

SEATON DELAVAL HALL
The Avenue, Seaton Sluice, Northumberland NE26 4QR
Tel: 0191 237 9100 **Email:** seatondelavalhall@nationaltrust.org.uk

WALLINGTON
Cambo, Morpeth, Northumberland NE61 4AR
Tel: 01670 773600 **Email:** wallington@nationaltrust.org.uk

WARKWORTH CASTLE
Warkworth, Alnwick, Northumberland NE65 0UJ
Tel: 01665 711423 **Email:** warkworth.castle@english-heritage.org.uk

WHALTON MANOR GARDENS
Whalton, Morpeth, Northumberland NE61 3UT
Tel: 01670 775205 **Email:** gardens@whaltonmanor.co.uk

BESSIE SURTEES HOUSE
41-44 Sandhill, Newcastle, Tyne & Wear NE1 3JF
Tel: 0191 269 1200 **Email:** customers@english-heritage.org.uk

GIBSIDE
Nr Rowlands Gill, Burnopfield, Newcastle upon Tyne NE16 6BG
Tel: 01207 541820 **Email:** gibside@nationaltrust.org.uk

HYLTON CASTLE
Castle Garth, Sunderland, Tyne and Wear SR5 3PB
Tel: 01912 611585

NEWCASTLE CASTLE
Nr Galgate, Newcastle, Tyne & Wear NE1 1RQ
Tel: 0191 230 6300 **Email:** info@newcastlecastle.co.uk

SOUTER LIGHTHOUSE
Coast Road, Whitburn, Sunderland, Tyne & Wear SR6 7NH
Tel: 0191 529 3161 **Email:** souter@nationaltrust.org.uk

TYNEMOUTH CASTLE & PRIORY
Tynemouth, Tyne & Wear NE30 4BZ
Tel: 01912 691215 **Email:** customers@english-heritage.org.uk

WASHINGTON OLD HALL
The Avenue, Washington Village, Tyne & Wear NE38 7LE
Tel: 0191 416 6879 **Email:** washington.oldhall@nationaltrust.org.uk

Durham Cathedral

SCOTLAND

BORDERS • SOUTH WEST SCOTLAND • EDINBURGH
GREATER GLASGOW • TAYSIDE • WEST HIGHLANDS & ISLANDS
GRAMPIAN HIGHLANDS • HIGHLANDS & SKYE

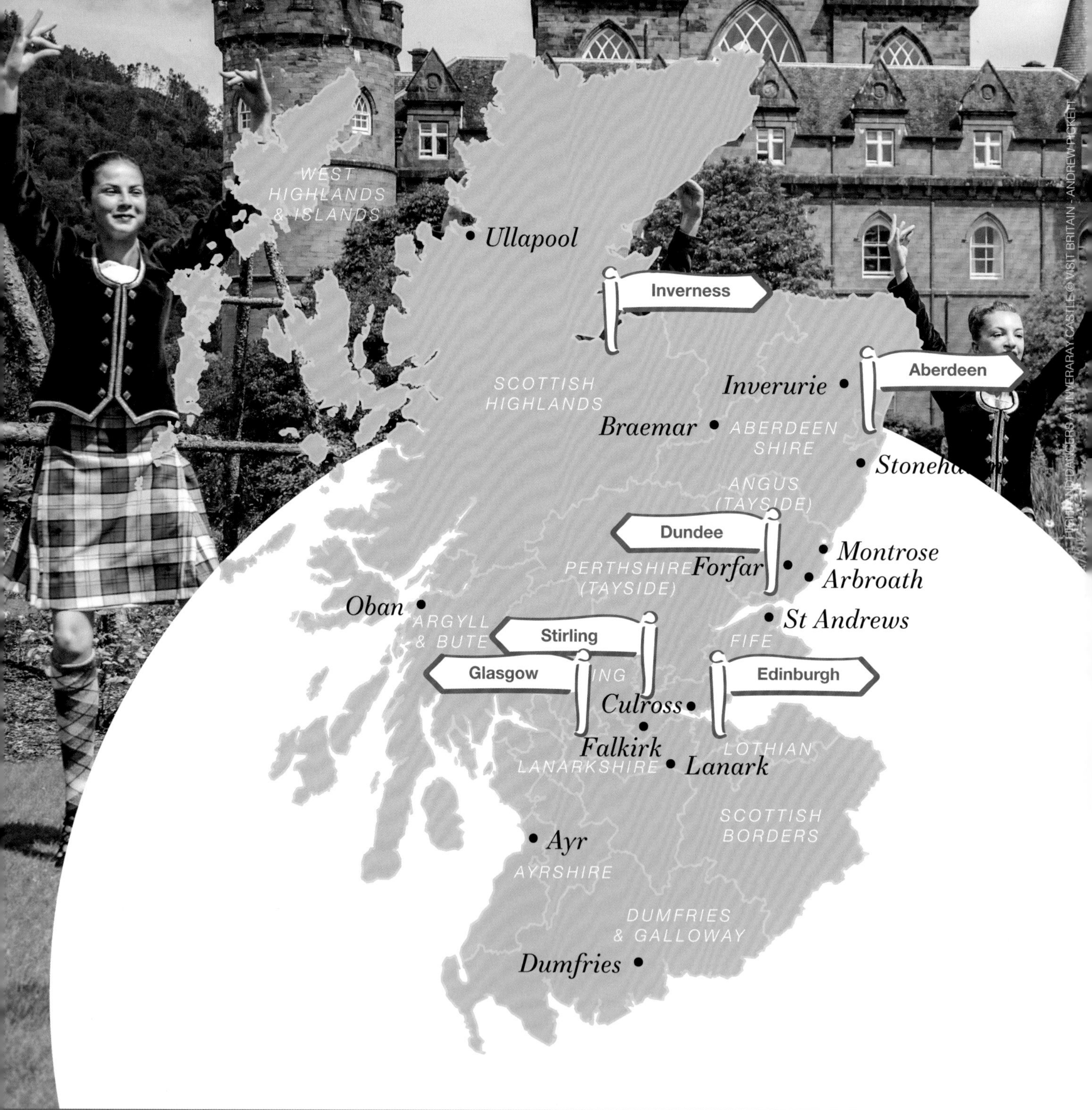

WEST
HIGHLANDS
& ISLANDS

• Ullapool

Inverness

SCOTTISH
HIGHLANDS

Inverurie •

Aberdeen

Braemar •   ABERDEEN
SHIRE

• Stoneha...

ANGUS
(TAYSIDE)

Dundee

Montrose
Forfar   Arbroath
PERTHSHIRE
(TAYSIDE)

• St Andrews

Oban •
ARGYLL
& BUTE

Stirling   FIFE

Glasgow   ...ING   Edinburgh

Culross •

Falkirk   LOTHIAN
LANARKSHIRE   • Lanark

SCOTTISH
BORDERS

• Ayr
AYRSHIRE

DUMFRIES
& GALLOWAY

Dumfries •

🌲 COUNTRYSIDE:

• Bens & glens
• Links golf courses
• Lochs & beaches

⏳ HERITAGE:

• Clan history
• Highland castles
• Lowland palaces

🍴 FOOD:

• Whisky
• Salmon
• Shortbread

DON'T MISS!

DUMFRIES HOUSE

The early masterpiece architecture of the Adam brothers with a superb collection of Thomas Chippendale and Scottish enlightenment furniture makers. The Palladian house and its collections were saved for the nation by the Trust set up by HRH Prince Charles in 2007.

Highlights:

- Chippendale bed & rosewood bookcase
- Flemish tapestries
- Murano glass chandeliers
- 5 acres walled gardens

BLUE DRAWING ROOM, DUMFRIES HOUSE

INVERARAY CASTLE

A romantic gothic revival castle on the shores of Loch Fyne, which is home to the Chieftain of Clan Campbell. Fine neo-classical interiors have sophisticated French decoration and Scottish and English art and furnishings.

Highlights:

- Armoury Hall
- Tapestry Drawing Room
- China Turrett
- Victorian kitchens

DUNVEGAN CASTLE FROM THE GARDENS

INVERARAY CASTLE

DUNVEGAN CASTLE

An iconic Scottish castle, developed between 1200 and 1850, home to Clan MacLeod for 800 years. See the legendary 4th century Fairy Flag carried by the clan to ensure victory in battle and a host of clan treasures.

Highlights:

- Family portraits
- The Fairy Flag
- The Water Garden
- Seal tours

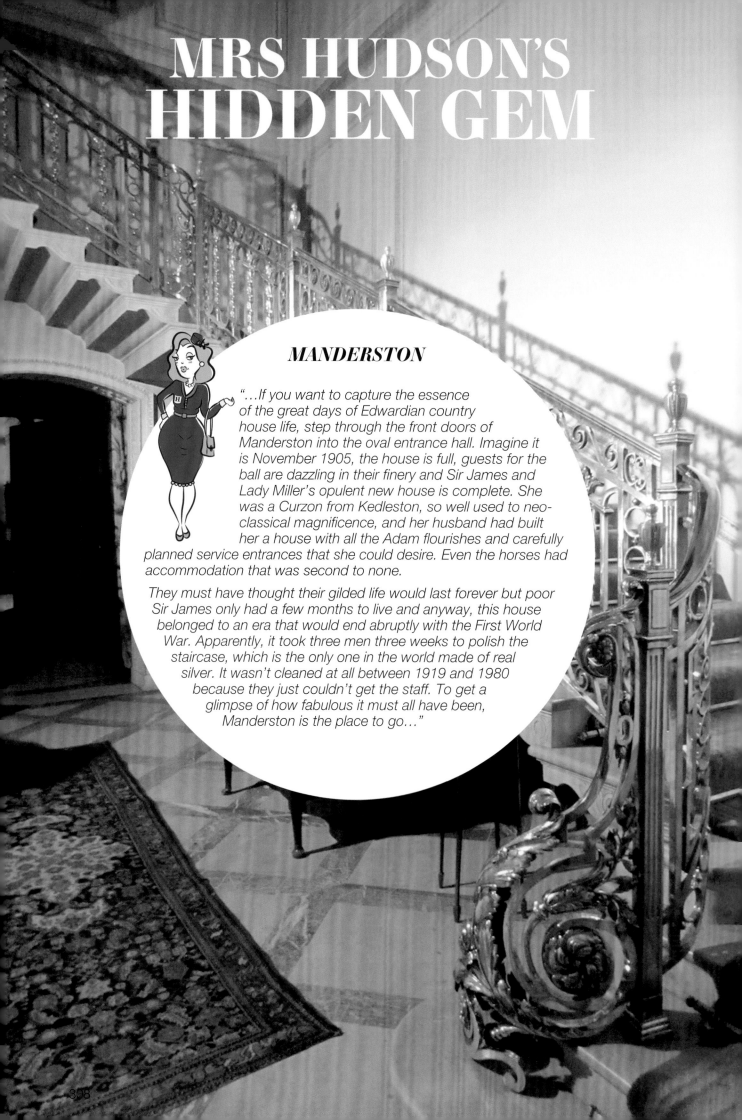

MRS HUDSON'S
HIDDEN GEM

MANDERSTON

"…If you want to capture the essence of the great days of Edwardian country house life, step through the front doors of Manderston into the oval entrance hall. Imagine it is November 1905, the house is full, guests for the ball are dazzling in their finery and Sir James and Lady Miller's opulent new house is complete. She was a Curzon from Kedleston, so well used to neo-classical magnificence, and her husband had built her a house with all the Adam flourishes and carefully planned service entrances that she could desire. Even the horses had accommodation that was second to none.

They must have thought their gilded life would last forever but poor Sir James only had a few months to live and anyway, this house belonged to an era that would end abruptly with the First World War. Apparently, it took three men three weeks to polish the staircase, which is the only one in the world made of real silver. It wasn't cleaned at all between 1919 and 1980 because they just couldn't get the staff. To get a glimpse of how fabulous it must all have been, Manderston is the place to go…"

MARK THE YEAR

300 YEARS
CHIPPENDALE

Celebrate our greatest furniture maker 300 years after his birth.
- Blair Castle
- Duff House
- Dumfries House
- Manderston
- Mellerstain House
- Paxton House

THE DRAWING ROOM, MELLERSTAIN

100 YEARS
WOMEN & SUFFRAGE

LADY GRISELL BAILLIE BY MARIA VERELST AT MELLERSTAIN

FLORA MACDONALD STATUE AT INVERNESS CASTLE

2. FLORA MACDONALD
Jacobite heroine
at Dunvegan Castle.

KATHERINE, DUCHESS OF ATHOLL ©BLAIR CASTLE

1. LADY GRISELL BAILLIE (1665-1746)
Songwriter, compiler of "The Household Book" at Mellerstain.

3. KITTY, DUCHESS OF ATHOLL
Politician, 1st Conservative woman in government at Blair Castle.

DID YOU KNOW?

1 CAWDOR CASTLE

When baby Muriel, heir to Cawdor Castle, was kidnapped by the Argylls to be brought up in their household, her canny grandmother branded her on the hip with a hot key to be sure it was the same girl who married John, son of the Earl of Argyll in 1510.

2 TRAQUAIR HOUSE

The 18th century brewery at Traquair House was re-opened in 1965. Beer was brewed at Traquair for Mary Queen of Scots and today's brew uses the original oak tuns and 200-gallon copper delivered in 1738. Traquair beer is exported all over the world.

3 ABBOTSFORD

Author Sir Walter Scott was "perhaps the most devoted dog lover that ever was". His favourite was Maida the deerhound who sits with him today on the Scott Monument in Edinburgh and waits for him at the door of his home, Abbotsford.

CAWDOR CASTLE

MAIDA, SCOTT'S FAVOURITE DOG AT ABBOTSFORD

BEER BREWED AT TRAQUAIR HOUSE

DALMENY HOUSE

BLACKADDIE HOTEL, DUMFRIESSHIRE

The name Blackaddie is derived from the black water of the River Nith which runs alongside. The 16th century hotel is set in two acres of gardens with magnificent views of the river and the breath-taking Lowther and Queensbury Hills. The house has connections to poet, Robert Burns and scholar, theAdmirable Crichton.

CRAIGADAM HOUSE, DUMFRIESSHIRE

Craigadam is a small country house in the midst of a 25,000 acre sporting estate. It is an imaginative conversion of 18th century farm buildings which open onto a delightful courtyard.

ROMAN CAMP COUNTRY HOUSE & RESTAURANT, PERTHSHIRE

The Roman Camp Country House & Restaurant, dating from 1625, was originally a hunting lodge for the Earls of Moray. It was remodelled and extended during the early 20th century becoming a hotel in the 1930's. The house lies in 20 acres of gardens by the river Teith, including a large walled flower and herb garden and rolling lawns.

TARR ON THE ROAD SCOTLAND:
A BORDERS TRINITY

Rambler Derek Tarr kept the three dominant peaks of the Eildon Hills as constant companions on a four day walk uncovering the heritage of Scottish Borders.

DEREK TARR TAKES IN SCOTT'S VIEW OF THE EILDON HILLS, ALL PHOTOGRAPHS © NICOLA BURFORD

WALK 1

Mellerstain to Dryburgh

9.4 miles approx

It was a 'dreich' morning with foreboding clouds cloaking Mellerstain House in mystery. On the western edge of The Merse, Mellerstain is the work of the architects William Adam and his son Robert and is home to the Earls of Haddington. The elder Adam was commissioned to build the wings by George Baillie and his wife Lady Grisell and work began in 1725. For 40 years the family lived in the East Wing and the servants in the West. Their grandson commissioned the younger Adam to join the two wings with a central block, finally finishing in 1778. The Library has one of Robert Adam's best decorated ceilings and exceptional plasterwork while the Great Gallery houses period clothing, toys and puppets. During the Second World War part of the house was used as a hospital to tend injured soldiers.

I left the estate in warmer weather and followed country lanes and paths to the village of Smailholm stopping at the Kinsman-Blake Gallery, a family-run craft studio. A short road walk brought me to brooding Smailholm Tower and my first connection to the writer, Sir Walter Scott. On a rocky outcrop high above the River Tweed, this fortified 'pele' tower, so common in The Borders, can be seen from miles around. The romantic setting where Scott played as a boy has a darker, older history of 'reivers' and skirmishes between border families. Today the tower, which is administered by Historic Scotland, contains an interesting museum. The rooftop viewing area is well worth the effort.

Since 2003, walkers have the 'right to roam' across any land abiding by stipulated rules, well suited to the mountains of The Highlands but less to the farmlands of the Borders. After a frustrating battle through fields, I finally arrived at Bemersyde Moss, a Site of Special Scientific Interest run by the Scottish Wildlife Trust, a good place to observe bird life from a hide.
The banks of the River Tweed and the Borders Abbeys Way led me to The Dryburgh Abbey Hotel.

Lunch: The Hoebridge Café at Mellerstain

Dinner & overnight: The Dryburgh Abbey Hotel

WALK 2

Dryburgh to Galashiels
9.8 miles approx

A few glimpses of the ruined Premonstratensian abbey can be seen through the trees from the hotel. Dewdrops glistened in the early morning sun as I entered the abbey grounds and wandered between the picturesque ruins. Although less influential than neighbouring Jedburgh, Kelso and Melrose, Dryburgh is for me the most beautiful. Founded in the mid-1100s, the abbey has been damaged over the centuries but much is still relatively intact. Two notable characters are buried here. First is Sir Walter Scott who, through his writings in the 1800s, created the romantic image of Scotland that we still have today. The second is the controversial figure of Field Marshall Douglas Haig, Commander-in-Chief of the British Expeditionary Forces during the 'blood bath' of the Western Front in the First World War.

From Dryburgh, a steady incline brought me to a monument for Scottish hero, William Wallace. Constructed of red sandstone and standing 21.5 feet tall, it was erected by the 11th Earl of Buchan in 1814. I passed Bemersyde House, former home of Field Marshall Haig, and upwards to Scott's View, the writers' favourite spot overlooking the Eildon Hills. The next mile or so was a gentle descent along lanes to cross the River Tweed at Leaderfoot. Here, three crossings reflect transport through the ages. Traffic on the busy A68, on a 1970s box girder bridge, thundered above as I crossed its predecessor, stone 1776 Drygrange Old Bridge. From here the path headed towards brick built Leaderfoot Viaduct that once carried the Berwickshire Railway over the Tweed.

Passing the site of the Roman camp of Trimontium and through the pretty village of Newstead, I arrived at Melrose. The Roman museum in the square holds artefacts from the camp and a replica of the Trimontium parade helmet. I was given a concise history by a knowledgeable elderly lady guide.

The Cistercian abbey near the centre of the town is where the heart of another Scottish hero, Robert the Bruce, is believed buried in the presbytery. With vaulted ceilings, towering columns and a splendid museum, a little time is needed for exploring. A short walk from the abbey is a site of significance to followers of Rugby Union, a sport in the blood of Borders folk, where most towns have a club of renown. The Greenyards is the home of Melrose RFC and it was here in 1883 that the Sevens version of the game was first played. An annual Sevens tournament is still held here.

I arrived at Tweedbank to join the South Uplands Way along a disused railway. To my surprise, there was a train! I rechecked my map – no railway line. I discovered that I was at the end of the recently opened Borders Railway relinking the area to Edinburgh and the national rail network. Re-crossing the river I ventured up a hill to my night's stop.

  Lunch: Coffee shop in Melrose

 Dinner & overnight: The Maplehurst Boutique Guest House, Tweedbank

MELLERSTAIN HOUSE

DEREK ON THE TERRACE AT MELLERSTAIN

SMAILHOLM TOWER, HISTORIC SCOTLAND

SCOTT'S BURIAL PLACE AT DRYBURGH ABBEY

Galashiels to St Boswells

9.8 miles approx

A short walk brought me to Abbotsford, the most important of all Sir Walter Scott connections; his creation, his home, his passion and the place he referred to as his 'Conundrum Castle'. This wonderfully romantic edifice reflects the very soul of the man and his work. He began buying the land in 1811 and embarked on creating a residence of Gothic splendour. In 1826, embroiled in financial difficulties, he agreed with his creditors literally to write himself out of debt. He died here on the banks of his beloved River Tweed in 1832. The wonderful library houses Scott's collection of books and the 'Byron Urn', a gift from his friend and contemporary Lord Byron. The atmospheric study is where he wrote many of his later works. The chapel contains an intricate carved and painted altar.

From Abbotsford, I followed country lanes back to Melrose before climbing to the top of Eildon Hill North. At 1300 ft the panorama is breathtaking; virtually all of my route was laid out in front of me.

A steep descent brought me to Rhymer's Stone named after a local man Thomas the Rhymer. The stone is on the site of the Eildon tree beneath which Thomas fell asleep to be awakened by a kiss from the Queen of Elfland.

Further along the Borders Abbeys Way, I reached the pleasant town of St Boswells with shops including The Mainstreet Trading Company, a multi-award winning independent bookshop and café.

Lunch: Ochiltrees Restaurant, Abbotsford

Dinner & overnight:. The Buccleuch Arms, St Boswells

SIR WALTER SCOTT'S STUDY AT ABBOTSFORD

MELROSE ABBEY

THE LEADERFOOT BRIDGES

THE GARDENS AT ABBOTSFORD

FLOORS CASTLE

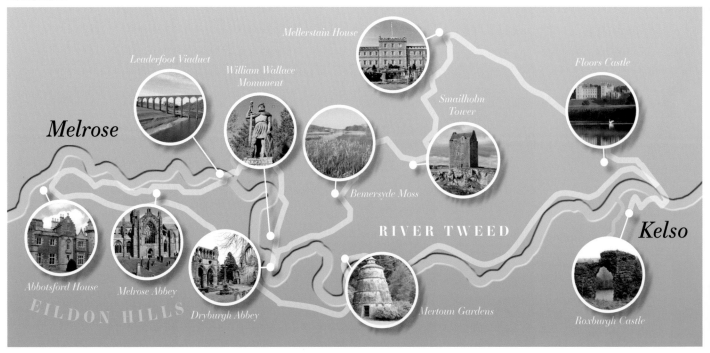

Mellerstain House

Leaderfoot Viaduct

William Wallace Monument

Melrose

Smailholm Tower

Floors Castle

Bemersyde Moss

RIVER TWEED

Kelso

Abbotsford House

Melrose Abbey

Dryburgh Abbey

EILDON HILLS

Mertoun Gardens

Roxburgh Castle

St Boswells to Roxburgh Castle

13.3 miles approx

An early start was required to cover 10 miles along the River Tweed to Floors Castle. The weather varied between showers and sunshine but the walking was easy and the scenery pleasant. I passed the entrance to Mertoun House but was too early to visit its fine gardens. I encountered few people save for a couple of lady golfers, one or two farmers and a couple of fly fishermen knee-deep in the river.

Approaching Floors via the north entrance, I first visited the walled garden. The castle is the home of the 10th Duke of Roxburghe and was designed by William Adam for the 1st Duke in 1721. In the 19th century the architect William Playfair arrayed the castle with turrets, pinnacles and cupolas. Fascinating interiors include the Bird Room, displaying mounted birds in mahogany cases and the Robe Room where the Roxburghe Coronation Robes and a collection of costumes can be seen. Among the impressive art collection, A View of Kelso by JMW Turner was used as the frontispiece of Scott's Minstrelsy of the Scottish Border.

A mile from the castle, at the confluence of the rivers Tweed and Teviot, is Kelso with the largest market square in Scotland and the site of a once powerful abbey, founded by Tironensian monks in the 12th century. The final leg of my journey was to cross the Kelso and Teviot bridges to Roxburgh Castle, today little more than a large mound, but an important site in the wars between England and Scotland. In 1460, the Scots successfully stormed and occupied it but, tragically, King James II was killed by an exploding cannon in the action. His Queen, Mary of Guelders, had the castle destroyed. Today it is a fine vantage point to Floors Castle across the river.

> ✕ Lunch: The Terrace Café, Floors Castle

On my Borders walk everything came in threes. Triple peaked Eildon Hill; the Leaderfoot bridges; three Scottish heroes; three abbeys; and three houses. Even Trimontium, the Roman camp, reflected this theme of trinity. It's easy to bypass this area while heading north, but detour to experience the culturally rich and romantic Scottish Borders. ∎

Mellerstain House & Gardens

www.mellerstain.com

One of Scotland's finest stately homes, this outstanding Georgian mansion house is a unique example of Adam design, begun in 1725 by Scottish architect William Adam and completed in 1778 by his more famous son, Robert. Some say this is one of Robert Adam's finest works, complemented by the fine art, period furniture, china and embroidery collections. Its idyllic location does not disappoint, with acres of parkland, gardens, lakeside walks, playground, coffee shop and holiday cottages.

KEY FACTS

 Outdoor shoes/ boots recommended for the grounds & gardens. No photography in the house.

 Accessible WC facility located in the courtyard.

 Free on site parking. Accessible parking and drop-off point at the main reception.

 Partially suitable for visitors with limited mobility.

 Dog friendly within grounds and gardens on leads. Guide dogs only in the house.

 Self-catering holiday cottages, The Clock House, Courtyard Cottage and West Lodge.

 Groups and guided tours welcome by prior arrangement.

 Educational and school visits by arrangement.

 Free entry to coffee shop/ ticket entry to House and Gardens.

 For corporate functions please contact.

 See the 'What's On' page on the website for all upcoming events at Mellerstain House.

CONTACT

Owner: The Mellerstain Trust
Contact: The Trust Office
Tel: 01573 410225
Email: enquiries@mellerstain.com

LOCATION

Mellerstain, Gordon, Berwickshire TD3 6LG **Map Ref:** 14:J10
From Edinburgh A68 to Earlston, turn left 5 miles, signed.

OPENING TIMES

Easter weekend (4 days), May-Sep on Fri-Mon.
House: 12.30pm-5pm. Last ticket 4.15pm.
Coffee shop & gardens: 11am-5pm.

ADMISSION

Please see our website or call us.

Abbotsford, Chinese Drawing Room

Thirlestane Castle

www.thirlestanecastle.co.uk

Thirlestane Castle nestles in the hills of the Scottish Borders just 35 minutes from Edinburgh. Built in 1590, it was originally a great stone keep but over the years became a grand ducal palace and then a country mansion. It is the ancient seat of the Earls and Duke of Lauderdale, and the Maitland family still live there. Explore and discover exquisite 17th Century plasterwork ceilings, fine furnishings, pictures, and historic toys. Facilities include free parking, a woodland walk, gift shop and Tea Room.

CONTACT
Owner: Thirlestane Castle Trust
Contact: Rhona Jamieson **Tel:** 01578 722430
Email: enquiries@thirlestanecastle.co.uk

LOCATION
Lauder, Scottish Borders TD2 6RU
Map Ref: 14:I9 - Signposted just off the A68 at Lauder.

OPENING TIMES
30 Apr-30 Sep 2018. Sun-Thus, 10am-4pm (Grounds 10am-5pm). For up-to-date opening times please visit website.

ADMISSION
Castle & Grounds
Adult: £8, Child: £3.50, Senior Citizens: £6.50, Family (2+3): £20, Groups: 15+ £6.50 (includes guided tour).
Grounds Only
Adult: £3.50, Child: £1.50.

KEY FACTS

 Public toilets are located on both the lower ground floor and the ground floor.

 Baby changing facilities available in both male and female toilets.

 Ample free parking for cars and coaches.

 Restricted access, no lift for first floor.

 Well-behaved dogs on leads are welcome in the castle grounds.

 Two self-catering apartments available within the castle.

 Groups welcome. Guided tours are available by arrangement.

 Enjoy delicious cakes or light lunch with tea and coffee in the cosy Tea Room.

 Gift shop selling a range of Thirlestane Castle souvenirs and gifts.

 Beautiful events venue for private dining, corporate and large outdoor events.

 Calendar of special events throughout the opening season. See website for details.

Thirlestane Castle is a fairytale setting for weddings.

Mellerstain House

Floors Castle

floorscastle.com

An architectural masterpiece overlooking the River Tweed and Cheviot Hills. Home to the 10th Duke of Roxburghe, Floors Castle showcases spectacular state rooms with outstanding collections of paintings, tapestries, ceramics and furniture. Explore the picturesque Victorian walled gardens, extensive grounds and new cycle trail. Enjoy seasonal homemade food at one of our Cafés serving morning coffee, delicious lunch or afternoon tea.

CONTACT
Owner: His Grace the Duke of Roxburghe
Contact: Louise Shaw / Natalie Cairns
Tel: 01573 223333
Email: enquiries@floorscastle.com
LOCATION
Floors Castle,Roxburghe Estates, Kelso TD5 7SF
Map Ref: 14:J10
OS Ref: NT11 374
From S A68, A698. From N A68.
OPENING
Castle & Grounds
1 May-30 Sep & WE's in Oct 10.30am-5pm.
Gardens & Terrace
Café open all year round.
10.30am-5pm, Apr-Oct.
10.30am-4pm Nov- Mar.
ADMISSION
Castle, Gardens & Grounds
Adult: £11.50, Conc: £10.50, Child (5-15): £6, Family: £29 (2+3).
Gardens & Grounds
Adult: £6.50, Conc: £5.50, Child (5-15): £3, Family: £16.

KEY FACTS

 Free parking for cars and coaches. Disabled parking available.

 Dog friendly grounds.

 Experienced guides throughout the Castle.

 Two Cafés, serving delicious homemade food created in the Castle kitchen.

 Two delightful gift shops to browse and pick up a special souvenir or Deli produce to take home.

Seasonal activities, corporate events and weddings.

Castle Kennedy Gardens

www.castlekennedygardens.com

Glorious 75 acre gardens situated on an isthmus between two natural lochs, with ruined Castle Kennedy at one end overlooking a beautiful herbaceous walled garden and Lochinch Castle at the other. Proximity to the gulf-stream provides an impressive collection of rare trees, including 20 Champion Trees, magnolias, and spectacular rhododendron displays. Guided walks, children's activities, theatre, tearoom, gift shop, plant centre - a 'must-visit'.

KEY FACTS

 For further information please visit the website.

 Toilet & disabled WC facilities available.

 Well-shaded car and bus parking is available adjacent to the entrance to the Gardens

 A free wheelchair is available at the main garden entrance. Please contact prior to visit for further details.

 Welcoming responsible dog owners and all friendly dogs on leads.

 Luxury self-catering holiday cottage accommodation on the Lochinch Castle Heritage Estate.

 Experience the beauty of Castle Kennedy Gardens on a Group Tour.

 Working with educational bodies under the Curriculum for Excellence & Outdoor Learning.

 Enjoy a quick coffee, a light lunch, a delicious cream tea or pudding at the Tea Room.

 Gift Shop sells original gifts, accessories, crafts, books, souvenirs, & postcards of the Gardens.

 Plant Centre has a wide selection of plants, including our famous rhododendrons.

 Corporate functions.

 Please see the 'What's On' section of the website for all upcoming walks, trails and other events.

Offering small private ceremonies & celebrations with 200 friends for your perfect wedding day.

CONTACT
Owner: The Earl and Countess of Stair
Contact: Stair Estates
Tel: 01776 702024 / 01581 400225
Email: info@castlekennedygardens.com

LOCATION
Stranraer, Dumfries and Galloway DG9 8SJ
Map Ref: 9:D3 - 3m E of Stranraer on A75.

OPENING TIMES
Gardens & Tea Room
29 Mar-31 Oct, daily 10am-5pm. Feb & Mar, weekends only.

ADMISSION
Adult: £5.50, Child: £2, Conc: £4.50, Family (2+2): £12.
Groups of 20 or more 10% discount.

Dumfries House

Gosford House

www.gosfordhouse.co.uk

1791 the 7th Earl of Wemyss, aided by Robert Adam, built one of the grandest houses in Scotland, with a 'paradise' of lakes and pleasure grounds. New wings, including the celebrated Marble Hall were added in 1891 by William Young. The house has a fine collection of paintings and furniture.

CONTACT
Owner/Contact: The Earl of Wemyss
Tel: 01875 870201
Email: info@gosfordhouse.co.uk

LOCATION
Longniddry, East Lothian EH32 0PX
Map Ref: 14:17 - Off A198 2 miles North East of Longniddry.

OPENING TIMES
Please check our website for most up-to-date opening times/days.

ADMISSION
Adult: £8
O.A.P/Students: £5
Child (under 16): Free

KEY FACTS

 NO photographs are allowed to be taken inside the house. NO bags are allowed into the house.

 Book in advance for groups of 8+. Each tour of the house lasts approximately 1 hour.

 Toilet facilities available.

 Providing the back drop you need for your event; such as black tie grandeur or party informality.

 Limited for coaches.

 Hosting a variety of large scale group activity days for groups.

 The house has very limited disabled access and part of the tour requires climbing stairs.

 Gosford House is available for a limited number of wedding receptions each year.

 Dogs allowed in grounds on leads.

 Played host to several major feature films, TV series and top brand fashion shoots etc.

Dalmeny House

www.dalmeny.co.uk

Dalmeny House, the family home of the Earls of Rosebery for over 300 years. Boasting superb collections of porcelain and tapestries, fine paintings by Gainsborough, Raeburn, Reynolds and Lawrence, together with exquisite 18th Century French furniture and a superb Napoleonic collection.

CONTACT
Owner:
The Earl of Rosebery
Contact: The Administrator
Tel: 0131 331 1888
Email: events@dalmeny.co.uk
LOCATION
South Queensferry,
Edinburgh EH30 9TQ
Map Ref: 13:G8
From Edinburgh A90, B924, 7 miles North, A90 ½m. On South shore of Firth of Forth.
OPENING TIMES
Jun & Jul Sun-Wed 2pm-5pm. Entry is by guided tour only & tours are 2.15pm & 3.30pm. Open at other times by appointment only.
ADMISSIONS
Summer: Adult, £10, Child (14-16yrs): £6.50, OAP: £9, Student: £9, Groups (20+): £9.

KEY FACTS

 60 cars, 3 coaches. Parking for functions in front of house.

 WCs.

 Dogs on leads in grounds only.

 Obligatory. Special interest tours can be arranged outside normal opening hours.

Café.

Lunches & Dinners.

Hopetoun House

hopetoun.co.uk

As you approach Hopetoun House the impressive panoramic view of the main façade is breathtakingly revealed. Designed by William Bruce and then altered and extended by William Adam, Hopetoun House is one of the finest examples of 18th Century architecture in Britain.

CONTACT
Owner: Hopetoun House Preservation Trust
Contact: Reception
Tel: 0131 331 2451
Email: enquiries@hopetoun.co.uk
LOCATION
South Queensferry,
EH30 9SL **Map Ref:** 13:F7
Exit A90 at A904,
Follow Brown Signs.
OPENING TIMES
Daily from Apr-Sep; 10.30am-4.30pm. Last admission 4pm.
ADMISSIONS
House & Grounds
Adult: £9.85, Child (5-16yrs): £5.25, Conc/Student: £8.60, Family (2+2): £27.
Grounds only
Adult: £4.55, Child (5-16yrs): £2.80, Conc/Student: £3.95; Family (2+2): £13.

KEY FACTS

 Cars and coaches welcome.

 Lift to 1st floor, Virtual access to upper floors. WC's.

 Dogs welcome (on leads) in grounds.

 Daily tour at 2pm. Groups (20+) welcome out of season by appointment.

 The Stables Tea Room serving traditional afternoon teas served in stunning surroundings.

Private functions, banquets & gala evenings, meetings, conferences, exhibitions & outdoor activities.

 Visit www.hopetoun.co.uk/events to see our calendar of events.

 Wedding ceremonies.

Scotland

New Lanark World Heritage Site

www.newlanark.org

Close to the famous Falls of Clyde, this cotton mill village c1785 became famous as the site of Robert Owen's radical reforms. Beautifully restored as a living community, attraction and hotel, the fascinating history of the village has been interpreted in New Lanark Visitor Centre.

KEY FACTS

 Toilet facilities available.

 Baby changing facilities available.

 Closed 25 Dec and 1 Jan.

 Cars & coaches. 5 min walk. The main Visitor Centre car park and spaces in the village are limited.

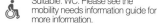 Suitable. WC. Please see the mobility needs information guide for more information.

 Hotel, self-catering & hostel.

 Book guided tours in advance.

Contact for information on education and school visits.

 Take time to sample the delicious fare in the family friendly Mill Café.

 Mill One Restaurant.

 The New Lanark Mill Shop offers a superb range of contemporary gifts, books & Scottish produce.

 New Lanark Mill Hotel.

 Please see the 'What's On' section of the website for a list of events and exhibitions.

 Wedding ceremonies and receptions.

 For filming or photography please fill out enquiry form on the website.

CONTACT
Owner: New Lanark Trust **Contact:** Trust Office
Tel: 01555 661345 **Email:** trust@newlanark.org

LOCATION
New Lanark Mills, Lanark, South Lanarkshire ML11 9DB
Map Ref: 13:E9 - Sat Nav code ML11 9BY. Nearest train station is Lanark. Glasgow > Lanark Bus from Buchanan Bus Station.

OPENING TIMES
10am-5pm Apr-Oct, 10am-4pm Nov-Mar. Shops/catering open until 5pm daily. Closed 25 Dec and 1 Jan.

ADMISSION
Visitor Centre
Adult: £12.50, Concs (Senior/Student): £10.50, Child: £9, Family (2+2): £38, Groups: 1 free/20 booked.

New Lanark Roof Garden

Drummond Gardens
drummondcastlegardens.co.uk

One of the finest formal gardens in Scotland. The Italianate parterre is revealed from a viewpoint at the top of the terrace. First laid out in the 17th Century and renewed in the 1950s. The perfect setting to stroll amongst the manicured plantings and absorb the atmosphere of this special place.

KEY FACTS

 The castle is not open to the public, but the gardens afford marvellous views of the buildings.

 By arrangement for groups. Special rates available for out of hours visits & guided garden tours.

 Lavatory facilities available.

 Cold drinks and ice cream available.

 Baby changing facilities available.

 Plant sales.

 Please drive to the castle courtyard (signposted for wheelchair user parking) and ticket office.

 Please see the website for special events.

 Partial. WC's. Viewing platform. Special vehicle access, ask on arrival. Gravel paths.

 Featured in Outlander. Looking for a location for your next film or TV series? Contact for more details.

 Dog friendly, but must be kept on leads.

CONTACT
Owner: Grimsthorpe & Drummond Castle Trust, A registered charity SC03964
Contact: The Caretaker
Tel: 01764 681433 **Fax:** 01764 681642
Email: info@drummondcastlegardens.co.uk

LOCATION
Drummond Castle, Muthill, Crieff, Perthshire PH7 4HZ
Map Ref: 13:E5 - 2 miles South of Crieff on Muthill Road (A822). 20 minutes drive from A9.

OPENING TIMES
Easter weekend, then daily. May, Sep, Oct at 1pm-6pm. Jun- Aug at 11am-6pm. Last admission 5pm.

ADMISSION
Adult: £6, Child: £2, Concession: £5.50, Family: £14, Groups (15+): From £5 per person.

Glamis Castle Gardens

Balcarres

16th Century tower house with 19th Century additions by Burn and Bryce.

Woodland and terraced gardens.

KEY FACTS

 Partial access.

Dogs welcome on leads only.

Guided tours by arrangement.

CONTACT
Owner:
Balcarres Heritage Trust
Contact: Lord Balniel
Tel: 01333 340206

LOCATION
Colinsburgh, Fife KY9 1HN
Map Ref:14:I6
½ mile North of Colinsburgh.

OPENING TIMES
Woodland & Gardens:
1 Mar-30 Sep, 2pm-5pm.

The house is not open except by written appointment and on 1-30 Apr, excluding Sun.

ADMISSION
House: £8
Garden: £8
House & Garden: £15

Strathtyrum
House & Gardens
www.strathtyrum.co.uk

The home of the Cheape family, the house was built in 1753 and a Georgian front added in 1820. The gardens include formal lawns, the restored Victorian walled garden, Doocot and Mausoleum. The walled garden is available to hire for weddings and events.

KEY FACTS

 Limited.

 Unsuitable.

 Plant sales.

 Please contact for corporate events.

 Please see the 'Events' section of the website.

 Weddings and celebrations may be held in a marquee within the walled garden.

CONTACT
Contact: Estate Office
Tel: 01334 473600
Email:
info@strathtyrumhouse.com

LOCATION
St Andrews, Fife KY16 9SF
Map Ref:14:I5
OS Ref: NO490 172
Entrance from the St Andrews/ Guardbridge Road, which is signposted when open.

OPENING TIMES
Apr 2-5, 10-13, 17-20, 24-27, 30-3 May. May 7-10, 23-25, 28. All dates inclusive. Guided tours 11am, 12 noon & 1pm. (Last admission 1pm).

ADMISSION
House: £5pp
House & Gardens: £8pp

Cortachy
Estate

www.airlieestates.com

Countryside walks including access through woodlands to Airlie Monument on Tulloch Hill with spectacular views of the Angus Glens and Vale of Strathmore. Footpaths are waymarked and colour coded.

KEY FACTS

 The estate network of walks are open all year round.

 Limited.

 Unsuitable.

 Dogs on leads only.

 Please contact for corporate events.

 Please see the 'Events' section of the website.

Weddings and Celebrations can be held either in a marquee or inside Downiepark House.

CONTACT
Owner: Trustees of Airlie Estates
Contact: Estate Office
Tel: 01575 570108
Fax: 01575 540400
Email: office@airlieestates.com

LOCATION
Cortachy, Kirriemuir, Angus DD8 4LX **Map Ref:**13:H3
Off the B955 Glens Road from Kirriemuir.

OPENING TIMES
Walks all year.

Gardens: 6-9 Apr, 30 Apr-20 May 2018
Last admission 3.30pm.

Please see estate website for admission prices and opening alterations.

Scone Palace & Grounds

Craigston Castle

www.craigston-castle.co.uk

Built between 1604 and 1607 by John Urquhart Tutor of Cromarty. Two wings were added in the early 1700s. The beautiful sculpted balcony, unique in Scottish architecture, depicts a piper, two grinning knights and David and Goliath. Remarkable carved oak panels of Scottish kings' biblical heroes, originally from the family seat at Cromarty Castle were mounted in doors and shutters in the early 17th Century. The house is a private home and is still owned and lived in by the Urquhart family.

The castle is available to rent at certain times of year and full details can be found on our website.

CONTACT
Owner: William Pratesi Urquhart
Contact: Barbara Perch
Tel: 01888551707 **Email:** info@craigston.co.uk

LOCATION
Turriff, Aberdeenshire AB53 5PX
Map Ref: 17:D8 - On B9105, 4.5 miles North East of Turriff.

OPENING TIMES
5-27 May and then 28-29 Sep 2018.
Plus throughout the year by appointment.

ADMISSION
Adult: £6, Child: £2 , Concession: £4.
Groups: Adult £5, Child/School £1.

KEY FACTS

 Please contact for any further details.

 Parking available on site.

 Very limited wheelchair access.

 Dogs welcome in the castle grounds.

 As guests of the Urquhart family you will have your choice of room, decorated with period furniture.

 Guided tours are obligatory.

 Courses held at specific times of year include painting & cookery, and open to other suggestions.

 Bespoke events can be organised with partner organisations. Let on an exclusive self-catering basis.

 Please see the 'Things to do' section of the website.

A spectacular wedding venue for the perfect mix of grand and relaxed.

Delgatie Castle

Delgatie Castle

www.delgatiecastle.com

Dating from 1030 the castle is steeped in Scottish history but still gives the feel of a lived in home. It has some of the finest painted ceilings in Scotland. Mary Queen of Scots stayed here for 3 days after the Battle of Corrichie.

Our pretty tearoom has a 'Taste Our Best Award' from Visit Scotland and also 'Scottish Home Baking Award' winner.

KEY FACTS

 No photography.

 Toilet facilities available.

 Open all year.

 Parking available.

 WC's.

 Two self-catering apartments in Castle.

 By arrangement.

 Educational and school visits by arrangement.

 The Laird's kitchen is open from 10am-5pm serving hot drinks, cakes, lunches & afternoon teas.

 Restaurant.

 Gift shop.

 The 'Yester' room or 'Ballroom' are perfect for business meetings, parties, anniversaries etc.

 Special events.

 For that once in a lifetime experience Delgatie Castle is the perfect wedding venue.

CONTACT
Owner: Delgatie Castle Trust **Contact:** Mrs Joan Johnson
Tel: 01888 563479
Email: joan@delgatiecastle.com

LOCATION
Turriff, Aberdeenshire AB53 5TD
Map Ref: 17:D9 - Off A947 Aberdeen to Banff Road.

OPENING TIMES
Daily 15 Jan-20 Dec. 1 Apr-30 Sep, 10am-5pm.
1 Oct-31 Mar, 10am-4pm.

ADMISSION
Adult: £8, Child/Con: £5, Family: £21 (2 Adults & 2 Children), Groups (10+): £5.

Crimonmogate

www.cmg-events.co.uk

Situated in Aberdeenshire, Crimonmogate is a Grade A listed mansion house and one of the most easterly stately homes in Scotland. It is now owned by William and Candida, Viscount and Viscountess Petersham. Pronounced 'Crimmon-moggat'. This exclusive country house stands within beautiful and seasonally-changing parkland and offers one of Aberdeenshire's most outstanding and unusual venues for corporate events, parties, dinners and weddings.

KEY FACTS

 Parking available.

 Only the principal rooms are part of the tour.

 Weddings & special events: max 60 in hall & up to 200 in marquee.

 Please see website for all upcoming events.

Fully licensed for civil ceremonies – and receptions are held in the unique marquee, or 'yurt'.

CONTACT
Owner/Contact:
Viscount Petersham
Tel: 01346 532401
Email: info@cmg-events.co.uk

LOCATION
Lonmay, Fraserburgh, Aberdeenshire AB43 8SE
Map Ref: 17:F8

OPENING TIMES
Please refer to the website for visiting dates.

ADMISSION
Adult: £7, Conc: £6, Child: £5.
Max of 12 at any one time, guided tours only.

Craigston Castle

Cawdor Castle

Dunvegan
Castle & Gardens
🏛 Ⓕ **www.dunvegancastle.com**

DUNVEGAN CASTLE ©MACLEOD ESTATE

DUNVEGAN CASTLE GARDENS @MACLEOD ESTATE

Experience living history at Dunvegan Castle, the ancestral home of the Chiefs of Clan MacLeod for 800 years.

Any visit to the Isle of Skye is incomplete without savouring the wealth of history on offer at Dunvegan Castle & Gardens, the ancestral home of the Chiefs of Clan MacLeod for 800 years. Originally designed to keep people out, it was first opened to visitors in 1933 and is one of Skye's most famous landmarks.

On display are many fine oil paintings and Clan treasures, the most famous of which is the Fairy Flag. Legend has it that this sacred Banner has miraculous powers and when unfurled in battle, the Clan MacLeod will defeat their enemies. Another of the castle's great treasures is the Dunvegan Cup, a unique 'mazer' dating back to the Middle Ages. It was gifted by the O'Neils of Ulster as a token of thanks to one of the Clan's most celebrated Chiefs, Sir Rory Mor, for his support of their cause against the marauding forces of Queen Elizabeth I of England in 1596. Today visitors can enjoy tours of an extraordinary castle and Highland estate steeped in history and clan legend, delight in the beauty of its formal gardens, take a boat trip onto Loch Dunvegan to see the seal colony, enjoy an appetising meal at the MacLeods Table Café or browse in one of its four shops offering a wide choice to suit everyone.

Over time, we have given a warm Highland welcome to visitors including Sir Walter Scott, Dr Johnson and Queen Elizabeth II and we look forward to welcoming you.

BOAT TRIPS TO SEAL COLONY ©MACLEOD ESTATE

KEY FACTS

 Boat trips to seal colony, fishing trips & loch cruises. Weather dependent. No photography in castle.

 Welcome by arrangement. Guide available on request.

 Toilet facilities available.

 MacLeod Table Café (seats 76).

 Baby changing facilities available.

 120 cars and 10 coaches. Coaches please book if possible.

 Gift shops sell a wide range of quality items, Harris Tweed products, knitwear, jewellery and small gifts.

 Partial. WC's. Laptop tour of Castle available.

 Offering an award-winning highland hospitality for every occasion.

 Dogs on leads in gardens only.

 For events and exhibitions please see the 'What's on' section of the website.

 4 self-catering holiday cottages sleeping up to 6 people.

 Perfect wedding venue in glorious surroundings, a warm highland welcome and rich in history.

 By appointment. Self-guided.

 A unique location for film, TV or advertising. Check website for details.

OWNER
Hugh Macleod of Macleod

CONTACT
Contact: Lynne Leslie, Office Manager
Tel: 01470 521206
Email: info@dunvegancastle.com

LOCATION
Dunvegan Castle, Dunvegan, Isle of Skye, Scotland IV55 8WF

Map Ref: 15:F9

1 mile North of village. North West corner of Skye. Kyle of Lochalsh to Dunvegan via Skye Bridge.

Rail: Inverness to Kyle of Lochalsh.

Ferry: Maillaig to Armadale.

OPENING TIMES
1 Apr-15 Oct Daily 10am-5.30pm.
Last admission 5pm. Closed 6 Oct-31 Mar.

Castle and Gardens closed Christmas & New Year.

ADMISSION
Castle & Gardens
Adult: £14, Child (5-15yrs): £9,
Senior/Student/Group (min 10 adults): £11,
Family Ticket (2 Adults, 4 Children): £34.

Gardens only
Adult: £12, Child (5-15yrs): £7,
Senior/Student/ Group: £9.

Seal Boat Trips
Adult: £7.50, Child (5-15yrs): £5.50, Senior/ Student/ Group £6.50, Infant (under 3yrs): Free.

Loch Cruises & Fishing Trips
Adult: £45, Child (5-15yrs): £35.

ABBOTSFORD, HOME OF SIR WALTER SCOTT 🏛ⓕ
The Abbotsford Trust, Abbotsford, Melrose, Roxburghshire TD6 9BQ
Tel: 01896 752043 **Email:** enquiries@scottsabbotsford.co.uk

BEMERSYDE GARDENS 🏛ⓕ
Melrose, Roxburghshire TD6 9DP
Tel: 01968 678465

BOWHILL HOUSE & COUNTRY ESTATE 🏛ⓕ
Bowhill, Selkirk TD7 5ET
Tel: 01750 22204

BUGHTRIG GARDEN 🏛ⓕ
Bughtrig, Coldstream TD12 4JP
Tel: 01890 840777 **Email:** ramsay@bughtrig.co.uk

DUNS CASTLE
Duns, Berwickshire TD11 3NW
Tel: 01361 883211

FERNIEHIRST CASTLE
Jedburgh, Roxburghshire, Scottish Borders TD8 6NX
Tel: 01450 870051 **Email:** curator@clankerr.co.uk

HERMITAGE CASTLE ◀▶
Scottish Borders TD9 0LU
Tel: 01387 376222

HIRSEL ESTATE 🏛ⓕ
Coldstream TD12 4LP
Tel: 01555 851536 **Email:** joy.hitchcock@daestates.co.uk

MANDERSTON 🏛ⓕ
Duns, Berwickshire TD11 3PP
Tel: 01361 883450 **Email:** palmer@manderston.co.uk

Mertoun Gardens 🏛ⓕ

St. Boswells, Melrose, Roxburghshire TD6 0EA
26 acres of beautiful grounds. Walled garden and well preserved circular dovecot.
Map Ref: 14:J10 **Tel:** 01835 823236
Email: estateoffice@mertoun.com **Website:** www.mertoungardens.co.uk
Open: Apr-Sep, Fri-Mon 2pm-6pm. Last Admission 5.30pm.
Admission: Adult: £5; Child: Free.

PAXTON HOUSE, GALLERY & COUNTRY PARK 🏛ⓕ
Berwick-Upon-Tweed TD15 1SZ
Tel: 01289 386291 **Email:** info@paxtonhouse.com

SMAILHOLM TOWER ◀▶
Smailholm, Kelso TD5 7PG
Tel: 01573 460365

TRAQUAIR HOUSE 🏛ⓕ
Innerleithen, Peeblesshire EH44 6PW
Tel: 01896 830323 **Email:** enquiries@traquair.co.uk

ARDWELL GARDENS 🏛ⓕ
Ardwell House, Ardwell, Stranraer, Wigtownshire DG9 9LY
Tel: 01776 860227 **Email:** info@ardwellestate.co.uk

AUCHINLECK ▪
Ochiltree, Ayrshire KA18 2LR
Tel: 01896 752043 **Email:** bookings@landmarktrust.org.uk

BLAIRQUHAN CASTLE
Maybole, Ayrshire KA19 7LZ
Tel: 01655 770239

BRODICK CASTLE ◀▶
Isle Of Arran KA27 8HY
Tel: 0131 243 9300

CAERLAVEROCK CASTLE ◀▶
Glencaple, Dumfries DG1 4RU
Tel: 01387 770244

CRAIGDARROCH HOUSE 🏛ⓕ
Moniaive, Dumfriesshire DG3 4JB
Tel: 01848 200202

CULZEAN CASTLE & COUNTRY PARK ♛
Maybole, Ayrshire KA19 8LE
Tel: 0844 493 2149 **Email:** culzean@nts.org.uk

DRUMLANRIG CASTLE 🏛ⓕ
Thornhill, Dumfriesshire DG3 4AQ
Tel: 01848 331555 **Email:** info@drumlanrigcastle.co.uk

DUMFRIES HOUSE 🏛ⓕ
Cumnock, East Ayrshire KA18 2NJ
Tel: 01290 421742/01290 427975 **Email:** DHtours@dumfries-house.org.uk

GLENMALLOCH LODGE ▪
Newton Stewart, Dumfries And Galloway DG8 6AG
Tel: 01628 825925 **Email:** bookings@landmarktrust.org.uk

KELBURN CASTLE & COUNTRY CENTRE 🏛ⓕ
Fairlie, By Largs, Ayrshire KA29 0BE
Tel: 01475 568685/568595 **Email:** admin@kelburncountrycentre.com

Rammerscales 🏛ⓕ

Lockerbie, Dumfriesshire DG11 1LD
Fine Georgian house with views over Annan valley.
Map Ref: 10:I2 - Directions available on website.
Tel: 01387 810229 **Email:** malcolm@rammerscales.co.uk
Website: www.rammerscales.co.uk
Open: 1-26 May, 1pm-4pm. Bus parties by appointment.
Admission: Adult: £5.

SORN CASTLE 🏛ⓕ
Sorn, Mauchline, Ayrshire KA5 6HR
Tel: 01290 551476 **Email:** info@sorncastle.com

Amisfield Mains

Nr Haddington, East Lothian EH41 3SA
Georgian farmhouse with gothic barn and cottage.
Location: Between Haddington and East Linton on A199.
Map Ref: 14:I8 **Tel:** 01875 870201 **Fax:** 01875 870620
Open: Exterior only: By appointment, Wemyss and March Estates Office, Longniddry, East Lothian EH32 0PY.
Admission: Please contact for details.

Arniston House 🏛ⓕ

Gorebridge, Midlothian EH23 4RY
Magnificent country setting, purchased 1571, beloved by Sir Walter Scott, William Adam Mansion commissioned 1726. **Map Ref:** 13:H9 - 1 mile from A7 at Gorebridge. **Tel:** 01875 830515 **Email:** info@arniston-house.co.uk
Website: www.arniston-house.co.uk **Open:** May & Jun: Tue & Wed; Jul-10 Sep: Tue, Wed & Sun, guided tours at 2pm & 3.30pm.
Pre-arranged groups. **Admission:** Adult: £6, Child: £3.

Beanston

Nr Haddington, East Lothian EH41 3SB
Georgian farmhouse with Georgian orangery.
Map Ref: 14:I8 - Between Haddington and East Linton on A199.
Tel: 01875 870201
Open: Exterior only: By appointment, Wemyss and March Estates Office, Longniddry, East Lothian EH32 0PY.
Admission: Please contact for details.

BLACKNESS CASTLE
Blackness, Linlithgow EH49 7NH
Tel: 01506 834807

DIRLETON CASTLE
North Berwick EH39 5ER
Tel: 01620 850 330

EDINBURGH CASTLE
Castle Hill, Edinburgh EH1 2NG
Tel: 0131 225 9846 **Email:** hs.explorer@scotland.gsi.gov.uk

GLADSTONE'S LAND
477B Lawnmarket, Royal Mile EH1 2NT
Tel: 0131 226 5856

Harelaw Farmhouse

Nr Longniddry, East Lothian EH32 0PH
Early 19th Century 2-storey farmhouse built as an integral part of the steading. Dovecote over entrance arch. **Location:** Between Longniddry and Drem on B1377. **Map Ref:** 14:I8 **Tel:** 01875 870201
Open: Exteriors only: By appointment, Wemyss and March Estates Office, Longniddry, East Lothian EH32 0PY.
Admission: Please contact for details.

HOUSE OF THE BINNS
Linlithgow, West Lothian EH49 7NA
Tel: 0844 493 2127 **Email:** information@nts.org.uk

INVERESK LODGE GARDEN
24 Inveresk Village, Musselburgh EH21 7TE
Tel: 0131 6651855 **Email:** inveresk@nts.org.uk

LENNOXLOVE HOUSE
Haddington, East Lothian EH41 4NZ
Tel: 01620 828614 **Email:** ken-buchanan@lennoxlove.com

LINLITHGOW PALACE
Linlithgow, West Lothian EH49 7AL
Tel: 01506 842896 **Email:** hs.explorer@scotland.gsi.gov.uk

NEWLISTON
Kirkliston, West Lothian EH29 9EB
Tel: 0131 333 3231

PALACE OF HOLYROODHOUSE
Edinburgh EH8 8DX
Tel: +44 (0)131 556 5100 **Email:** bookinginfo@royalcollection.org.uk

Red Row

Aberlady, East Lothian EH32 0DE
Terraced Cottages.
Map Ref: 14:I7 - Main Street, Aberlady, East Lothian.
Tel: 01875 870201 **Fax:** 01875 870620
Open: Exterior only. By appointment, Wemyss and March Estates Office, Longniddry, East Lothian EH32 0PY.
Admission: Please contact for details.

ROSSLYN CHAPEL
Chapel Loan, Roslin, Midlothian EH25 9PU
Tel: 0131 440 2159 **Email:** mail@rosslynchapel.com

COREHOUSE
Lanark ML11 9TQ
Tel: 01555 663126

GLASGOW CATHEDRAL
Castle Street, Glasgow G4 0QZ
Tel: 0141 552 6891

THE HILL HOUSE
Upper Colquhoun Street, Helensburgh G84 9AJ
Tel: 0844 493 2208 **Email:** thehillhouse@nts.org.uk

POLLOK HOUSE
2060 Pollokshaws Road, Glasgow G43 1AT
Tel: 0844 493 2202 **Email:** information@nts.org.uk

ABERDOUR CASTLE
Aberdour KY3 0SL
Tel: 01383 860519

ARBROATH ABBEY
Arbroath, Abbotsford, Tayside DD11 1EG
Tel: 01241 878756

ARBUTHNOTT HOUSE & GARDEN
Arbuthnott, Laurencekirk AB30 1PA
Tel: 01561 361226

BLAIR CASTLE & GARDENS
Blair Atholl, Pitlochry, Perthshire PH18 5TL
Tel: 01796 481207 **Email:** bookings@blair-castle.co.uk

BRANKLYN GARDEN
116 Dundee Road, Perth PH2 7BB
Tel: 0844 493 2193 **Email:** information@nts.org.uk

BRECHIN CASTLE
Brechin, Angus DD9 6SG
Tel: 01356 624566 **Email:** enquiries@dalhousieestates.co.uk

CAMBO GARDENS
Cambo Estate, Kingsbarns, St. Andrews, Fife KY16 8QD
Tel: 01333 450054 **Email:** cambo@camboestate.com

Charleton House

Colinsburgh, Leven, Fife KY9 1HG
Map Ref: 14:I6 - Off A917
1 mile North West of Colinsburgh. 3 miles North West of Elie.
Tel: 01333 340249 / 00467 35463865
Open: 1 Sep-2 Oct: daily, 12 noon-3pm.
Guided tours obligatory, admission every ½hr.
Admission: £12.

CLUNY HOUSE
Aberfeldy PH15 2JT
Email: wmattingley@btinternet.com

DUNNINALD, CASTLE & GARDENS
Montrose, Angus TD6 9BQ
Tel: 01674 672031 **Email:** visitorinformation@dunninald.com

EDZELL CASTLE
Perthshire DD9 7UE
Tel: 01356 648 631

FALKLAND PALACE & GARDEN
Falkland, Fife KY15 7BU
Tel: 0844 493 2186 **Email:** information@nts.org.uk

GLAMIS CASTLE & GARDENS
Glamis, Forfar, Angus DD8 1RJ
Tel: 01307 840393 **Email:** enquiries@glamis-castle.co.uk

GLENEAGLES
Auchterarder, Perthshire PH3 1PJ
Tel: 01764 682388 **Email:** jmhaldane@gleneagles.org

HILL OF TARVIT MANSION HOUSE
Cupar, Fife KY15 5PB
Tel: 0844 493 2185 **Email:** hilloftarvit@nts.org.uk

HOUSE OF DUN
Montrose, Angus DD10 9LQ
Tel: 0844 493 2144 **Email:** houseofdun@nts.org.uk

HOUSE OF PITMUIES GARDENS
Guthrie, By Forfar, Angus DD8 2SN
Tel: 01241 828245

HUNTINGTOWER CASTLE
Perth PH1 3JL
Tel: 01738 627 231

KELLIE CASTLE & GARDEN
Pittenweem, Fife KY10 2RF
Tel: 0844 493 2184 **Email:** information@nts.org.uk

Monzie Castle

Crieff, Perthshire PH7 4HD
Built in 1791. Destroyed by fire in 1908 and rebuilt and furnished by Sir Robert Lorimer. **Map Ref:** 13:E5 - 2 miles North East of Crieff.
Tel: 01764 653110
Open: 19 May-17 Jun, daily, 2pm-4.30pm. By appointment at other times. **Admission:** Adult: £5, Child: £1. Group rates available, contact property for details.

SCONE PALACE & GROUNDS
Perth PH2 6BD
Tel: 01738 552300 **Email:** visits@scone-palace.co.uk

ST ANDREW'S CASTLE
St Andrews, Fife KY16 9AR
Tel: 01334 477196

Tullibole Castle

Crook Of Devon, Kinross KY13 0QN
Scottish tower house c1608 with ornamental fishponds, a roofless lectarn doocot, 9th Century graveyard. **Map Ref:** 13:F6 - B9097 1m E of Crook of Devon. **Tel:** 01577 840236 **Email:** info@tullibole.co.uk
Website: www.tullibole.co.uk **Open:** Last week in Aug-30 Sep: Tue-Sun, 1pm-4pm. **Admission:** Adult: £5.50, Child/Conc: £3.50. Free for Doors Open weekend.

ARDCHATTAN PRIORY GARDENS
Connel, Argyll PA37 1RQ
Tel: 01796 481355

ARDENCRAIG GARDENS
Ardencraig, Rothesay, Isle Of Bute, West Highlands PA20 9ZE
Tel: 01700 504644 **Email:** enquires@argyll-bute.gov.uk

ARDKINGLAS HOUSE & WOODLAND GARDEN
Estate Office, The Square, Cairndow, Argyll PA26 8BH
Tel: 01499 600261 **Email:** info@ardkinglas.com

ARDTORNISH ESTATE & GARDENS
Morvern, Nr. Oban, Argyll & Bute PA80 5UZ
Tel: 01967 421288 **Email:** stay@ardtornish.co.uk

ARDUAINE GARDEN
Arduaine, Oban PA34 4XQ
Tel: 0844 493 2216 **Email:** information@nts.org.uk

ATTADALE GARDENS
Attadale Gardens, Strathcarron, Wester Ross IV54 8YX
Tel: 01520 722217 **Email:** houseofkeil@hotmail.com

CASTLE STALKER
Portnacroish, Appin, Argyll PA38 4BL
Tel: 01631 730354 **Email:** enquiries@scottsabbotsford.co.uk

CRARAE GARDEN
Inveraray, Argyll, Bute & Loch Lomond PA32 8YA
Tel: 0844 493 2210 **Email:** CraraeGarden@nts.org.uk

DOUNE CASTLE
Doune FK16 6EA
Tel: 01786 841742

DUART CASTLE
Isle Of Mull, Argyll PA64 6AP
Tel: 01680 812309 **Email:** guide@duartcastle.com

INVERARAY CASTLE & GARDENS
Inveraray Castle, Inveraray, Argyll PA32 8XE
Tel: 01499 302203 **Email:** enquiries@inveraray-castle.com

KISIMUL CASTLE
Castlebay, Isle of Barra HS9 5UZ
Tel: 01871 810313

MOUNT STUART
Isle Of Bute PA20 9LR
Tel: 01700 503877 **Email:** contactus@mountstuart.com

STIRLING CASTLE
Stirling FK8 1EJ
Tel: 01786 450000 **Email:** hs.explorer@scotland.gsi.gov.uk

BALFLUIG CASTLE
Alford, Aberdeenshire AB33 8EJ
Tel: 020 7624 3200

CASTLE FRASER & GARDEN
Sauchen, Inverurie AB51 7LD
Tel: 0131 243 9300

CRAIG CASTLE
Rhynie, Huntly, Aberdeenshire AB54 4LP
Tel: 01464 861705

CRATHES CASTLE, GARDEN & ESTATE ♛
Banchory, Aberdeenshire AB31 3QJ
Tel: 0844 493 2166 **Email:** crathes@nts.org.uk

DRUM CASTLE & GARDEN ♛
Drumoak, Melrose, By Keith, Banffshire AB55 5JE
Tel: 01542 810332

DRUMMUIR CASTLE
Drummuir, Abbotsford, Melrose, Roxburghshire TD6 9BQ
Tel: 01542 810332

DUFF HOUSE ⛊
Banff AB45 3SX
Tel: 01261 818181 **Email:** hs.explorer@scotland.gsi.gov.uk

DUNOTTAR CASTLE 🏰ⓕ
Stonehaven, Aberdeenshire AB39 2TL
Tel: 01569 762173 **Email:** dunnottarcastle@btconnect.com

FORT GEORGE ⛊
Grampian Highlands IV2 7TD
Tel: 01667 460232

FYVIE CASTLE & GARDEN ♛
Turriff, Aberdeenshire AB53 8JS
Tel: 0844 493 2182 **Email:** information@nts.org.uk

GORDON CASTLE 🏰ⓕ
Estate Office, Fochabers, Morayshire IV32 7PQ
Tel: 01343 820244

HADDO HOUSE ♛
Tarves, Ellon, Aberdeenshire AB41 0ER
Tel: 0844 493 2179 **Email:** information@nts.org.uk

HUNTLY CASTLE ⛊
Huntly, North and Grampian AB54 4SH
Tel: 01466 793191

KILDRUMMY CASTLE ⛊
Alford, Aberdeenshire AB33 8RA
Tel: 01975 571331

Lickleyhead Castle

Auchleven, Insch, Aberdeenshire AB52 6PN
Beautifully restored Laird's Castle, built by the Leslies c1450,
renovated in 1629 by John Forbes of Leslie. Boasts many interesting
architectural features.
Map Ref: 17:C10 2m S of Insch on B992. **Tel:** 07495756122
Open: 4-26 May (inclusive). Sat 9 & Sun 10 Jun, 10am-12 noon.
Admission: Free

PITMEDDEN GARDEN ♛
Pitmedden Garden, Ellon, Aberdeenshire AB41 7PD
Tel: 01651 842352 **Email:** information@nts.org.uk

SPYNIE PALACE ⛊
Spynie Palace, Elgin IV30 5QG
Tel: 01343 546358

DAVID WELCH WINTER GARDENS
Duthie Park, Polmuir Road, Aberdeen AB11 7TH
Tel: 01224 585310 **Email:** wintergardens@aberdeencity.gov.uk

---

ARMADALE CASTLE & GARDENS
Aramadale, Sleat, Isle of Skye IV45 8RS
Tel: 01471 844305 **Email:** jan@armadalecastle.com

BALLINDALLOCH CASTLE 🏰ⓕ
Ballindalloch, Banffshire AB37 9AX
Tel: 01807 500205 **Email:** enquiries@ballindallochcastle.co.uk

CASTLE & GARDENS OF MEY 🏰
Mey, Thurso, Caithness KW14 8XH
Tel: 01847 851473 **Email:** enquiries@castleofmey.org.uk

CAWDOR CASTLE & GARDENS 🏰ⓕ
Cawdor Castle, Nairn IV12 5RD
Tel: 01667 404401 **Email:** info@cawdorcastle.com

THE DOUNE OF ROTHIEMURCHUS
By Aviemore PH22 1QP
Tel: 01479 812345 **Email:** info@rothie.net

DUNROBIN CASTLE & GARDENS 🏰ⓕ
Golspie, Sutherland KW10 6SF
Tel: 01408 634081 **Email:** info@dunrobincastle.co.uk

EILEAN DONAN CASTLE 🏰
Dornie, Kyle Of Lochalsh, Wester Ross IV40 8DX
Tel: 01599 555202 **Email:** eileandonan@btconnect.com

INVEREWE GARDEN ♛
Poolewe IV22 2LG
Tel: 01445 712952 **Email:** 01445 712952

SKAILL HOUSE
Breckness Estate, Sandwick, Orkney KW16 3LR
Tel: 01856 841501 **Email:** info@skaillhouse.co.uk

URQUHART CASTLE ⛊
Drumnadrochit, Loch Ness, Inverness-shire IV63 6XJ
Tel: 01456 450551

Dunvegan Castle

WALES

SOUTH WALES • MID WALES • NORTH WALES

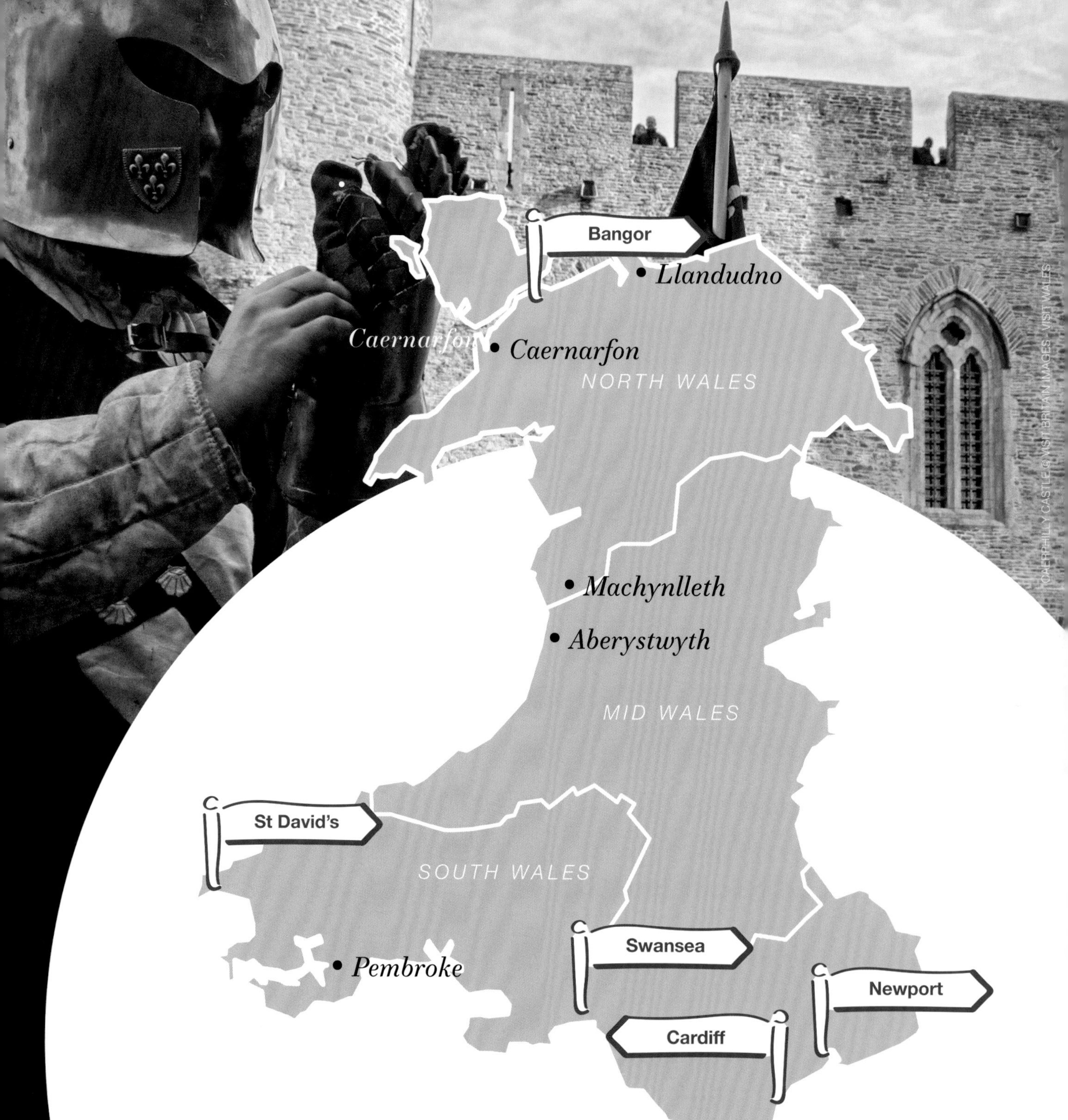
Bangor
Llandudno
Caernarfon
Caernarfon
NORTH WALES
Machynlleth
Aberystwyth
MID WALES
St David's
SOUTH WALES
Pembroke
Swansea
Newport
Cardiff

CAERPHILLY CASTLE © VISIT BRITAIN IMAGES, VISIT WALES

COUNTRYSIDE:

- Snowdonia
- Brecon Beacons
- Pembrokeshire Coast

HERITAGE:

- Medieval castles
- Tudor manor houses
- Mining heritage

FOOD:

- Welsh cakes
- Welsh rarebit
- Lamb cawl

BODNANT GARDENS

80 acre Victorian garden, created by 5 generations of the McLaren family. Formal Italianate rose terraces and informal plantings. National Collections of Magnolias, Embothriums, Eucryphias and Rhododendron Forestii.

Highlights:

• Laburnum Arch (May/June)
• Himalayan Blue poppy Meconopsis betonicifolia (June/July)
• Pinetum

THE LILY TERRACE, BODNANT GARDENS

FONMON CASTLE

The transformation of the castle at Fonmon in the 1760s by Robert Jones III created a series of spacious rococo interiors while castellations add the air of a gothic fort to the exterior.

Highlights:

• Cantilevered staircase
• Library
• Walled garden

THE DRAWING ROOM, FONMON CASTLE

POWIS CASTLE

Once the stronghold of the Princes of Powys, the panelled interiors belong to the late 17th century and the garden is worthy of an Italian baroque palace. Marriage to the heir of fabulously wealthy Clive of India in 1774 brought furniture, paintings and tapestries and important Indian works of art.

Highlights:

• State Bedroom
• Tipu Sultan's State Tent
• Terraced gardens

TIPU SULTAN'S STATE TENT AT POWIS CASTLE © NATIONAL TRUST IMAGES/ERIK PELHAM

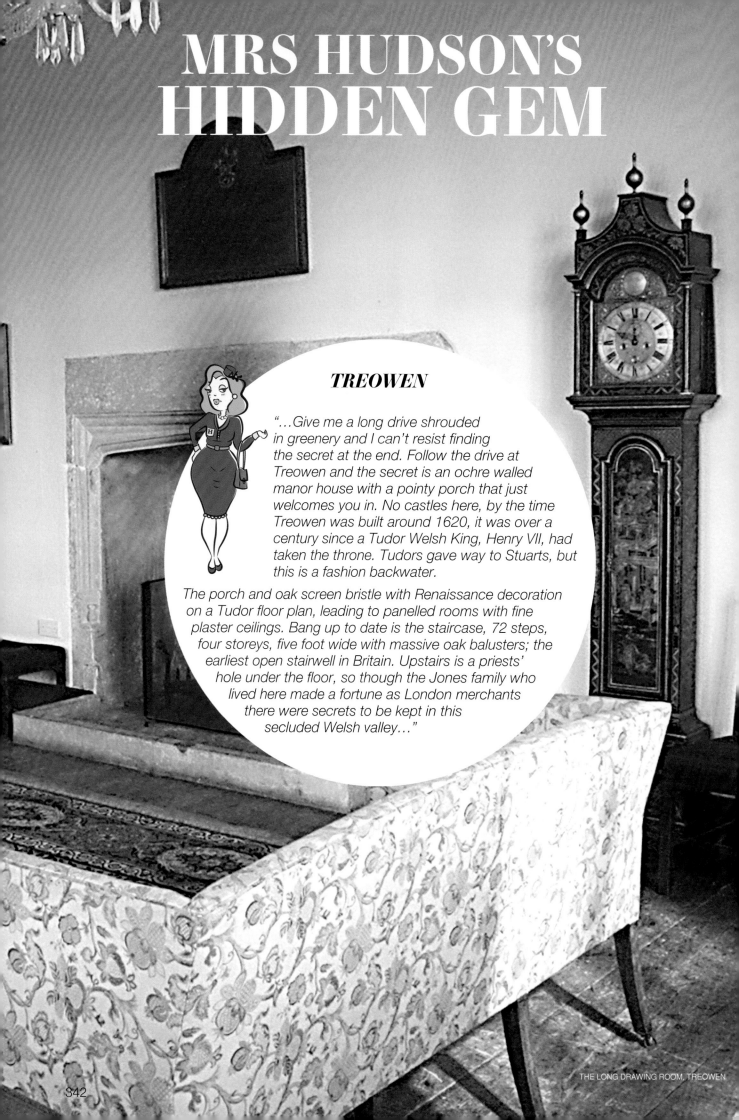

MRS HUDSON'S HIDDEN GEM

TREOWEN

"…Give me a long drive shrouded in greenery and I can't resist finding the secret at the end. Follow the drive at Treowen and the secret is an ochre walled manor house with a pointy porch that just welcomes you in. No castles here, by the time Treowen was built around 1620, it was over a century since a Tudor Welsh King, Henry VII, had taken the throne. Tudors gave way to Stuarts, but this is a fashion backwater.

The porch and oak screen bristle with Renaissance decoration on a Tudor floor plan, leading to panelled rooms with fine plaster ceilings. Bang up to date is the staircase, 72 steps, four storeys, five foot wide with massive oak balusters; the earliest open stairwell in Britain. Upstairs is a priests' hole under the floor, so though the Jones family who lived here made a fortune as London merchants there were secrets to be kept in this secluded Welsh valley…"

THE LONG DRAWING ROOM, TREOWEN

342

MARK THE YEAR

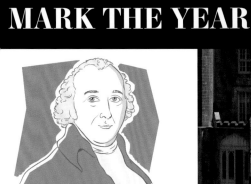

200 YEARS
REPTON
Enjoy the gardens of Humphry Repton 200 years after his death.
✔ *Plas Newydd*

PLAS NEWYDD © NATIONAL TRUST IMAGES/JOHN MILLAR

100 YEARS
WOMEN & SUFFRAGE

THE DRAWING ROOM, FONMON CASTLE

1. ISABEL DE CLARE, COUNTESS OF PEMBROKE (1172-1220)
Linguist, heiress, wife of William Marshall
at Pembroke Castle.

THE DAVIES SISTERS © GREGYNOG

2. GWENDOLINE (1882-1951) & MARGARET DAVIES (1884-1963)
Patrons & collectors of art and music
at Gregynog.

LADY CAROLINE PAGET BY REX WHISTLER © NATIONAL TRUST IMAGES

3. LADY CAROLINE PAGET (1913-73)
Muse of artist, Rex Whistler
at Plas Newydd.

343

DID YOU KNOW?

1 CAERPHILLY CASTLE

The leaning tower of Caerphilly Castle leans even more than the Leaning Tower of Pisa.

2 ABERGLASNEY GARDENS

The Elizabethan cloister garden at Aberglasney Gardens is the best preserved Elizabethan garden in the UK. The Cloister has allowed strollers to enjoy the garden even in the rain for 500 years.

3 LLANFAIACH FAWR

In August 1645 Charles I came to stay with his Commissioner Edward Pritchard at Llanfaiach Fawr Manor. Unfortunately, Pritchard's brother-in-law was Bussy Mansell, soon to be Commander in Chief for Parliament in Wales. When civil war broke out in November, Edward switched sides, defending Cardiff for Parliament.

CRESSELLY

CAERPHILLY CASTLE © ROSS

4 CRESSELLY

The new Georgian house at Cresselly, built in 1769 by John Bartlett Allen, was needed because the old one was uncomfortably close to the family coal mine.

5 GWYDIR CASTLE

In 1921 Charles Wynn-Carrrington, Marquess of Lincolnshire sold Gwydir Castle and the contents were scattered. Amazingly, the carved panelling of the Dining Room is back, having been tracked to the Metropolitan Museum of Art in New York and brought triumphantly home.

6 LAUGHARNE CASTLE

The sea-facing gazebo at Laugharne Castle provided inspiration for two important 20th century writers. It belonged to Richard Hughes, author of A High Wind in Jamaica, who lent it to poet,Dylan Thomas.

3 TOP CASTLES

CAERNARFON CASTLE FROM THE INNER BAILEY
© CROWN COPYRIGHT 2017 - VISIT WALES

1. CAERNARVON CASTLE, GWYNEDD

The greatest of Edward I's defensive ring of North Wales castles built in the 1290s after the suppression of Llywelyn ap Gruffydd. Formidable firepower could be launch from the towers, gatehouses & galleries while banded stonework & polygonal towers recall Byzantium.

2. BEAUMARIS CASTLE, ANGLESEY

The masterpiece of Master James of St George, genius architect of the castles of Edward I. Left unfinished at his death in 1309, Beaumaris Castle has perfect concentric walls and a tide filled moat.

BEAUMARIS CASTLE © VISIT BRITAIN - DAVID ANGEL

3. CARDIFF CASTLE, CARDIFF

Roman outer walls, a Norman motte and round shell keep but also living quarters designed in extravagant high Victorian gothic revival by William Burges for the 3rd Marquess of Bute. Henry I imprisoned his elder brother Robert Curthose here for 20 years.

THE BANQUETING HALL, CARDIFF CASTLE © CROWN COPYRIGHT 2017 - VISIT WALES

NANTEOS MANSION, CEREDIGION

Elegant Georgian mansion house of 1731 with Palladian carriage house set in landscaped grounds and woodlands. The Nanteos Cup, a holy relic of the True Cross now in the National Library of Wales, was brought here by the monks of Glastonbury.

WARPOOL COURT HOTEL, PEMBROKESHIRE

The first building on this site, 'Bryn-y-garn' ('hill of the rock'), was constructed in 1870 to re-house the long-established St Davids' Cathedral School. In 1956 Warpool Court was transformed into a country house hotel by Mr and Mrs Glyn Lloyd.

TRE YSGAWEN COUNTRY HOUSE HOTEL & SPA, ANGLESEY

A rural Victorian mansion built for the Pritchard-Rayner family in 1882 where they followed the Anglesey Hunt. The hotel spa makes use of the converted stable buildings; there are 4-posters, a sculpture garden and woodland walks. Afternoon teas.

WOLFSCASTLE COUNTRY HOTEL, PEMBROKESHIRE

Beginning as a simple cottage known as "Allt yr Afon" in the 1600s, it was redesigned in the 1880s into a seven bedroom vicarage by the Edwardes family who owned nearby Sealyham House. It was acquired by present owner Andy Stirling in 1976.

GLEN-YR-AFON HOUSE HOTEL, MONMOUTHSHIRE

Victorian gothic villa with extensive grounds offering individually styled rooms and walks along the river Usk. Afternoon teas.

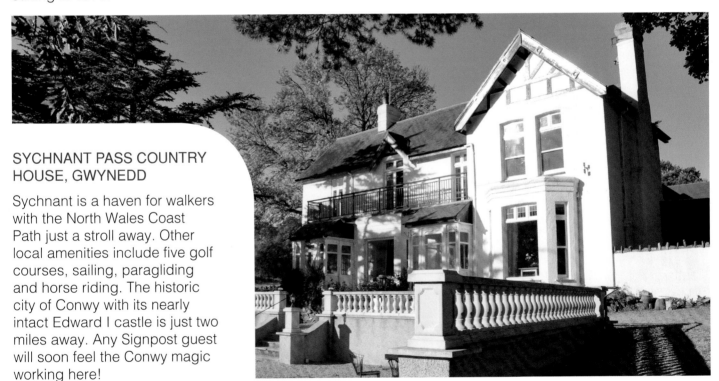

SYCHNANT PASS COUNTRY HOUSE, GWYNEDD

Sychnant is a haven for walkers with the North Wales Coast Path just a stroll away. Other local amenities include five golf courses, sailing, paragliding and horse riding. The historic city of Conwy with its nearly intact Edward I castle is just two miles away. Any Signpost guest will soon feel the Conwy magic working here!

Y TALBOT, CEREDIGION

Y Talbot is a Welsh country inn, set in the centre of Tregaron, a small town nestling at the foot of the Cambrian Mountains. Twenty miles west is Cardigan Bay and 20 miles east over the mountains, on a single track former drover's road, to Abergwesyn and the Elan Valley.

Wales

Aberglasney Gardens

www.aberglasney.org

Made famous by the BBC television series 'A Garden Lost in Time', this followed its restoration. Today it is quite simply one of Wales' finest gardens. A renowned plantsman's paradise with a unique Elizabethan cloister garden at its heart, Aberglasney offers the opportunity to explore more than 10 acres of magnificent gardens which along with the fully restored ground floor of Aberglasney's Grade II* listed mansion offer a stunning venue for weddings, exhibitions and events.

KEY FACTS

 Membership: 364 days of unlimited entry to the gardens, mansion & tea rooms with more benefits.

 Toilet facilities available.

 Baby changing facilities available.

 Closed on Christmas Day.

 Free parking, also large coach park.

 Mostly suitable. Two wheelchairs available for visitors to use free of charge (first come first serve basis).

 Two 5* self-catering holiday cottages on site. The Gardener's Cottage & The Coachman's Cottage.

 Access Aberglasney's App on your iOS device or hire an iPad on site.

 Pre-booked for groups. Experience the history tour and the head gardener tour.

 School visits offer garden tours (either historical/horticultural) & hands-on activities in the gardens.

 The tearooms, idyllically located overlooking the pool garden. Enjoy lunches, tea & homemade cake.

 Pick up a souvenir with pieces from many local craftspeople on sale as well as a large range of books.

 In the plant sales area you'll find many of the plants you will see growing in the gardens.

 Offering a unique venue for product launches, exhibitions, meetings and conferences.

 For upcoming events and exhibitions, please see the website.

Mansion house and garden weddings. Contact for information.

CONTACT
Owner: Aberglasney Restoration Trust (Private Charitable Trust)
Contact: Booking Department
Tel: 01558 668998
Email: info@aberglasney.org

LOCATION
Llangathen, Carmarthenshire, Wales SA32 8QH
Map Ref: 5:F10
Aberglasney is 12 miles East of Carmarthen and 4 miles West of Llandeilo on the A40 at Broad Oak.

OPENING TIMES
All year: daily (except Christmas day). Apr-Oct: 10am-6pm, last entry 5pm. Nov-Mar: 10.30am-4pm, last entry 3pm.

ADMISSION
Adult/Concessions: £8.50
Children (16 years & under): FREE
Groups 10+: Adult £7.25 - By arrangement.

Fonmon Castle

www.fonmoncastle.com

Just 25 minutes from Cardiff and the M4, Fonmon is one of few medieval castles still lived in as a home, since being built c1200, it has only changed hands once. Visitors are welcomed by an experienced guide and the 45 minute tour walks through the fascinating history of the Castle, its families, architecture and interiors. The Fonmon gardens are an attraction in their own right for enthusiasts and amateurs alike and visitors are free to wander and explore. Available as an exclusive wedding and party venue, corporate and team building location, visitor attraction and host for product launches and filming.

KEY FACTS

 Accepts credit cards.

 Toilet facilities available.

 Baby changing facilities available.

 Ample free parking for cars and coaches.

 Suitable. WC's.

Guided tours are obligatory. Group tours are accompanied by a delicious, Afternoon tea.

 Educational visits by arrangement.

 Ideal corporate location for conferences, meetings, away days & team building by prior arrangement.

Please see the 'What's On' section of the website for all upcoming events.

 Licensed for civil ceremonies for up to 110 people. Offering wedding receptions.

 A popular destination for film shoots and photographic projects.

CONTACT
Owner: Sir Brooke Boothby Bt **Contact:** Casey Govier
Tel: 01446 710206 **Email:** fonmon_castle@msn.com

LOCATION
Fonmon, Barry, Vale Of Glamorgan CF62 3ZN
Map Ref: 2:L2 15 miles W of Cardiff, 1 mile W of Cardiff Airport.

OPENING TIMES
Public opening: 1 Apr-30 Sep on Tue & Wed afternoons for individuals, families & small groups. Midday-5pm, no need to book. Tours at 2pm, 3pm & 4pm & last 45 mins, last entrance to gardens at 4pm. Groups 20+ welcome by appointment throughout the year. Varied group hospitality options available including very popular afternoon teas.

ADMISSION
Entry & Tour of the Castle - Adult: £6, Child: Free.
Access to Garden & Grounds: Free.

Llancaiach Fawr Manor

www.llancaiachfawr.co.uk

This superbly restored gentry manor house is no ordinary heritage attraction. History here is tangible. The costumed servants of the house are living and working in 1645 and allow you to share and engage in their world. Fires crackle, candles flicker and the sounds and smells of domestic life make your visit a memorable experience of the past. Meet ordinary people living in extraordinary times.

CONTACT
Owner: Caerphilly County Borough Council
Contact: Reception
Tel: 01443 412248
Email: llancaiachfawr@caerphilly.gov.uk

LOCATION
Gelligaer Road, Nelson, Treharris, Caerphilly County Borough CF46 6ER **Map Ref:** 2:M1
South side of B4254, 1 mile North of A472 at Nelson.

TYPICALLY OPEN
10am-5pm Tue-Sun and BH Mons all year round. Last entry to the Manor 4pm. Closed 24 Dec-1 Jan inclusive.

ADMISSION
Adult: £8.50
Concessions: £6.95
Child: £6.95
Family (2+3): £25

KEY FACTS

 No photography indoors.

 Lavatory facilities available.

 Baby changing facilities available.

 Closed 24 Dec-1 Jan inclusive.

 90 free spaces. Disabled spaces close to visitor centre entrance.

 Accessible WC's. Lift for access to upper floors.

 Dogs in grounds only. Not in walled gardens.

 Costumed 17th Century servants lead tours. Approx 1.5 hours.

 Tours, activities, trails & workshops.

 Licensed. 10am-4pm. Hot & cold drinks, sandwiches cakes & snacks. Hot food served 12pm-2pm.

 Licensed. Sun lunches and private functions.

 Boutique gift shop.

Plant sales available.

Provides a distinctive environment for any conference, business meeting, banquet or dinner party.

Please see the 'Events' section of the website for all upcoming events.

Ideal location for your wedding; overlooking the peaceful surroundings of the Rhymney Valley.

Sunken Garden at Aberglasney

Abercamlais House

www.abercamlais.com

Splendid Grade I mansion dating from 16th Century, altered extensively in early 18th Century with 19th Century additions, in extensive grounds beside the river Usk. Beautiful octagonal pigeon house, formerly a privy.

CONTACT
Owner: Mr & Mrs Ballance
Contact: Mrs Ballance
Tel: 07789930064
Email: andrea.ballance@blueyonder.co.uk

LOCATION
Abercamlais, Brecon, Powys LD3 8EY **Map Ref:** 6:I10
5 miles West of Brecon on A40.

OPENING TIMES
Apr-end Sep.
See website for further details.

ADMISSION
Adult: £5, Child: Free.

KEY FACTS

 No photography in house.

 Parking available.

 Accessible.

 Dogs on leads only.

 Obligatory. The tour lasts for about 2 hours.

Wales

The Judge's Lodging

www.judgeslodging.org.uk

Explore the fascinating world of the Victorian judges, their servants and felonious guests at this award-winning, totally hands-on historic house. Through sumptuous judge's apartments and the gas-lit servants' quarters below, follow an 'eavesdropping' audio tour featuring actor Robert Hardy. Damp cells, vast courtroom and new interactive local history rooms included.

KEY FACTS

 Parking available in town.

 Partial. Disabled parking is at the top of Broad Street, approximately 50 yards from the front entrance.

 Guided tours by arrangement.

 An invaluable resource and learning experience for primary, secondary and higher education.

The gift shop sells a wide selection of books, gifts and toys to suit all ages and pockets.

 Wedding and civil partnership ceremony venue.

CONTACT
Owner:
The Judge's Lodging Trust
Contact: Gabrielle Rivers
Tel: 01544 260650
Email: info@judgeslodging.org.uk
LOCATION
Broad St, Presteigne, Powys
LD8 2AD **Map Ref:** 6:K8
In town centre, off A44 and A4113. Within easy reach from Herefordshire, Shropshire and mid-Wales.
OPENING TIMES
1 Mar-31 Oct: Tues-Sun, 10am-5pm. 1 Nov-31 Nov: Wed-Sun, 10am-4pm.
1 Dec-22 Dec: Sat-Sun 10am-4pm. Open BH Mons.
ADMISSION
Adult: £7.95, Child: £3.95, Conc: £6.95, Family: £21.50.
Groups (10-80): Adult: £7.50, Conc: £6.50, Schools: £5.50..

Gregynog

The Judge's Lodging

Iscoyd Park

www.iscoydpark.com

A red brick Georgian House in an idyllic 18th Century parkland setting situated on the Welsh/Shropshire border. Still a family home, Iscoyd has undergone a complete restoration over the last seven years whilst building a reputation as an award-winning wedding venue. We have 14 double bedrooms with plans to increase this number over the next few years. From September 2017 we have bought all catering 'in-house'

under the direction of our Michelin trained Head Chef. While continuing to focus on weddings, we will also be open for company retreats, private parties and photography/film shoots as well as hosting 'in-house' ticketed events such as pop-up restaurants, residential events and cooking classes. The house is only let on an exclusive basis meaning there is never more than one event occurring at any time.

CONTACT
Contact/Owner: Philip L Godsal
Tel: 01948 780785
E-mail: info@iscoydpark.com

LOCATION
Nr Whitchurch, Shropshire SY13 3AT

Map Ref: 6:L4

2 miles West of Whitchurch off A525.

OPENING TIMES
House visits by written appointment.

KEY FACTS

 Open all year.

 Limited for coaches.

 WC's.

 Rooms in the Stable Rooms & the Laundry Cottage are let on a B&B basis.

 Obligatory.

 By arrangement.

 Licensed.

 Private dinners and weddings a speciality.

 Please see website for special events.

 Licensed.

Wales

Cochwillan Old Hall

A fine example of medieval architecture with the present house dating from 1450. It is thought to have been built by William Gryffydd who fought for Henry VII at Bosworth. Once owned in the 17th Century by John Williams who became Archbishop of York. The house was restored from a barn in 1971.

KEY FACTS

 For all further enquiries please contact.

 Parking available on site.

 Accompanied tours available.

CONTACT
Owner: R C H Douglas Pennant
Contact:
Mark & Christopher Chenery
Tel: 01248 355139
Email: risboro@hotmail.co.uk

LOCATION
Halfway Bridge, Bangor, Gwynedd LL57 3AZ
Map Ref: 5:G2 - 3 ½ miles South East of Bangor. 1 mile South East of Talybont off A55.

OPENING TIMES
By appointment.

ADMISSION
Please email or telephone for details.

Wern Isaf

This Arts and Crafts house was built in 1900 by the architect H L North as his family home and contains much of the original furniture and William Morris fabrics.

Situated in a woodland garden with extensive views over the Menai Straits and Conwy Bay.

KEY FACTS

 For all further enquiries please contact.

 Parking available on site.

 Guided tours available.

CONTACT
Owner/Contact:
Mrs P J Phillips
Tel: 01248 680437

LOCATION
Penmaen Park, Llanfairfechan, Conwy LL33 0RN

Map Ref: 5:G2

Off A55 midway between Bangor and Conwy.

OPENING TIMES
1-29 May
(excluding Weds)
11:30am-2:30pm.

ADMISSION
Free.

Hartsheath ⅢⒻ

A rock-faced stone Neo-Classical house substantially remodelled in the early 19th Century around an earlier 18th Century house.

Situated in a fine 19th Century landscaped park.

KEY FACTS

 For all further enquiries please contact.

 Parking available on site.

 Guided tours available.

CONTACT
Owner: Dr M.C. Jones-Mortimer Will Trust
Contact:
Dr Miranda Dechazal
Tel: 01352 770204

LOCATION
Pontblyddyn, Mold, Flintshire CH7 4HP
Map Ref: 6:J3

Access from A5104, 3.5 miles South East of Mold between Pontblyddyn and Penyffordd.

OPENING TIMES
2pm-5pm
May: 1, 7, 8, 26, 27, 28
Jun: 3,10
Aug: 26, 27, 28
Sep: 20, 21, 22, 23, 24, 25, 26, 27

ADMISSION
£5

Y Fferm

A late 16th Century small manorial house which underwent major alteration in the 17th Century.

KEY FACTS

 For all further enquiries please contact.

 Parking available on site.

 Guided tours available.

CONTACT
Owner: Dr M.C. Jones-Mortimer Will Trust
Contact:
Dr Miranda Dechazal
Tel: 01352 770204

LOCATION
Pontblyddyn, Mold, Flintshire CH7 4HN
Map Ref: 6:J3 - Access from A541 in Pontblyddyn, 3½ miles South East of Mold.

OPENING TIMES
2pm-5pm
May: 1, 7, 8, 26, 27, 28
Jun: 3,10
Aug: 26, 27, 28
Sep: 20, 21, 22, 23, 24, 25, 26, 27

ADMISSION
£5

ABERDEUNANT 🌿
Taliaris, Llandeilo, Carmarthenshire SA19 6DL
Tel: 01588 650177 **Email:** aberdeunant@nationaltrust.org.uk

CAERPHILLY CASTLE ✚
Caerphilly CF83 1JD
Tel: 029 2088 3143

CASTLE CASTLE
Castle Street, Cardiff CF10 3RB
Tel: 029 2087 8100

CARDIGAN CASTLE
Green Street, Cardigan, Ceredigion SA43 1JA
Tel: 01239 615131 **Email:** cadwganbpt@btconnect.com

CARREG CENNEN CASTLE ✚
Tir y Castell Farm, Llandeilo, Carmarthenshire SA19 6UA
Tel: 01558 822291

CASTELL COCH ✚
Tongwynlais, Cardiff CF15 7JS
Tel: 029 2081 0101

CHEPSTOW CASTLE ✚
Chepstow, Monmouthshire NP16 5EY
Tel: 01291 624065

CILGERRAN CASTLE 🌿 ✚
Cardigan, Pembrokeshire SA43 2SF
Tel: 01239 621339 **Email:** cilgerrancastle@nationaltrust.org.uk

Cornwall House 🏠©

58 Monnow Street, Monmouth NP25 3EN
Town house, Georgian street façade, walled garden.
Location: Half way down main shopping street, set back from street. Please use centre door. **Map Ref:** 6:L11
Tel: 01600 712031 **Email:** jane2harvey@tiscali.co.uk
Open: 2pm-5pm on Fridays in Jul & Aug and on 29 Mar-2 Apr, 7 & 8 Apr, 5-7 May, 26-28 May, 25-27 Aug. **Admission:** Adult £4, Conc. £2.

CRESSELLY 🏠
Kilgetty, Pembrokeshire SA68 0SP
Email: hha@cresselly.com

ST DAVIDS BISHOP'S PALACE ✚
St Davids, Pembrokeshire SA62 6PE
Tel: 01437 720517

DINEFWR 🌿
Llandeilo, Carmarthenshire SA19 6RT
Tel: 01443 336000 **Email:** cadw@wales.gsi.gov.uk

DYFFRYN GARDENS 🌿
St Nicholas, Vale of Glamorgan CF5 6SU
Tel: 02920 593328 **Email:** dyffryn@nationaltrust.org.uk

DYLAN THOMAS BIRTHPLACE ◇
5 Cwmdonkin Drive, Uplands, Swansea, SA3 5AR
Tel: 01792 472 555 **Email:** info@dylanthomasbirthplace.com

ST FAGANS: NATIONAL HISTORY MUSEUM
Cardiff CF5 6XB
Tel: 029 2057 3500

GROSMONT CASTLE ✚
Nr Abergavenny, Monmouthshire NP7 8EQ
Tel: 01443 336000 **Email:** cadw@wales.gsi.gov.uk

KIDWELLY CASTLE ✚
Kidwelly, Carmarthenshire SA17 5BQ
Tel: 01554 890104

THE KYMIN 🌿
The Round House, The Kymin, Monmouth NP25 3SF
Tel: 01600 719241 **Email:** kymin@nationaltrust.org.uk

LAUGHARNE CASTLE ✚
King Street, Laugharne, Carmarthenshire SA33 4SA
Tel: 01994 427906

LLANDAFF CATHEDRAL
Llandaff Cathedral Green, Cardiff CF5 2LA
Tel: 02920 564554 **Email:** office@llandaffcathedral.org.uk

LLANVIHANGEL COURT 🏠
Nr Abergavenny, Monmouthshire NP7 8DH
Tel: 01873 890217 **Email:** jclarejohnson@googlemail.com

MARGAM COUNTRY PARK & CASTLE
Margam, Port Talbot, West Glamorgan SA13 2TJ
Tel: 01639 881635 **Email:** margampark@npt.gov.uk

MONMOUTH CASTLE ✚
Castle Hill, Monmouth NP25 3BS
Tel: 01443 336000 **Email:** cadw@wales.gsi.gov.uk

NATIONAL BOTANIC GARDEN OF WALES
Llanarthne, Carmarthenshire SA32 8HG
Tel: 01558 667149 **Email:** info@gardenofwales.org.uk

OGMORE CASTLE & STEPPING STONES ✚
Ogmore, St Brides Major, Vale Of Glamorgan CF32 0QP
Tel: 01443 336000 **Email:** cadw@wales.gsi.gov.uk

OXWICH CASTLE ✚
Oxwich, Swansea SA3 1NG
Tel: 01792 390359

PEMBROKE CASTLE
Pembroke SA71 4LA
Tel: 01646 681510 **Email:** info@pembrokecastle.co.uk

PICTON CASTLE & WOODLAND GARDENS 🏠©
Taliaris, Nr Haverfordwest, Pembrokeshire SA62 4AS
Tel: 01437 751326 **Email:** info@pictoncastle.co.uk

RAGLAN CASTLE ✚
Raglan, Monmouthshire NP15 2BT
Tel: 01291 690228

SKENFRITH CASTLE ✚
Skenfrith, Nr Abergavenny, Monmouthshire NP7 8UH
Tel: 01443 336000 **Email:** cadw@wales.gsi.gov.uk

STRADEY CASTLE 🏠©
Llanelli, Carmarthenshire SA15 4PL
Tel: 01554 774626 **Email:** info@stradeycastle.com

TINTERN ABBEY ✛
Tintern NP16 6SE
Tel: 01291 689251 **Email:** TinternAbbey@wales.gsi.gov.uk

Trebinshwn

Llangasty, Nr Brecon, Powys LD3 7PX
16th Century mid-sized manor house. Extensively rebuilt 1780. Fine courtyard and walled garden. **Map Ref:** 6:I10 - 1½m NW of Bwlch.
Tel: 01874 730653 **Fax:** 01874 730843
Email: liza.watson@trebinshunhouse.co.uk
Open: Easter-31 Aug: Mon-Tue, 10am-4.30pm.
Admission: Free.

TREDEGAR HOUSE & PARK ❧
Newport, South Wales NP10 8YW
Tel: 01633 815880 **Email:** tredegar@nationaltrust.org.uk

Treowen ▥ⓕ

Wonastow, Monmouth NP25 4DL
The most important early 17th Century gentry house in the county. Particularly fine open well staircase.
Map Ref: 6:K11 - 3m WSW of Monmouth. **Tel:** 07530 357390
Website: www.treowen.co.uk **Open:** May-Aug Fri 10am-4pm.
Also Sat & Sun 14-15, 21-22 & 28-29 Apr, 12-13 May and 22-23 Sep 2pm-5pm. **Admission:** £6. Free to HHA Friends on Fridays only.

TRETOWER COURT & CASTLE ✛
Taliaris, Llandeilo, Carmarthenshire SA19 6DL
Tel: 01588 650177 **Email:** aberdeunant@nationaltrust.org.uk

TUDOR MERCHANT'S HOUSE ❧
Quay Hill, Tenby, Pembrokeshire SA70 7BX
Tel: 01834 842279 **Email:** tudormerchantshouse@nationaltrust.org.uk

USK CASTLE ▥
Monmouth Road, Usk, Monmouthshire NP5 1SD
Tel: 01291 672563 **Email:** info@uskcastle.com

ABERYSTWYTH CASTLE
Aberystwyth, Ceredigion SY23 2AG
Tel: 01970 612125

CANOLFAN OWAIN GLYNDWR
Heol Maengwyn, Machylleth, Powys SY20 8EE
Tel: 01654 703336 **Email:** glyndwr.enquiries@canolfanglyndwr.org

GLANSEVERN HALL GARDENS
Glansevern, Berriew, Welshpool, Powys SY21 8AH
Tel: 01686 640644 **Email:** glansevern@yahoo.co.uk

GREGYNOG ▥
Tregynon, Nr Newtown, Powys SY16 3PW
Tel: 01686 650224 **Email:** enquiries@gregynog.org

HAFOD ESTATE
Pontrhyd-y-groe, Ystrad Meurig, Ceredigion SY25 6DX
Tel: 01974 282568 **Email:** trust@hafod.org

THE HALL AT ABBEY-CWM-HIR
Nr Llandrindod Wells, Powys LD1 6PH
Tel: 01597 851727 **Email:** info@abbeycwmhir.com

LLANERCHAERON ❧
Ciliau Aeron, Nr Aberaeron, Ceredigion SA48 8DG
Tel: 01545 570200 **Email:** llanerchaeron@nationaltrust.org.uk

POWIS CASTLE & GARDEN ❧
Welshpool, Powys SY21 8RF
Tel: 01938 551929 **Email:** powiscastle@nationaltrust.org.uk

TREWERN HALL
Trewern, Welshpool, Powys SY21 8DT
Tel: 01938 570243

ABERCONWY HOUSE ❧
Castle Street, Conwy LL32 8AY
Tel: 01492 592246 **Email:** aberconwyhouse@nationaltrust.org.uk

BEAUMARIS CASTLE ✛
Beaumaris, Anglesey LL58 8AP
Tel: 01248 810361

BODNANT GARDEN ❧
Tal-Y-Cafn, Colwyn Bay LL28 5RE
Tel: 01492 650460 **Email:** bodnantgarden@nationaltrust.org.uk

BODRHYDDAN HALL ▥ⓕ
Bodrhyddan, Rhuddlan, Rhyl, Denbighshire LL18 5SB
Tel: 01745 590414

CAERNARFON CASTLE ✛
Castle Ditch, Caernarfon LL55 2AY
Tel: 01286 677617

CHIRK CASTLE ❧
Chirk LL14 5AF
Tel: 01691 777701 **Email:** chirkcastle@nationaltrust.org.uk

CONWY CASTLE ✛
Conwy LL32 8AY
Tel: 01492 592358

CRICCIETH CASTLE ✛
Castle Street, Criccieth, Gwynedd LL52 0DP
Tel: 01766 522227 **Email:** cadw@wales.gsi.gov.uk

DOLBELYDR ✛
Trefnant, Denbighshire LL16 5AG
Tel: 01628 825925 **Email:** bookings@landmarktrust.org.uk

ERDDIG ❧
Wrexham LL13 0YT
Tel: 01978 355314 **Email:** erddig@nationaltrust.org.uk

FLINT CASTLE ✛
Castle St, Flint, Flintshire CH6 5HF
Tel: 01443 336000

GWYDIR CASTLE
Llanrwst, Conwy LL26 0PN
Tel: 01492 641687 **Email:** info@gwydircastle.co.uk

HARLECH CASTLE ✛
Castle Square, Harlech LL46 2YH
Tel: 01766 780552

PENRHYN CASTLE ❧
Bangor, Gwynedd LL57 4HN
Tel: 01248 353084 **Email:** penrhyncastle@nationaltrust.org.uk

PLAS BRONDANW GARDENS, CAFFI & SHOP
Plas Brondanw, Llanfrothen, Gwynedd LL48 6SW
Tel: 01766 772772 / 01743 239236 **Email:** enquiries@plasbrondanw.com

PLAS MAWR ✿
High Street, Conwy LL32 8DE
Tel: 01492 580167

PLAS NEWYDD
Hill Street, Llangollen, Denbighshire LL20 8AW
Tel: 01978 862834 **Email:** heritage@denbighshire.gov.uk

PLAS NEWYDD HOUSE & GARDENS ❦
Llanfairpwll, Anglesey LL61 6DQ
Tel: 01248 714795 **Email:** plasnewydd@nationaltrust.org.uk

PLAS YN RHIW ❦
Rhiw, Pwllheli, Gwynedd LL53 8AB
Tel: 01758 780219 **Email:** plasynrhiw@nationaltrust.org.uk

PORTMEIRION
Minffordd, Penrhyndeudraeth, Gwynedd LL48 6ER
Tel: 01766 772311 **Email:** enquiries@portmeirion-village.com

RHUDDLAN CASTLE ✿
Castle Street, Rhuddlan, Rhyl LL18 5AD
Tel: 01745 590777

TOWER
Nercwys Road, Mold, Flintshire CH7 4EW
Tel: 01352 700220 **Email:** enquiries@towerwales.co.uk

Iscoyd Park ©Country Life

NORTHERN IRELAND

ANTRIM • ARMAGH • DOWN
FERMANAGH • LONDONDERRY • TYRONE

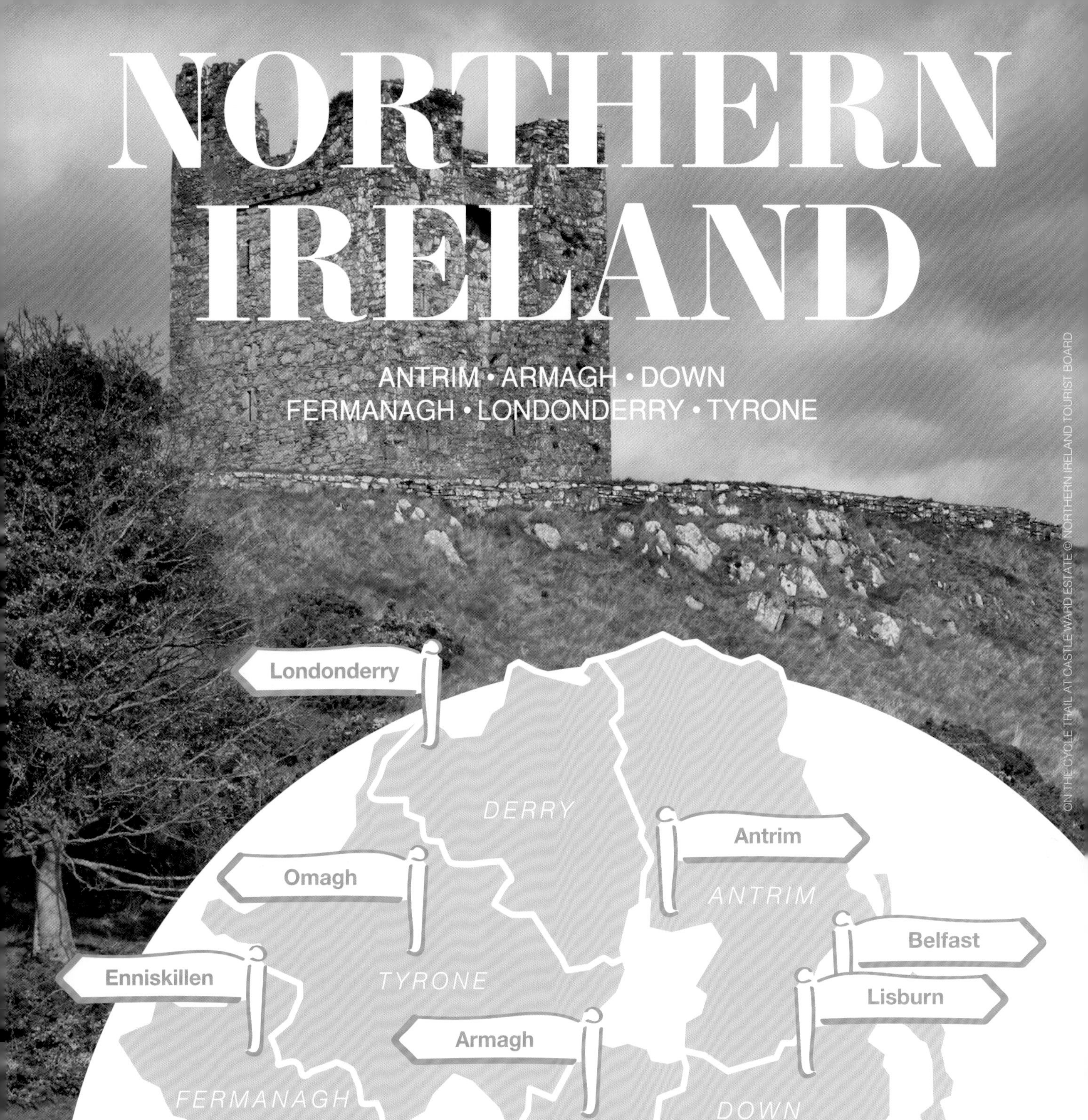

Londonderry

Antrim

Omagh

DERRY

ANTRIM

Belfast

Enniskillen

TYRONE

Lisburn

Armagh

FERMANAGH

DOWN

ARMAGH

Newry

🌲 **COUNTRYSIDE:**

- Causeway Coast
- Mourne Mountains
- Lough Neagh

⌛ **HERITAGE:**

- Norman castles
- Plantation houses
- Game of Thrones locations

🍴 **FOOD:**

- Stout & whiskey
- Potato breads
- Irish stew

TERRACE GARDENS AT HILLSBOROUGH CASTLE

ANTRIM CASTLE GARDENS

The restored gardens are a rare survival of a 17th century Anglo-Dutch garden with vistas, allées and canals plus formal parterre and flower gardens.

Highlights:

- The Canals
- The Masserene Wolfhound
- The 10th Viscountess' garden (1840)

MOUNT STEWART GARDENS © NATIONAL TRUST IMAGES/NAOMI GOGGINS

CASTLE COOLE

The masterpiece of neo-classical architect James Wyatt, built for the 1st Earl of Belmore in 1797. The family spent much time in Dublin and George IV failed to turn up to stay in the specially prepared staterooms, so the preservation is remarkable.

Highlights:

- State Bedroom
- French empire Drawing Room
- Basement servant's quarters

HILLSBOROUGH CASTLE

The official governor's residence of Northern Ireland started out as a Georgian home for Wills Hill, political adviser to George III and is now beloved by the Royal family. Gardens are being revealed by restoration, lake and extensive woodlands.

Highlights:

- Dining Room
- Old Masters on loan from the Royal Collection
- Irish silver and crystal

THE LONG CANALS AT ANTRIM CASTLE GARDENS

MOUNT STEWART

A neo-classical mansion that was a political powerhouse in the early 20th century. Superb paintings by Stubbs, Hoppner, Lawrence and de Lazlo. Sub-tropical and woodland gardens with lake, terraces and borders.

Highlights:

- The Dodo Terrace garden
- The Hambletonian by George Stubbs
- Dining chairs from the Congress of Vienna

VISITORS AT CASTLE COOLE ©NATIONAL TRUST IMAGES - JOHN MILLAR

MRS HUDSON'S HIDDEN GEM

LISSAN HOUSE

"…Don't you love finding eccentrics in the past? Lissan is a house with eccentricity in spade-loads. How about Robert Ponsonby Staples, the Edwardian patriarch? He only inherited because his elder brother was in an asylum - bad sign? - but Robert P was a man of talent, a successful artist, friend of the Prince of Wales and co-founder of the Grosvenor Gallery. He was also 'The Barefoot Baronet' convinced of the health benefits of natural electricity. He refused to wear shoes which might prevent him absorbing electricity from the ground and, if he felt in need of an extra boost of energy, would travel to Belfast to stand on the tramlines. At Lissan, he built a crazy staircase that careers around the entrance hall like something designed for Hogwarts.

In 1865, Sir Thomas Staples' will contained an eccentric decision. He left the house to his cousin but the contents to two other families. In no time the estate was in financial gloom, far from the heady days of the 18th century when it was one of the richest in Ireland. Today it's is one of those places where you just have to scratch the surface to uncover another eccentric detail…"

MARK THE YEAR

WORLD WAR ONE CENTENARY

The Ulster Tower at Thriepval was built as a memorial to the 36th (Ulster) Division who fought heroically in the Battle of the Somme but were almost wiped out in the Spring 1918 Offensive, the last battle of World War One. The Tower is a copy of Helen's Tower at Clandeboye where the soldiers trained.

WW1 VICTORIA CROSSES 36TH ULSTER DIVISION © CC KERESASPIA

100 YEARS
WOMEN & SUFFRAGE

FLORENCE WREY, ENGLISH SCHOOL ©NATIONAL TRUST IMAGES - JOHN HAMMOND

1. FLORENCE WREY (D.1718)
Eponymous inspiration for Florence Court at Florence Court.

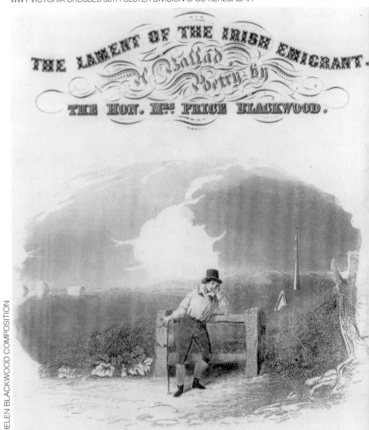

HELEN BLACKWOOD COMPOSITION

2. HELEN BLACKWOOD, LADY DUFFERIN & CLANDEBOYE (1807-67)
Songwriter, composer & author at Helen's Tower & Clandeboye Estate.

EDITH, LADY LONDONDERRY BY PHILIP DE LAZLO ©NATIONAL TRUST IMAGES - JOHN HAMMOND

3. EDITH VANE - TEMPEST - STEWART, MARCHIONESS OF LONDONDERRY (1878-1958)
Children's author, conservationist at Hill Top farm.

DID YOU KNOW ?

1 CASTLE WARD

The half of Castle Ward that faces Strangford Lough reflects Lady Anne Bligh's taste for fashionable Gothick but her husband Bernard Ward, Viscount Bangor's half is all Palladian. They couldn't agree on the design.

2 CARRICKFERGUS CASTLE

Off Carrickfergus Castle in 1778, American commander John Paul Jones' ship Ranger overcame the Royal Navy sloop, Drake, in the first victory over the British in home waters in the American War of Independence.

3 MUSSENDEN TEMPLE

Mussenden Temple was built in 1783 as a library, a gift from Frederick Hervey, Earl-Bishop of Derry to his married niece, Frideswide Mussenden. He was in his 50s, she was 20, leading to nasty rumours, but she died before it was finished.

THE PALLADIAN HALL, CASTLE WARD © NATIONAL TRUST IMAGES

LADY ANNE'S BOUDOIR © NATIONAL TRUST IMAGES - ANDREAS VON EINSIEDEL

4 ANTRIM CASTLE ▶

When Clotworthy Skeffington, 2nd Earl of Massereene's dog died at Antrim Castle, he organised a formal funeral and recruited 50 local dogs wearing white mourning scarves to follow in procession.

5 HILLSBOROUGH CASTLE ▶

Hillsborough Castle has the largest rhododendron bush in the United Kingdom, part of the gardens developed from the 1760s. The first rhododendrons arrived here from China in the 1850s.

6 DUNLUCE CASTLE ▶

Dunluce Castle was the inspiration for the castle of Cair Paravel in Ulsterman C S Lewis' Narnia stories.

CARRICKFERGUS CASTLE

3 TOP PICNIC SPOTS

1.
ANTRIM CASTLE GARDENS, CO ANTRIM

Make the most of the secluded woodlands, open lawns, garden benches and riverside banks in the restored 17th century garden, now a public park. Pick up supplies from the café in restored stables of Clotworthy House.

2.
CASTLE WARD, CO DOWN

Don your wolf cloak for a Game of Thrones picnic at the location for Winterfell from the hit HBO series. Or just enjoy the views over Strangford Lough or the gardens.

BY THE SIXMILEWATER, ANTRIM CASTLE GARDENS

GET YOUR OWN GAME OF THRONES PICNIC SPOT AT CASTLE WARD

3.
ROWALLANE GARDENS

Spread your rug under one of the magnificent magnolias of the National Trust's Victorian gardens at Rowallane. Spot wildlife or grab a coffee from the café to round off your picnic.

PLACES TO STAY
HISTORIC PLACES TO STAY

www.signpost.co.uk

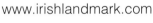

HELEN'S TOWER, CO DOWN

Three-storey Victorian tower commissioned from Scottish architect, William Burn as a memorial to Helen, Lady Dufferin & Clandeboye. Views as far as Scotland. Sleeps 2.

www.irishlandmark.com

THE CLOCKTOWER, BARONSCOURT, CO TYRONE

Dating from 1749, the stableyard at Baronscourt offers two adjoining cottages on the estate, with easy walking access to woodland, three loughs and plentiful wildlife. Sleeps 4.

MONTALTO, CO DOWN

The best rooms of this Palladian mansion of the 1750s, with exceptional plasterwork ceilings, are on the first floor after renovations in the 1830s. Nine luxurious rooms provide a true stately home experience for guests and wedding parties.

Ballywalter Park

www.ballywalterpark.com

NI A ⛪ Ⓕ

Ballywalter Park was built in the Italianate Palazzo style, by Sir Charles Lanyon for Andrew Mulholland. A Gentleman's wing was added in 1870 for Andrew's son, John Mulholland, later 1st Baron Dunleath. The house has a fine collection of original furniture and paintings, complemented by contemporary pieces.

KEY FACTS

 No photography indoors.

 Toilet facilities available.

 Accepts Euros.

 By appointment only.

 Parking available.

 Twelve en suite bedrooms available for group tours and corporate events.

 Obligatory.

 Educational visits by prior arrangement.

 Refreshments by prior arrangement.

 Lunches and dinners can be booked by prior arrangement.

 The house is available for corporate and incentive events, lunches and dinners.

 Special events on occasion throughout the year.

Film and television location.

CONTACT
Owner: The Lord and Lady Dunleath
Contact: Mrs Sharon Graham, The Estate Office
Tel: 028 4275 8264 **Fax:** 028 4275 8818
Email: enq@dunleath-estates.co.uk

LOCATION
Ballywalter, Newtownards, County Down BT22 2PP
Map Ref: 18:P4
Off A2 on unclassified road, 1 km South of Ballywalter village.

OPENING TIMES
By prior appointment only; please contact The Estate Office.

ADMISSION
House or Gardens: £10 per person
House & Gardens: £17 per person
Groups: Max 50 people (No group discount)
Refreshments by arrangement.

Ballywalter Park

Hillsborough Castle

www.hrp.org.uk/hillsborough-castle

The late Georgian mansion was built in the 1770s and is a working royal residence, functioning as the official residence of the Royal Family when they are in Northern Ireland, and it has been the home of the Secretary of State since the 1970s. A tour of the house will guide you through the elegant State Rooms, still in use today, including the majestic Throne Room. Don't miss 98 acres of stunning gardens.

CONTACT
Owner: Historic Royal Palaces
Tel: 028 9268 1300
Email: hillsboroughcastle@hrp.org.uk

LOCATION
Hillsborough BT26 6AG **Map Ref:** 18:N5

OPENING TIMES
Re-opening Jul 2018. House open specific days for guided tours, gardens open daily 10am-5pm, closing 4pm from 29 Oct. Please see website or call for details before visiting.

ADMISSION
See website.
House by guided tour only, advance booking recommended.

KEY FACTS

 Toilet changing facilities.

 Baby changing facilities.

 No parking on site.

 Complimentary tickets for adult carers are available to collect on the day of your visit.

 Assistance dogs only.

 Offer reduced admission for group bookings.

 Ambitious plans are underway to transform the castle and gardens for everyone to explore.

 The local area has a number of dining options available within a walking distance from the site.

 Available to host private and corporate dinners, conferences and other celebrations.

 See the 'Explore' page on the website for all upcoming events.

 Celebrate your wedding at Hillsborough Castle, see details on our website.

Hillsborough Castle

Barons Court

www.barons-court.com

The home of the Duke and Duchess of Abercorn, Barons Court was built between 1779 and 1782, and subsequently extensively remodelled by John Soane (1791), William and Richard Morrison (1819-1841), Sir Albert Richardson (1947-49) and David Hicks (1975-76).

CONTACT
Contact: The Estate Office
Tel: 028 8166 1683
Email: info@barons-court.com

LOCATION
Newtownstewart, Omagh, Co Tyrone BT78 4EZ
Map Ref:18:M3 - 5km South West of Newtownstewart.

OPENING TIMES
By appointment only.

ADMISSION
Tour of House and/or Gardens:
£14 per person
Tour inc. tea/coffee/scones:
£19 per person
Groups max. 50.

KEY FACTS

 No photography.

 Open all year by appointment.

 Parking available.

 Partially accessible.

 Holiday cottages, 4 star rated by Northern Ireland Tourist Board.

 Guided tours by arrangement.

The Carriage Room in the Stable Yard.

ARTHUR ANCESTRAL HOME
Cullybackey, County Antrim BT42 1AB
Tel: 028 2563 8494 **Email:** devel.leisure@ballymena.gov.uk

BELFAST CASTLE
Cave Hill, Antrim Road, Belfast BT15 5GR
Tel: 028 9077 6925

BOTANIC GARDENS
Stransmillis Road, Belfast BT7 1LP
Tel: 028 9031 4762

GLENARM CASTLE WALLED GARDEN
2 Castle Lane, Glenarm, Larne, County Antrim BT44 0BQ
Tel: 028 2884 1305

MONTALTO HOUSE
5 Craigaboney Road, Bushmills, County Antrim BT57 8XD
Tel: 028 2073 1257 **Email:** montaltohouse@btconnect.com

NORTHERN IRELAND ASSEMBLY ◇
Parliament Buildings , Ballymiscaw, Stormont, Belfast BT4 3XX
Tel: 028 90 521137 **Email:** info@niassembly.gov.uk

SENTRY HILL
Ballycraigy Road, Newtownabbey BT36 5SY
Tel: 028 9034 0000

ARDRESS HOUSE 🌿
64 Ardress Road, Portadown, Co Armagh BT62 1SQ
Tel: 028 8778 4753 **Email:** ardress@nationaltrust.org.uk

BENBURB CASTLE
Servite Priory, Main Street, Benburb, Co Tyrone BT71 7JZ
Tel: 028 3754 8241 **Email:** servitepriory@btinternet.com

DERRYMORE 🌿
Bessbrook, Newry, Co Armagh BT35 7EF
Tel: 028 8778 4753 **Email:** derrymore@nationaltrust.org.uk

GILFORD CASTLE ESTATE
Banbridge Road, Gilford BT63 6DT
Tel: 028 4062 3322 **Email:** gilford@irishfieldsports.com

AUDLEYS CASTLE
Strangford, County Down BT30 7LP
Tel: 028 9054 3034

BANGOR ABBEY
Bangor, County Down BT20 4JF
Tel: 028 9127 1200

BANGOR CASTLE
Bangor, County Down BT20 4BN
Tel: 028 9127 0371

CLOUGH CASTLE
Clough Village, Downpatrick, County Down 028 9054 3034
Tel: 028 9054 3034

DUNDRUM CASTLE
Dundrum Village, Newcastle, County Down BT33 0QX
Tel: 028 9054 3034

GREENCASTLE ROYAL CASTLE
Cranfield Point, Kilkeel, County Down BT34 4LR
Tel: 028 9054 3037

GREY ABBEY
9-11 Church Street, Greyabbey, County Down BT22 2NQ
Tel: 028 9054 6552

GREY POINT FORT
Crawfordsburn Country Park, Helens Bay, Co. Down BT19 1LE
Tel: 028 9185 3621

HELENS TOWER
Clandeboye Estate, Bangor BT19 1RN
Tel: 028 9185 2817

INCH ABBEY
Downpatrick, County Down BT30 9AX
Tel: 028 9181 1491

KILCLIEF CASTLE
Strangford, County Down
Tel: 028 9054 3034

MAHEE CASTLE
Mahee Island, Comber, Newtownards BT23 6EP
Tel: 028 9182 6846

MOVILLA ABBEY
63 Movilla Road, Newtownards BT23 8EZ
Tel: 028 9181 0787

NEWRY CATHEDRAL
38 Hill Street, Newry, County Down BT34 1AT
Tel: 028 3026 2586

PORTAFERRY CASTLE
Castle Street, Portaferry, County Down BT22 1NZ
Tel: 028 9054 3033

THE PRIORY
Newtownards, County Down
Tel: 028 9054 3037

QUOILE CASTLE
Downpatrick, County Down BT30 7JB
Tel: 028 9054 3034

RINGHADDY CASTLE
Killyleagh, County Down
Tel: 028 9054 3037

ROWALLANE GARDEN 🌿
Ballynahinch, Co Down BT24 7LH
Tel: 028 9751 0721 **Email:** rowallane@nationaltrust.org.uk

SKETRICK CASTLE
Whiterock, County Down BT23 6QA
Tel: 028 4278 8387

STRANGFORD CASTLE
Strangford, County Down
Tel: 028 9054 3034

CROM ESTATE ❧
Newtownbutler, County Fermanagh BT92 8AP
Tel: 028 6773 8118

ENNISKILLEN CASTLE ❧
Castle Barracks, Enniskillen, County Fermanagh BT74 7HL
Tel: 028 6632 5000 **Email:** castle@fermanagh.gov.uk

FLORENCE COURT ❧
Enniskillen, Co Fermanagh BT92 1DB
Tel: 028 6634 8249 **Email:** florencecourt@nationaltrust.org.uk

BELLAGHY BAWN
Castle Street, Bellaghy, County Londonderry BT45 8LA
Tel: 028 7938 6812

DUNGIVEN CASTLE
Main Street, Dungiven, Co Londonderry BT47 4LF
Tel: 028 7774 2428 **Email:** enquiries@dungivencastle.com

DUNGIVEN PRIORY & O CAHANS TOMB
Dungiven, County Londonderry BT47 4PF
Tel: 028 7772 2074

THE GUILDHALL
Guildhall Square, Londonderry BT48 6DQ
Tel: 028 7137 7335

MOUNTSANDAL FORT
Mountsandal Road, Coleraine, Co Londonderry BT52 1PE
Tel: 027 7034 4723 **Email:** coleraine@nitic.net

PREHEN HOUSE
Prehen Road, Londonderry BT47 2PB
Tel: 028 7131 2829 **Email:** colinpeck@yahoo.com

SAINT COLUMB'S CATHEDRAL
London Street, Derry, County Londonderry BT48 6RQ
Tel: 028 7126 7313 **Email:** stcolumbs@ic24.net

SAMPSON'S TOWER
Limavady TIC, 7 Connell Street, Limavady BT49 0HA
Tel: 028 7776 0307

ANTRIM CASTLE GARDENS & CLOTWORTHY HOUSE
Randalstown Road, Antrim BT41 4LH
Tel: 028 9448 1338 **Email:** culture@antrimandnewtwonabbey.gov.uk

BENVARDEN GARDEN
Benvarden, Dervock, County Antrim BT53 6NN
Tel: 028 2074 1331

CARRICKFERGUS CASTLE
Marine Highway, Carrickfergus, County Antrim BT38 7BG
Tel: 028 9335 1273 **Email:** scmenquiries@communities-ni.gov.uk

CASTLE COOLE ❧
Enniskillen, Co Fermanagh BT74 6JY
Tel: 028 6632 2690 **Email:** castlecoole@nationaltrust.org.uk

CASTLE WARD HOUSE & DEMESNE ❧
Strangford, Downpatrick, Co Down BT30 7LS
Tel: 028 4488 1204 **Email:** castleward@nationaltrust.org.uk

DOWN CATHEDRAL
Cathedral Office, English Street, Downpatrick, County Down BT30 6AB
Tel: 028 4461 4922 **Email:** info@downcathedral.org

DUNLUCE CASTLE
87 Dunluce Road, Portrush, County Antrim BT57 8UY
Tel: 028 2073 1938 **Email:** scmenquiries@communities-ni.gov.uk

KILLYLEAGH CASTLE
Killyleagh, Downpatrick, Co Down BT30 9QA
Tel: 028 4482 8261 **Email:** gawnrh@gmail.com

LISSAN HOUSE
Drumgrass Road, Cookstown, County Tyrone BT80 9SW
Tel: 028 8676 3312 **Email:** lissan.house@btconnect.com

MONTALTO ESTATE & CARRIAGE ROOMS
Ballynahinch, Co. Down BT24 8AY
Tel: 028 9756 6100 **Email:** info@montaltoestate.com

MOUNT STEWART ❧
Newtonards, Co Down BT22 2AD
Tel: 028 4278 8387 **Email:** mountstewart@nationaltrust.org.uk

SEAFORDE GARDENS ❧
Seaforde, County Down BT30 8PG
Tel: 028 4481 1225 **Email:** springhill@nationaltrust.org.uk

SPRINGHILL HOUSE ❧
20 Springhill Road, Moneymore, Co Londonderry BT45 7NQ
Tel: 028 8674 8210 **Email:** devel.leisure@ballymena.gov.uk

THE ARGORY ❧
Moy, Dungannon, Co Tyrone BT71 6NA
Tel: 028 8778 4753 **Email:** argory@nationaltrust.org.uk

CASTLEDERG CASTLE
Castle Park, Castlederg, County Tyrone BT81 7AS
Tel: 028 7138 2204

HARRY AVERYS CASTLE
Old Castle Road, Newtownstewart BT82 8DY
Tel: 028 7138 2204

KILLYMOON CASTLE
Killymoon Road, Cookstown, County Tyrone
Tel: 028 8676 3514

NEWTOWNSTEWART CASTLE
Townhall Street, Newtownstewart BT78 4AX
Tel: 028 6862 1588 **Email:** nieainfo@doeni.gov.uk

SAINT MACARTAN'S CATHEDRAL
Clogher, County Tyrone BT76 0AD
Tel: 028 0478 1220

SIR JOHN DAVIES CASTLE
Castlederg, County Tyrone BT81 7AS
Tel: 028 7138 2204

TULLYHOGUE FORT
B162, Cookstown, County Tyrone BT80 8UB
Tel: 028 8676 6727

MAPS

©VisitBritain/Rod Edwards

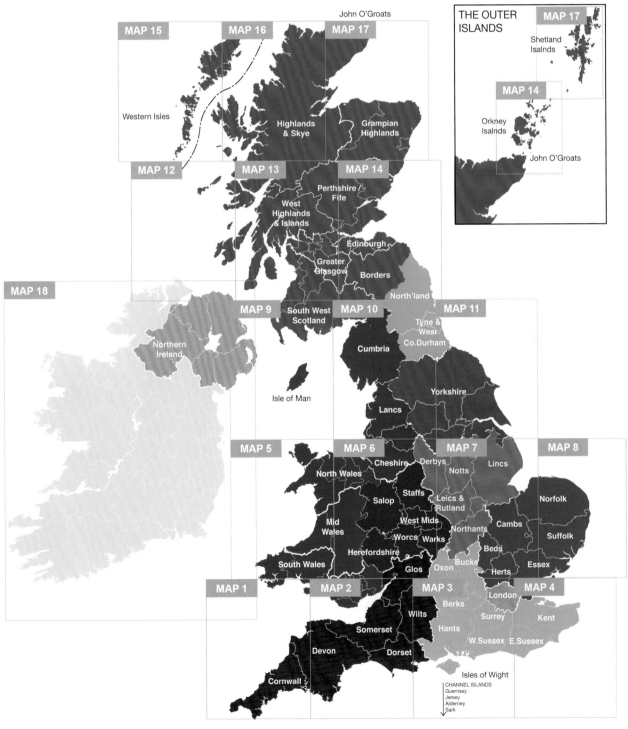

THE OUTER ISLANDS

MAP 15

MAP 16

MAP 17

John O'Groats

MAP 17

Shetland Isalnds

MAP 14

Orkney Isalnds

John O'Groats

Western Isles

Highlands & Skye

Grampian Highlands

MAP 12

MAP 13

MAP 14

West Highlands & Islands

Perthshire / Fife

Edinburgh

Greater Glasgow

Borders

MAP 18

MAP 9

South West Scotland

MAP 10

North'land

MAP 11

Tyne & Wear

Co.Durham

Northern Ireland

Cumbria

Isle of Man

Yorkshire

Lancs

MAP 5

MAP 6

Cheshire

Derbys

MAP 7

Lincs

MAP 8

North Wales

Notts

Mid Wales

Salop

Staffs

Leics & Rutland

Norfolk

West Mids

Cambs

Suffolk

Worcs

Warks

Northants

Herefordshire

Beds

South Wales

Glos

Oxon

Bucks

Herts

Essex

MAP 1

MAP 2

MAP 3

Berks

London

MAP 4

Wilts

Surrey

Kent

Somerset

Hants

Devon

Dorset

W.Sussex

E.Sussex

Cornwall

Isles of Wight

CHANNEL ISLANDS
Guernsey
Jersey
Alderney
Sark

MAP 1

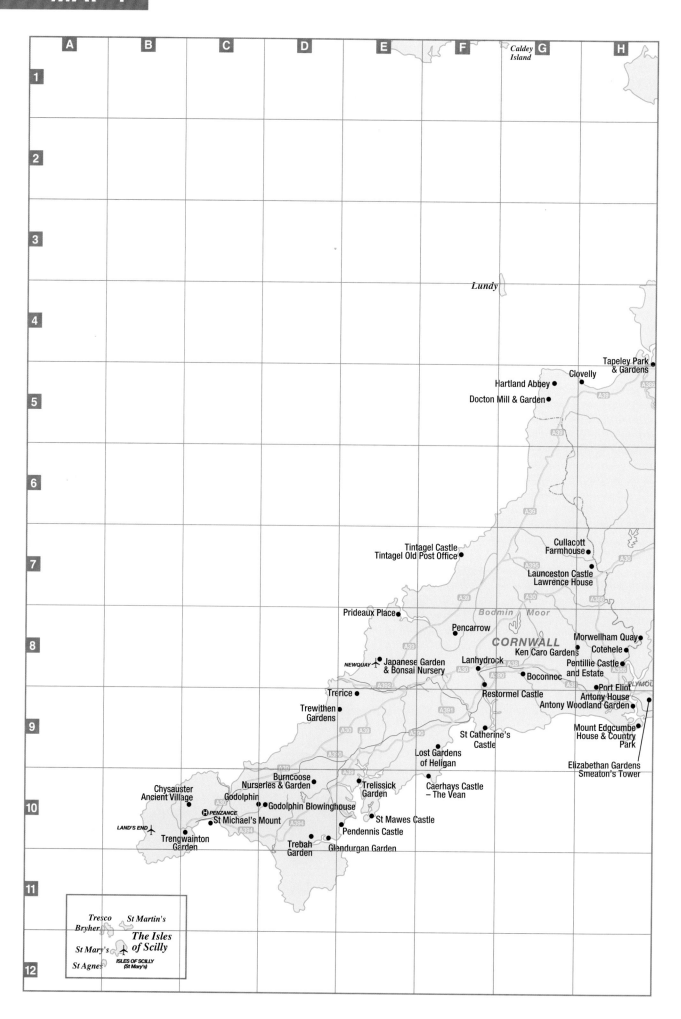

MAP 2

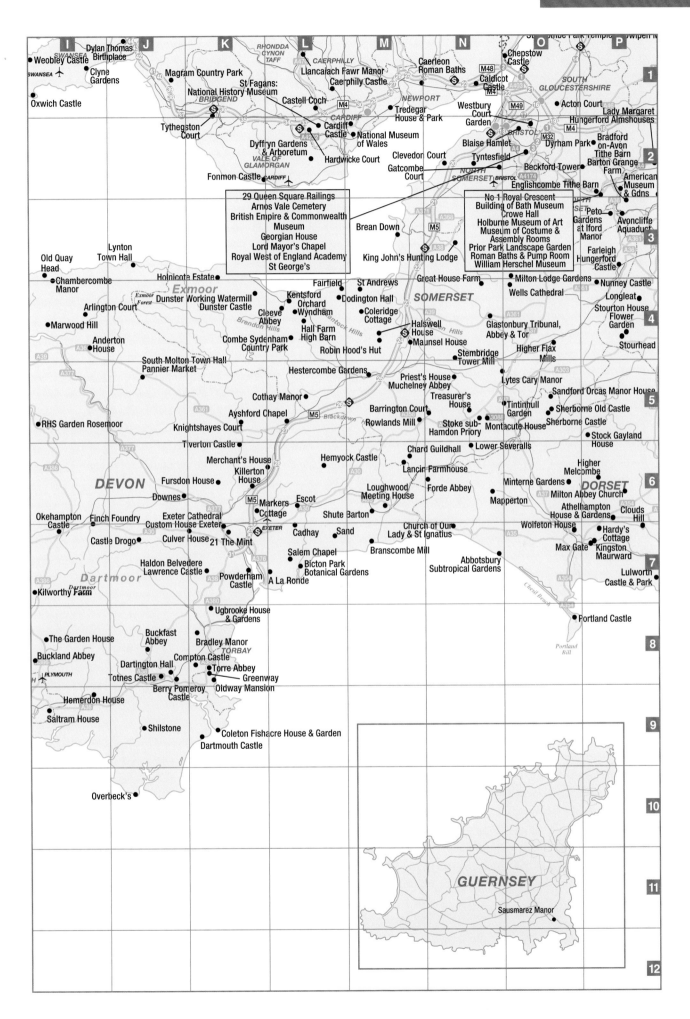

MAP 3

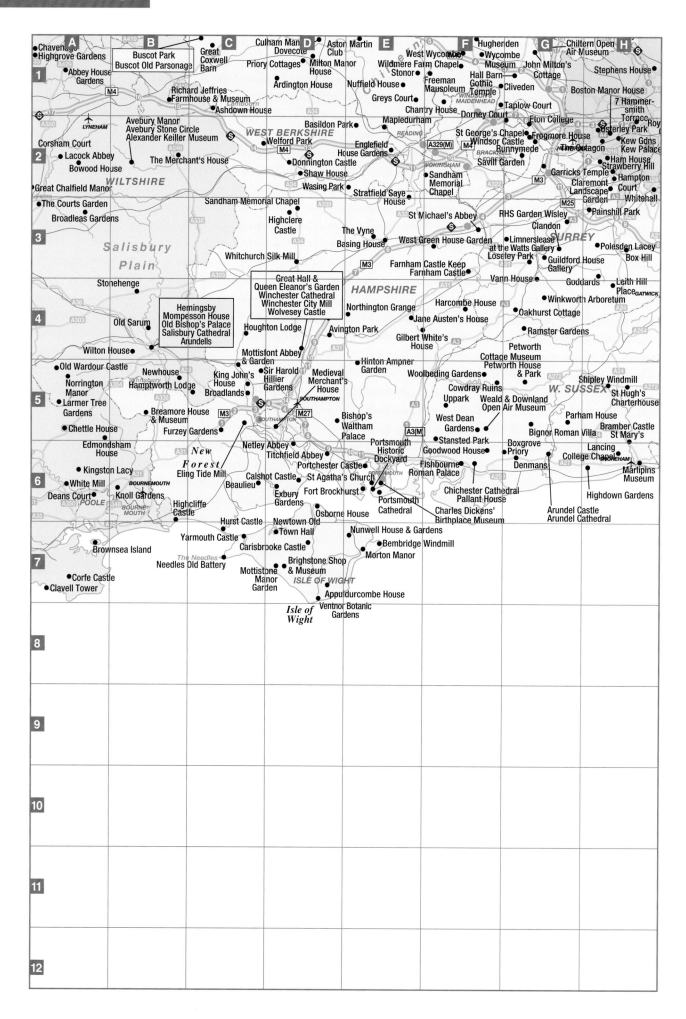

Chavenage
Highgrove Gardens
Abbey House Gardens
Buscot Park
Buscot Old Parsonage
Great Coxwell Barn
Culham Man Dovecote
Priory Cottages
Milton Manor House
Ardington House
Aston Martin Club
Wildmere Farm Chapel
Stonor
Nuffield House
Greys Court
Mapledurham
Chantry House
West Wycombe
Wycombe Museum
Freeman Mausoleum
Hall Barn
Gothic Temple
Dorney Court
Cliveden
Taplow Court
Eton College
Hughenden
John Milton's Cottage
Chiltern Open Air Museum
Stephens House
Boston Manor House
7 Hammersmith Terrace
Hampton
Osterley Park
Roy
Kew Gdns
Kew Palace

Richard Jeffries Farmhouse & Museum
Ashdown House
Avebury Manor
Avebury Stone Circle
Alexander Keiller Museum
Corsham Court
Lacock Abbey
Bowood House
The Merchant's House
WILTSHIRE
Welford Park
Donnington Castle
Shaw House
Wasing Park
WEST BERKSHIRE
Basildon Park
Englefield House Gardens
READING
St George's Chapel
Windsor Castle
Runnymede
Savill Garden
Frogmore House
The Cottage
Ham House
Strawberry Hill
Garricks Temple
Claremont Landscape Garden
Whitehall

Great Chalfield Manor
The Courts Garden
Broadleas Gardens
Sandham Memorial Chapel
Highclere Castle
Salisbury Plain
Stonehenge
Old Sarum
Wilton House
Whitchurch Silk Mill
The Vyne
Basing House
West Green House Garden
Stratfield Saye House
Sandham Memorial Chapel
St Michael's Abbey
St Michael's Abbey
West Green House Garden
Farnham Castle Keep
Farnham Castle
RHS Garden Wisley
Clandon
Limnerslease at the Watts Gallery
Loseley Park
Vann House
SURREY
Guildford House Gallery
Goddards
Winkworth Arboretum
Oakhurst Cottage
Polesden Lacey
Box Hill
Leith Hill Place GATWICK

Great Hall & Queen Eleanor's Garden
Winchester Cathedral
Winchester City Mill
Wolvesey Castle
HAMPSHIRE
Northington Grange
Harcombe House
Jane Austen's House
Gilbert White's House
Houghton Lodge
Avington Park
Hemingsby Mompesson House Old Bishop's Palace Salisbury Cathedral Arundells
Mottisfont Abbey & Garden
Hinton Ampner Garden
Petworth Cottage Museum
Petworth House & Park
Ramster Gardens

Old Wardour Castle
Newhouse
Hamptworth Lodge
King John's House
Sir Harold Hillier Gardens
Broadlands
Medieval Merchant's House
SOUTHAMPTON
Norrington Manor
Larmer Tree Gardens
Chettle House
Breamore House & Museum
Furzey Gardens
Woolbeding Gardens
Cowdray Ruins
Uppark
Weald & Downland Open Air Museum
West Dean Gardens
Shipley Windmill
W. SUSSEX
St Hugh's Charterhouse
Parham House
Bignor Roman Villa
Bramber Castle
St Mary's

Edmondsham House
Kingston Lacy
White Mill
Deans Court
Knoll Gardens
POOLE
BOURNEMOUTH
New Forest
Eling Tide Mill
Netley Abbey
Titchfield Abbey
Portchester Castle
Bishop's Waltham Palace
Portsmouth Historic Dockyard
Stansted Park
Goodwood House
Fishbourne Roman Palace
Boxgrove Priory
Denmans
Lancing College Chapel
Marlipins Museum
Highdown Gardens

Highcliffe Castle
Calshot Castle
Beaulieu
Exbury Gardens
St Agatha's Church
Fort Brockhurst
Portsmouth Cathedral
Chichester Cathedral
Pallant House
Charles Dickens' Birthplace Museum
Arundel Castle
Arundel Cathedral

Brownsea Island
Corfe Castle
Clavell Tower
Hurst Castle
Yarmouth Castle
Needles Old Battery
The Needles
Mottistone Manor Garden
Brighstone Shop & Museum
Carisbrooke Castle
Newtown Old Town Hall
Osborne House
Morton Manor
Nunwell House & Gardens
Bembridge Windmill
ISLE OF WIGHT
Appuldurcombe House
Ventnor Botanic Gardens
Isle of Wight

372

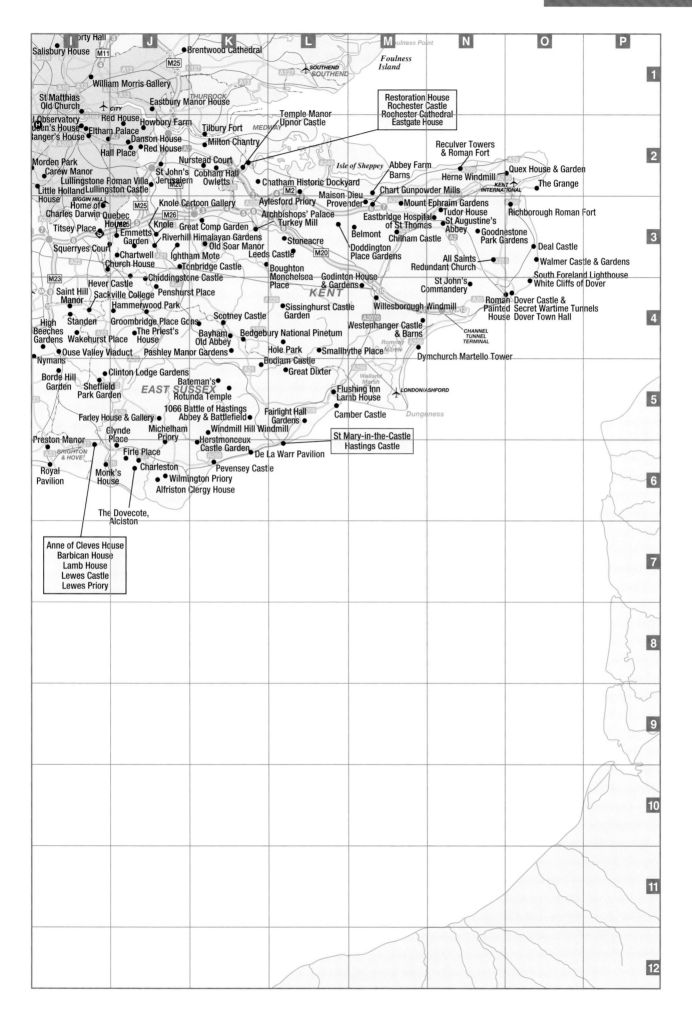

MAP 4

Salisbury House
rty Hall
William Morris Gallery
St Matthias Old Church
Observatory
Queen's House
Ranger's House
Eltham Palace
Morden Park
Carew Manor
Lullingstone Roman Villa
Little Holland House
Home of Charles Darwin
Titsey Place
Squerryes Court
Chartwell
Church House
High Beeches Gardens
Standen
Wakehurst Place
Nymans
Borde Hill Garden
Preston Manor
Royal Pavilion
Monk's House
The Dovecote, Alciston

Brentwood Cathedral
Eastbury Manor House
Red House
Howbury Farm
Danson House
Red House
Hall Place
St John's Jerusalem
Owletts
Knole Cartoon Gallery
Quebec House
Knole
Emmetts Garden
Riverhill Himalayan Gardens
Old Soar Manor
Ightham Mote
Hever Castle
Sackville College
Hammerwood Park
Penshurst Place
Chiddingstone Castle
Groombridge Place Gdns
The Priest's House
Pashley Manor Gardens
Ouse Valley Viaduct
Clinton Lodge Gardens
Sheffield Park Garden
Bateman's
Rotunda Temple
Farley House & Gallery
1066 Battle of Hastings Abbey & Battlefield
Glynde Place
Michelham Priory
Firle Place
Charleston
Wilmington Priory
Alfriston Clergy House

Tilbury Fort
Milton Chantry
Nurstead Court
Cobham Hall
Temple Manor
Upnor Castle
Chatham Historic Dockyard
Aylesford Priory
Archbishops' Palace
Turkey Mill
Great Comp Garden
Stoneacre
Leeds Castle
Tonbridge Castle
Scotney Castle
Bayham Old Abbey
Bedgebury National Pinetum
Hole Park
Bodiam Castle
Great Dixter
Sissinghurst Castle Garden
Boughton Monchelsea Place
Smallhythe Place
Flushing Inn
Lamb House
Camber Castle
Fairlight Hall Gardens
Windmill Hill Windmill
Herstmonceux Castle Garden
Pevensey Castle
De La Warr Pavilion

Restoration House
Rochester Castle
Rochester Cathedral
Eastgate House

KENT
EAST SUSSEX

Maison Dieu
Provender
Mount Ephraim Gardens
Eastbridge Hospital of St Thomas
Belmont
Chilham Castle
Doddington Place Gardens
Godinton House & Gardens
Willesborough Windmill
Westenhanger Castle & Barns
Dymchurch Martello Tower

Abbey Farm Barns
Chart Gunpowder Mills
Reculver Towers & Roman Fort
Herne Windmill
Quex House & Garden
The Grange
Richborough Roman Fort
Goodnestone Park Gardens
Deal Castle
Walmer Castle & Gardens
South Foreland Lighthouse
White Cliffs of Dover
St Augustine's Abbey
All Saints Redundant Church
St John's Commandery
Roman Painted House
Dover Castle & Secret Wartime Tunnels
Dover Town Hall

St Mary-in-the-Castle
Hastings Castle

Anne of Cleves House
Barbican House
Lamb House
Lewes Castle
Lewes Priory

373

MAP 5

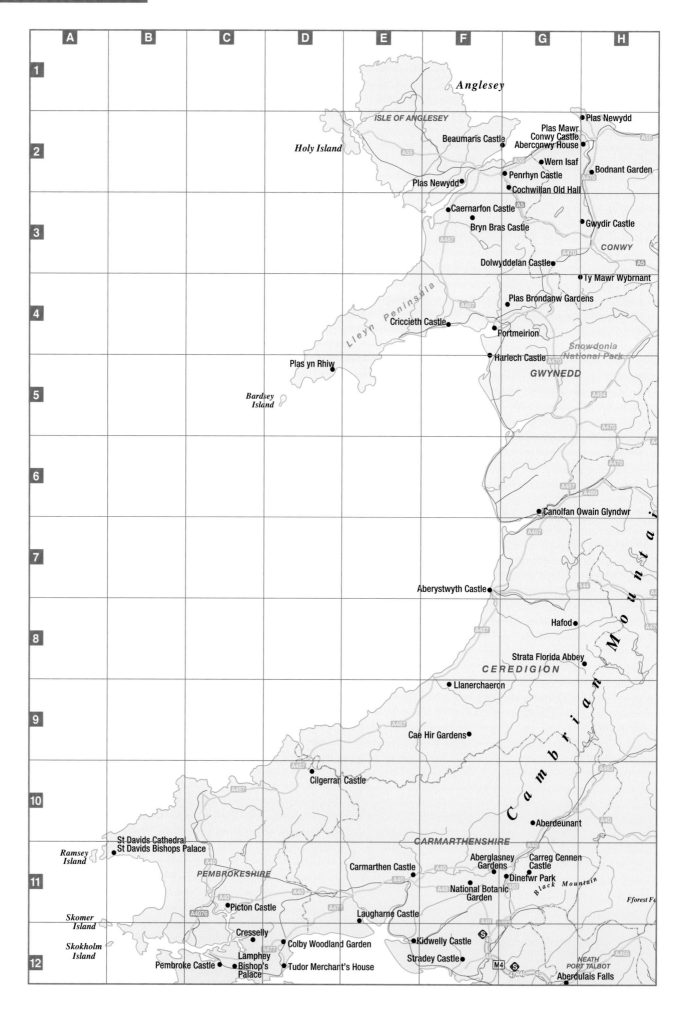

Anglesey

ISLE OF ANGLESEY

Holy Island

Plas Newydd

Plas Mawr
Conwy Castle
Beaumaris Castle
Aberconwy House

Wern Isaf

Bodnant Garden

Penrhyn Castle

Plas Newydd

Cochwillan Old Hall

Caernarfon Castle

Gwydir Castle

Bryn Bras Castle

CONWY

Dolwyddelan Castle

Ty Mawr Wybrnant

Plas Brondanw Gardens

Lleyn Peninsula

Criccieth Castle

Portmeirion

Snowdonia
National Park

Plas yn Rhiw

Harlech Castle

GWYNEDD

Bardsey
Island

Canolfan Owain Glyndwr

Aberystwyth Castle

Cambrian Mountains

Hafod

Strata Florida Abbey

CEREDIGION

Llanerchaeron

Cae Hir Gardens

Cilgerran Castle

Aberdeunant

St Davids Cathedral
St Davids Bishops Palace

CARMARTHENSHIRE

Ramsey
Island

Aberglasney
Gardens

Carreg Cennen
Castle

Carmarthen Castle

PEMBROKESHIRE

Dinefwr Park

Black Mountain

Fforest Fa

National Botanic
Garden

Skomer
Island

Picton Castle

Laugharne Castle

Skokholm
Island

Cresselly

Colby Woodland Garden

Kidwelly Castle

Lamphey
Bishop's
Palace

Stradey Castle

NEATH
PORT TALBOT

Pembroke Castle

Tudor Merchant's House

Aberdulais Falls

MAP 6

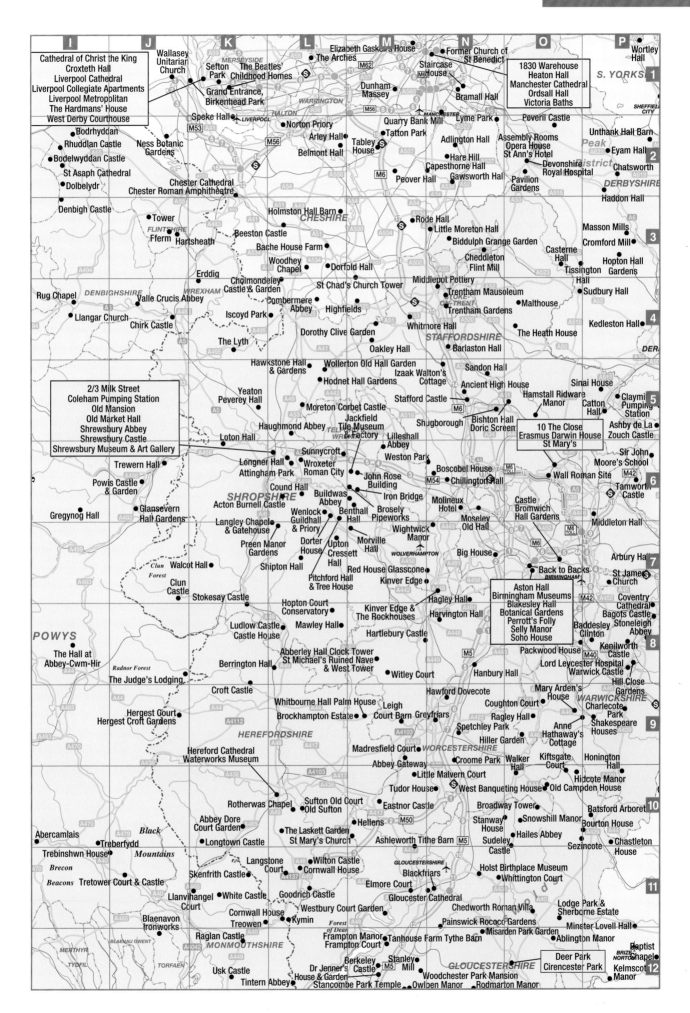

MAP 7

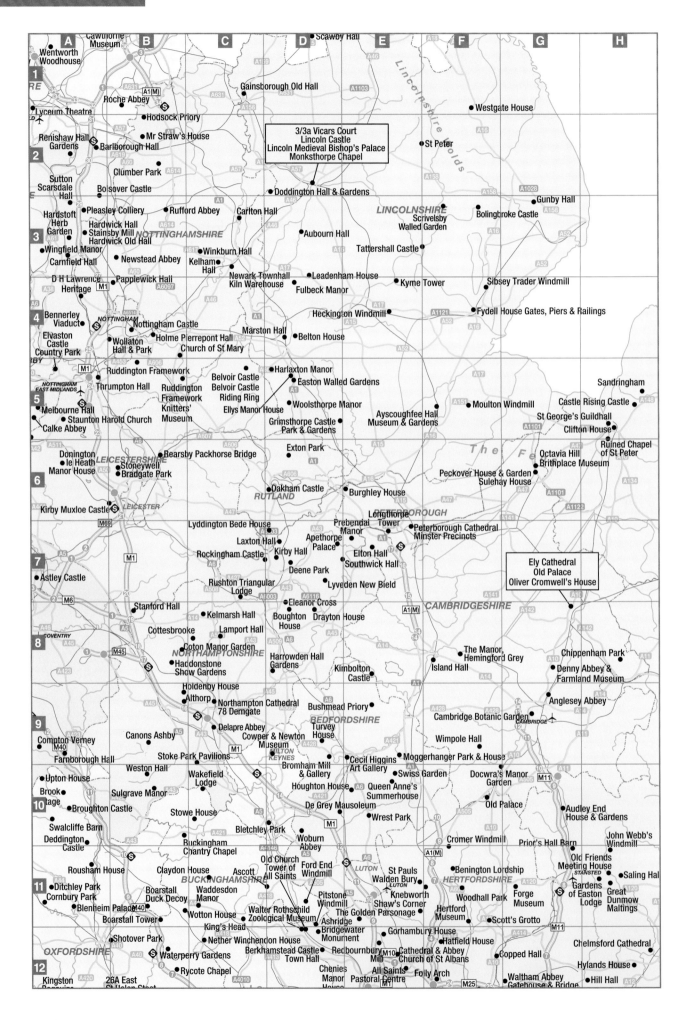

MAP 8

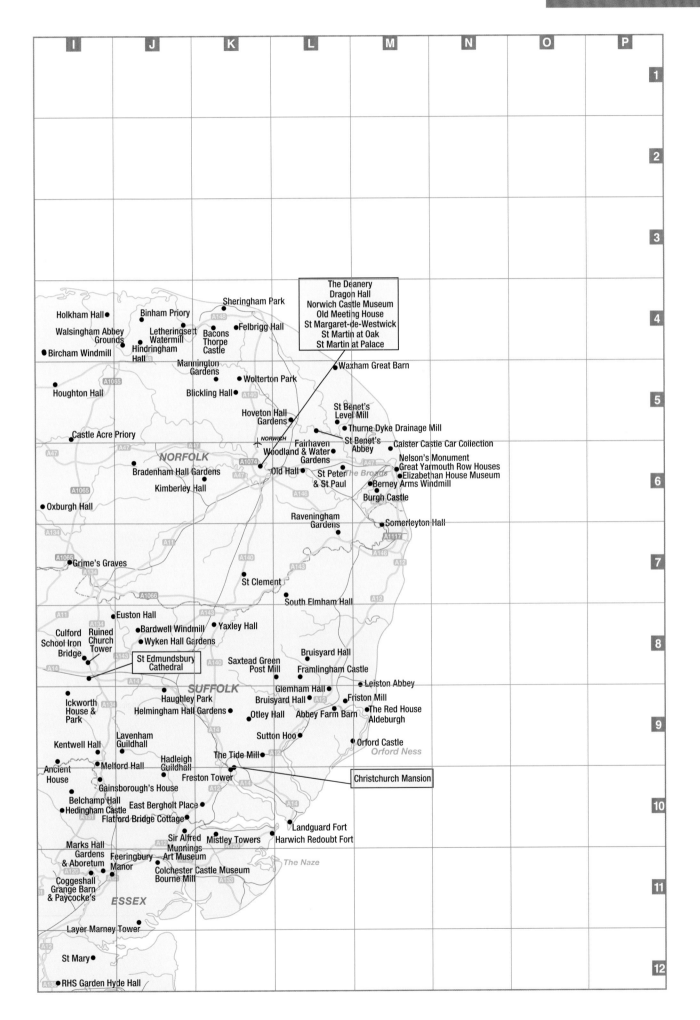

I   J   K   L   M   N   O   P

1
2
3
4
5
6
7
8
9
10
11
12

Holkham Hall
Binham Priory
Sheringham Park
Walsingham Abbey Grounds
Letheringsett Watermill
Bacons Thorpe Castle
Felbrigg Hall
Bircham Windmill
Hindringham Hall
Mannington Gardens

The Deanery
Dragon Hall
Norwich Castle Museum
Old Meeting House
St Margaret-de-Westwick
St Martin at Oak
St Martin at Palace

Waxham Great Barn
Wolterton Park
Houghton Hall
Blickling Hall
Hoveton Hall Gardens
St Benet's Level Mill
Thurne Dyke Drainage Mill
Castle Acre Priory
NORFOLK
NORWICH
Fairhaven Woodland & Water Gardens
St Benet's Abbey
Caister Castle Car Collection
Nelson's Monument
Great Yarmouth Row Houses
Bradenham Hall Gardens
Old Hall
St Peter & St Paul
The Broads
Elizabethan House Museum
Kimberley Hall
Berney Arms Windmill
Burgh Castle
Oxburgh Hall
Raveningham Gardens
Somerleyton Hall
Grime's Graves
St Clement
South Elmham Hall
Euston Hall
Bardwell Windmill
Yaxley Hall
Culford School Iron Bridge
Ruined Church Tower
Wyken Hall Gardens
Bruisyard Hall
St Edmundsbury Cathedral
Saxtead Green Post Mill
Framlingham Castle
SUFFOLK
Leiston Abbey
Glemham Hall
Friston Mill
Ickworth House & Park
Haughley Park
Bruisyard Hall
Otley Hall
Abbey Farm Barn
The Red House Aldeburgh
Helmingham Hall Gardens
Sutton Hoo
Lavenham Guildhall
Kentwell Hall
Orford Castle
Ancient House
Hadleigh Guildhall
The Tide Mill
Orford Ness
Melford Hall
Freston Tower
Christchurch Mansion
Gainsborough's House
Belchamp Hall
East Bergholt Place
Hedingham Castle
Flatford Bridge Cottage
Landguard Fort
Marks Hall Gardens & Aboretum
Sir Alfred Munnings Art Museum
Mistley Towers
Harwich Redoubt Fort
Feeringbury Manor
The Naze
Coggeshall Grange Barn & Paycocke's
Colchester Castle Museum
Bourne Mill
ESSEX
Layer Marney Tower
St Mary
RHS Garden Hyde Hall

MAP 9

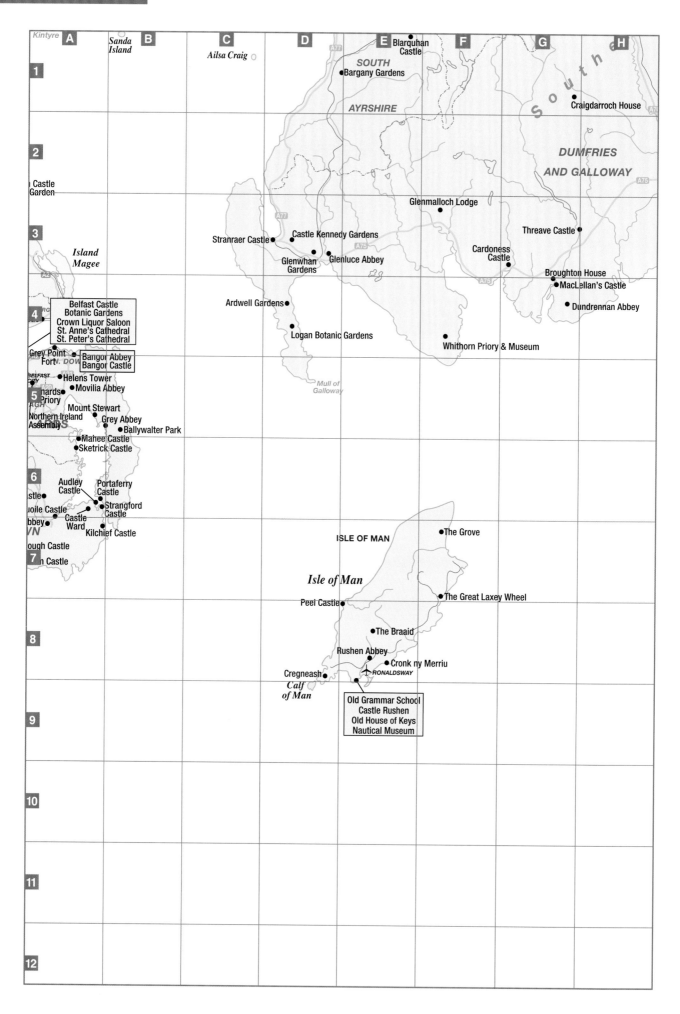

Kintyre **A**

Sanda Island **B**

Ailsa Craig ○ **C**

D

Blarquhan Castle **E**

F

G

South **H**

1

Bargany Gardens

Craigdarroch House

SOUTH AYRSHIRE

2

Castle Garden

DUMFRIES AND GALLOWAY

Glenmalloch Lodge

3

Island Magee

Stranraer Castle

Castle Kennedy Gardens

Threave Castle

Glenwhan Gardens

Glenluce Abbey

Cardoness Castle

Broughton House

MacLellan's Castle

4

Belfast Castle
Botanic Gardens
Crown Liquor Saloon
St. Anne's Cathedral
St. Peter's Cathedral

Ardwell Gardens

Dundrennan Abbey

Grey Point Fort

N. DOWN

Bangor Abbey
Bangor Castle

Logan Botanic Gardens

BELFAST CITY

Helens Tower

5

hards Priory

Movilia Abbey

Mull of Galloway

Whithorn Priory & Museum

Mount Stewart

Northern Ireland Assembly

Grey Abbey

Ballywalter Park

Mahee Castle

Sketrick Castle

6

Audley Castle

Portaferry Castle

stle

uoile Castle

Strangford Castle

Castle Ward

bbey

Kilchief Castle

7

ough Castle

n Castle

ISLE OF MAN

The Grove

Isle of Man

The Great Laxey Wheel

Peel Castle

8

The Braaid

Rushen Abbey

Cronk ny Merriu

Cregneash

RONALDSWAY

Calf of Man

Old Grammar School
Castle Rushen
Old House of Keys
Nautical Museum

9

10

11

12

MAP 10

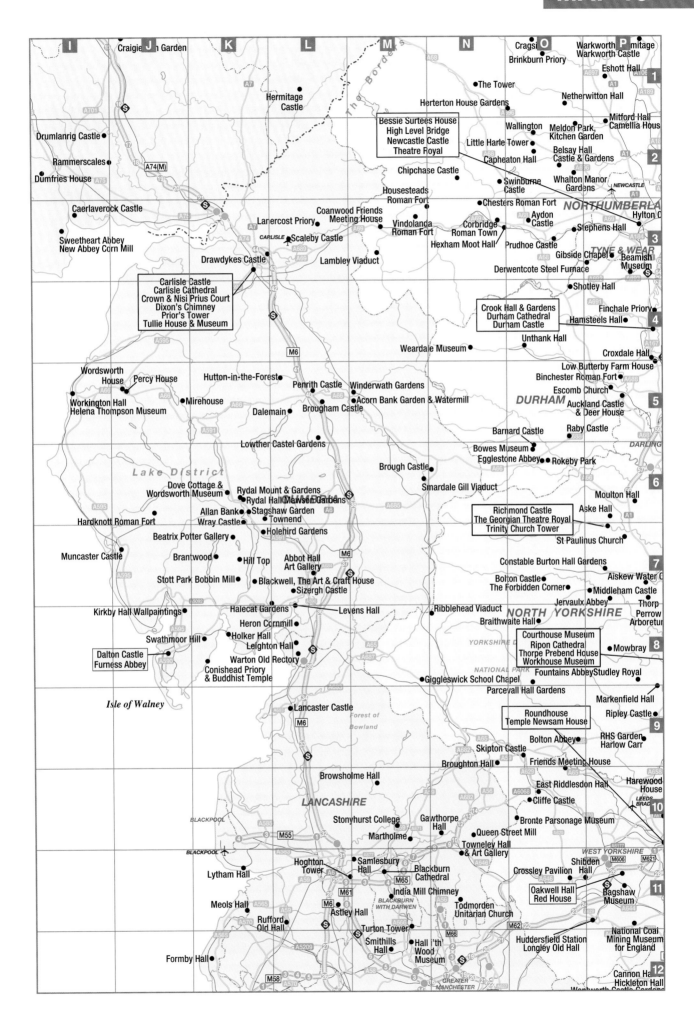

MAP 11

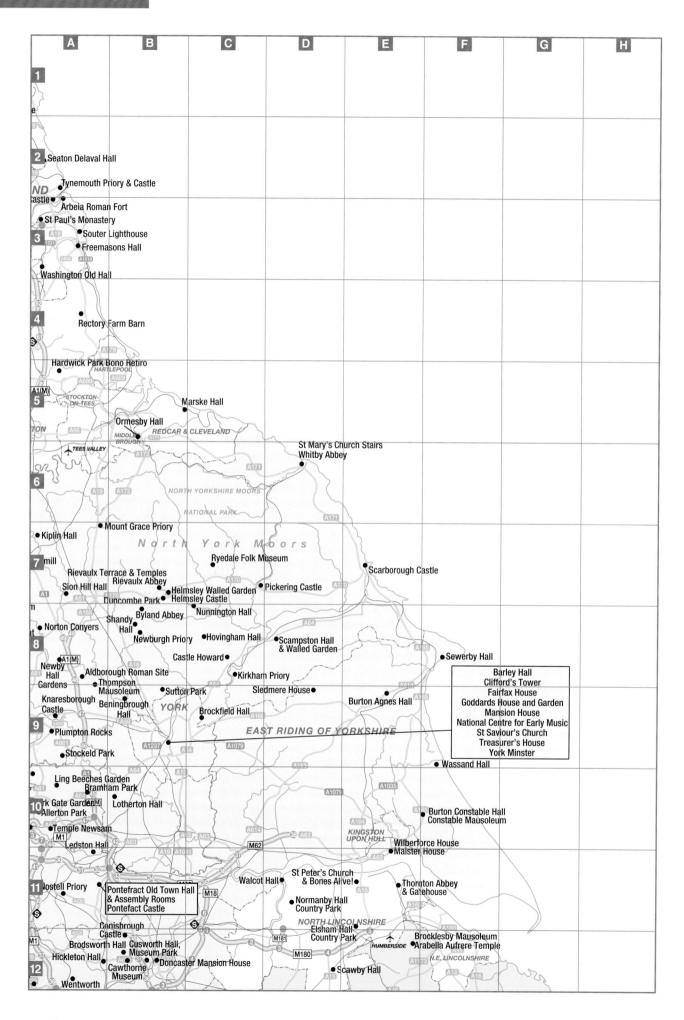

A　B　C　D　E　F　G　H

1

2 Seaton Delaval Hall

Tynemouth Priory & Castle

Arbeia Roman Fort
St Paul's Monastery
3 Souter Lighthouse
Freemasons Hall

Washington Old Hall

4 Rectory Farm Barn

Hardwick Park Bono Retiro
HARTLEPOOL

STOCKTON-
ON-TEES
5 Marske Hall

Ormesby Hall
MIDDLES-
BROUGH REDCAR & CLEVELAND
TEES VALLEY St Mary's Church Stairs
Whitby Abbey

6 NORTH YORKSHIRE MOORS

NATIONAL PARK

Mount Grace Priory
Kiplin Hall North York Moors

mill Ryedale Folk Museum
7 Scarborough Castle
Rievaulx Terrace & Temples
Rievaulx Abbey
Sion Hill Hall Helmsley Walled Garden Pickering Castle
Duncombe Park Helmsley Castle

Byland Abbey Nunnington Hall
Shandy
Hall
Norton Conyers Newburgh Priory Hovingham Hall Scampston Hall
8 & Walled Garden
Newby Castle Howard Sewerby Hall
Hall Aldborough Roman Site Kirkham Priory
Gardens Thompson
Knaresborough Mausoleum Sutton Park Sledmere House
Castle Beningbrough YORK Burton Agnes Hall
Hall Brockfield Hall
9 EAST RIDING OF YORKSHIRE
Plumpton Rocks

Stockeld Park

Wassand Hall
Ling Beeches Garden
Bramham Park
10 rk Gate Garden Lotherton Hall Burton Constable Hall
Allerton Park Constable Mausoleum

Temple Newsam KINGSTON
UPON HULL
Ledston Hall Wilberforce House
Maister House

11 ostell Priory St Peter's Church
Pontefract Old Town Hall Walcot Hall & Bones Alive! Thornton Abbey
& Assembly Rooms & Gatehouse
Pontefact Castle Normanby Hall
Country Park
Conisbrough NORTH LINCOLNSHIRE
Castle Elsham Hall Brocklesby Mausoleum
Brodsworth Hall Cusworth Hall, Country Park HUMBERSIDE Arabella Aufrere Temple
Hickleton Hall Museum Park N.E. LINCOLNSHIRE
12 Cawthorne Doncaster Mansion House
Museum Scawby Hall
Wentworth

Barley Hall
Clifford's Tower
Fairfax House
Goddards House and Garden
Mansion House
National Centre for Early Music
St Saviour's Church
Treasurer's House
York Minster

380

MAP 12

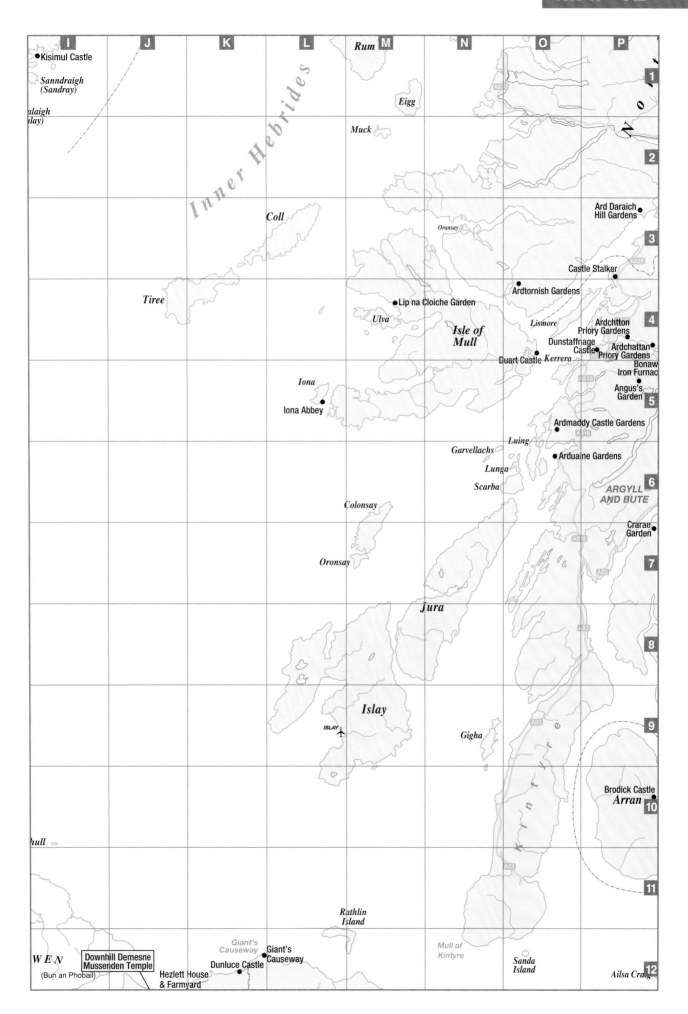

I · Kisimul Castle

Sanndraigh (Sandray)

alaigh (lay)

Inner Hebrides

Rum M

Eigg

Muck

Coll

Oransay

Ard Daraich Hill Gardens ·

Tiree

Castle Stalker *·*

Lip na Cloiche Garden *·*

· Ardtornish Gardens

Ulva

Lismore

Isle of Mull

Ardchtton Priory Gardens *·*

Dunstaffnage Castle *·* Ardchattan · Priory Gardens

Duart Castle *·* *Kerrera* Bonaw Iron Furnac

Iona

Angus's Garden

Iona Abbey *·*

· Ardmaddy Castle Gardens

Luing

Garvellachs

· Arduaine Gardens

Lunga

Scarba

ARGYLL AND BUTE

Colonsay

Crarae Garden *·*

Oronsay

Jura

Islay

ISLAY

Gigha

Brodick Castle *·*
Arran

hull

Rathlin Island

Giant's Causeway

Giant's Causeway *·*

Mull of Kintyre

W E N | Downhill Demesne Mussenden Temple

(Bun an Phobail) | Dunluce Castle *·*

Hezlett House & Farmyard

Sanda Island

Ailsa Craig

MAP 13

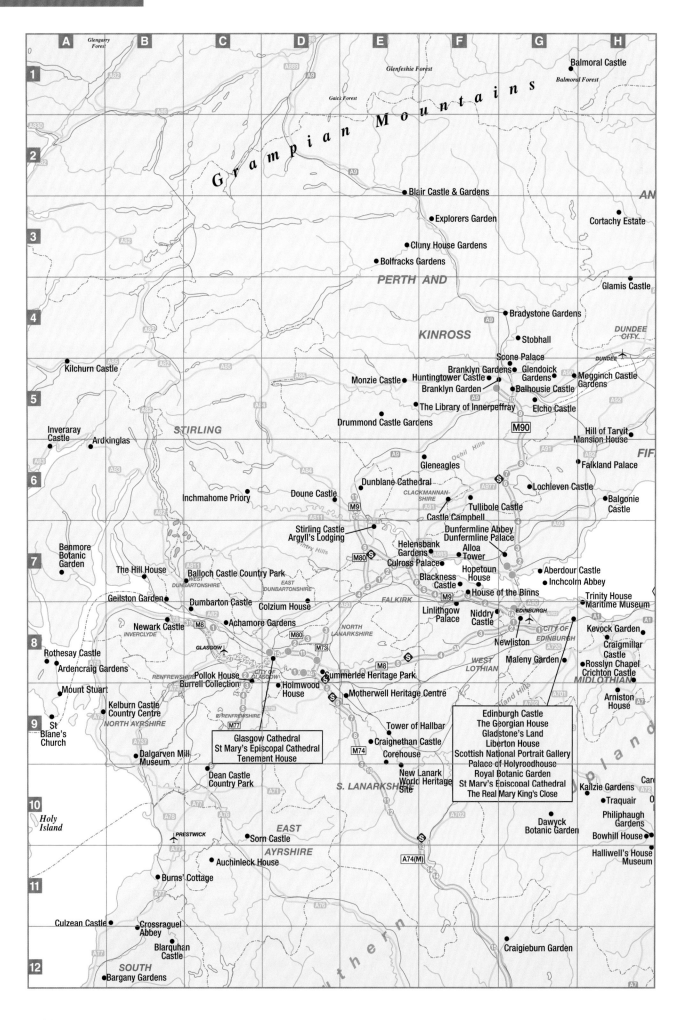

A **B** **C** **D** **E** **F** **G** **H**

Glengarry Forest

Balmoral Castle

1

Glenfeshie Forest

Balmoral Forest

2

Gaick Forest

G r a m p i a n M o u n t a i n s

AN

Blair Castle & Gardens

Explorers Garden

Cortachy Estate

3

Cluny House Gardens

Bolfracks Gardens

PERTH AND

Glamis Castle

4

Bradystone Gardens

KINROSS

Stobhall

DUNDEE CITY

Scone Palace

Kilchurn Castle

Branklyn Gardens Glendoick Gardens

DUNDEE

Monzie Castle Huntingtower Castle

Megginch Castle Gardens

5

Branklyn Garden Balhousie Castle

The Library of Innerpeffray Elcho Castle

STIRLING

Drummond Castle Gardens

M90

Inveraray Castle

Hill of Tarvit Mansion House

FIF

Ardkinglas

Gleneagles

Falkland Palace

6

Ochil Hills

Dunblane Cathedral

Lochleven Castle

Inchmahome Priory

Doune Castle

CLACKMANNAN-SHIRE

Tullibole Castle

Balgonie Castle

M9

Castle Campbell

Dunfermline Abbey Dunfermline Palace

7

Benmore Botanic Garden

Helensbank Gardens Alloa Tower

The Hill House

Balloch Castle Country Park

WEST DUNBARTONSHIRE

EAST DUNBARTONSHIRE

Culross Palace

Aberdour Castle

Hopetoun House

Inchcolm Abbey

Geilston Garden

Dumbarton Castle

Colzium House

FALKIRK

Blackness Castle

House of the Binns

Trinity House Maritime Museum

Newark Castle

M8

Achamore Gardens

M80

Linlithgow Palace

Niddry Castle

EDINBURGH

Kevock Garden

INVERCLYDE

M73

NORTH LANARKSHIRE

M9

CITY OF EDINBURGH

Craigmillar Castle

8

Rothesay Castle

GLASGOW

Newliston

Maleny Garden

Rosslyn Chapel

Ardencraig Gardens

Pollok House

CITY OF GLASGOW

Summerlee Heritage Park

WEST LOTHIAN

Crichton Castle

MIDLOTHIAN

Mount Stuart

Burrell Collection

Holmwood House

Arniston House

Kelburn Castle Country Centre

RENFREWSHIRE

M8

9

St Blane's Church

NORTH AYRSHIRE

M77

Motherwell Heritage Centre

Glasgow Cathedral
St Mary's Episcopal Cathedral
Tenement House

Tower of Hallbar

Edinburgh Castle
The Georgian House
Gladstone's Land
Liberton House
Scottish National Portrait Gallery
Palace of Holyroodhouse
Royal Botanic Garden
St Mary's Episcopal Cathedral
The Real Mary King's Close

Holy Island

Dalgarven Mill Museum

Craignethan Castle

Corehouse

M74

Kailzie Gardens

Car

10

Dean Castle Country Park

New Lanark World Heritage Site

Traquair

S. LANARKSHIRE

Philiphaugh Gardens

EAST

PRESTWICK

Sorn Castle

Dawyck Botanic Garden

Bowhill House

AYRSHIRE

A74(M)

Halliwell's House Museum

11

Auchinleck House

Burns' Cottage

Culzean Castle

Crossraguel Abbey

Craigieburn Garden

Blarquhan Castle

12

SOUTH

Bargany Gardens

MAP 14

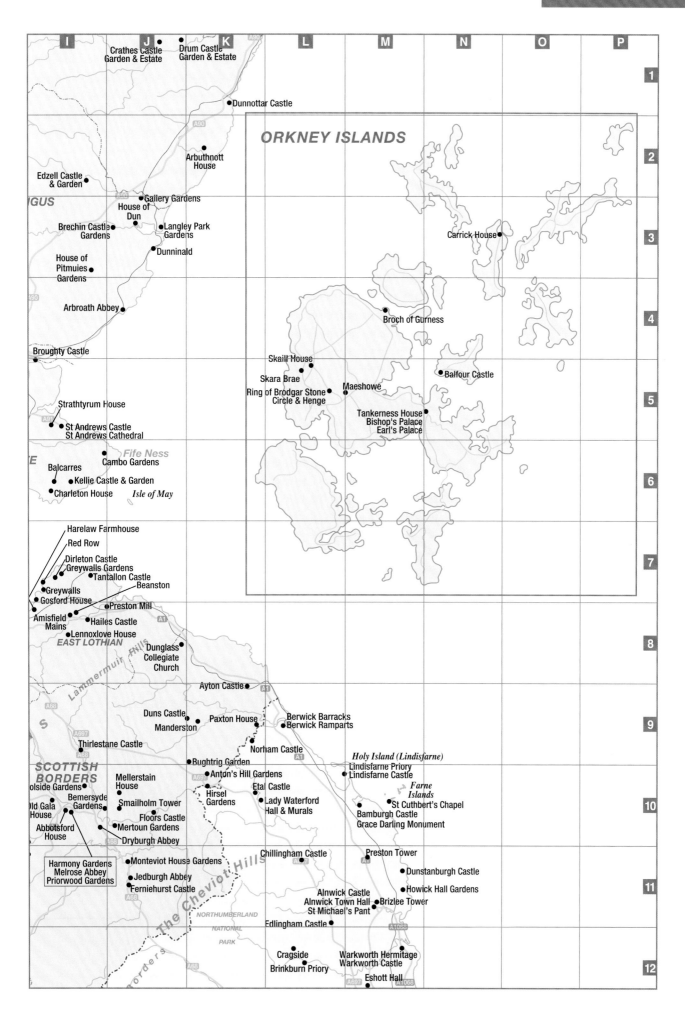

ORKNEY ISLANDS

I J K L M N O P

1
2
3
4
5
6
7
8
9
10
11
12

Crathes Castle Garden & Estate
Drum Castle Garden & Estate
Dunnottar Castle
Arbuthnott House
Edzell Castle & Garden
Gallery Gardens
House of Dun
IGUS
Brechin Castle Gardens
Langley Park Gardens
Dunninald
House of Pitmuies Gardens
Arbroath Abbey
Broughty Castle
Strathtyrum House
St Andrews Castle
St Andrews Cathedral
Fife Ness
Cambo Gardens
Balcarres
Kellie Castle & Garden
Charleton House
Isle of May

Carrick House

Broch of Gurness

Skaill House
Skara Brae
Ring of Brodgar Stone Circle & Henge
Maeshowe
Balfour Castle
Tankerness House
Bishop's Palace
Earl's Palace

Harelaw Farmhouse
Red Row
Dirleton Castle
Greywalls Gardens
Tantallon Castle
Beanston
Greywalls
Gosford House
Preston Mill
Amisfield Mains
Hailes Castle
Lennoxlove House
EAST LOTHIAN
Dunglass Collegiate Church

Ayton Castle

Duns Castle
Paxton House
Berwick Barracks
Berwick Ramparts
Manderston
Thirlestane Castle
Norham Castle

SCOTTISH BORDERS
Bughtrig Garden
Holy Island (Lindisfarne)
Lindisfarne Priory
Lindisfarne Castle
olside Gardens
Mellerstain House
Anton's Hill Gardens
Etal Castle
Farne Islands
Bemersyde Gardens
Hirsel Gardens
St Cuthbert's Chapel
ld Gala House
Smailholm Tower
Lady Waterford Hall & Murals
Bamburgh Castle
Grace Darling Monument
Floors Castle
Abbotsford House
Mertoun Gardens
Dryburgh Abbey
Harmony Gardens
Melrose Abbey
Priorwood Gardens
Monteviot House Gardens
Chillingham Castle
Preston Tower
Dunstanburgh Castle
Jedburgh Abbey
Howick Hall Gardens
Ferniehurst Castle
Alnwick Castle
Alnwick Town Hall
Brizlee Tower
St Michael's Pant
Edlingham Castle
NORTHUMBERLAND
NATIONAL
PARK
Cragside
Warkworth Hermitage
Warkworth Castle
Brinkburn Priory
Eshott Hall
The Cheviot Hills
Lammermuir Hills
Borders

383

MAP 15

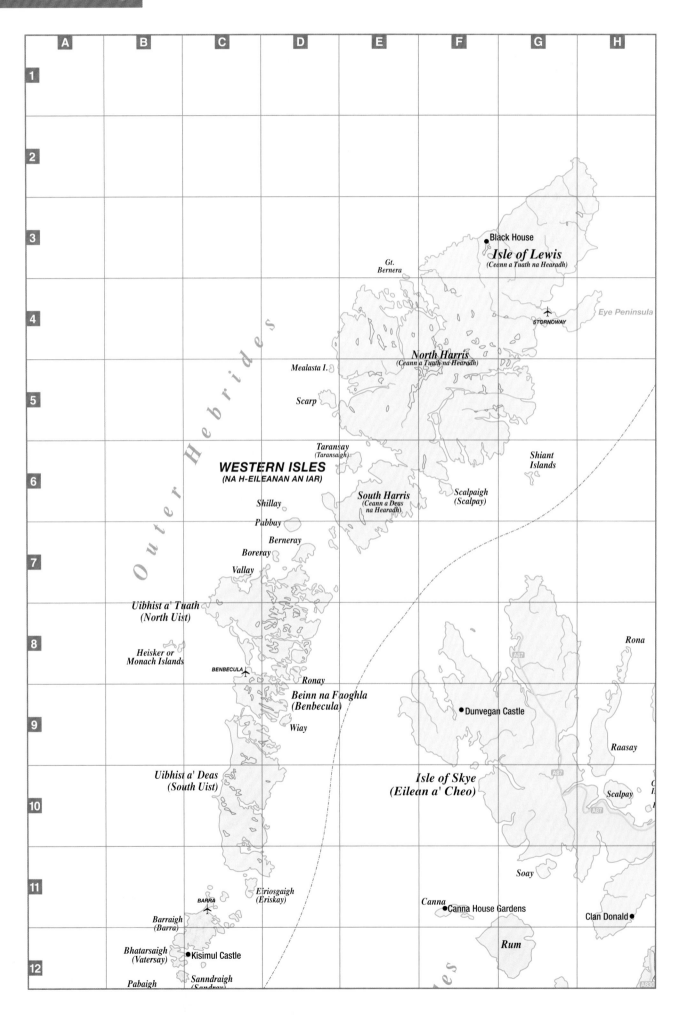

	A	B	C	D	E	F	G	H

Black House

Isle of Lewis
(Ceann a Tuath na Hearadh)

Gt.
Bernera

STORNOWAY

Eye Peninsula

North Harris
(Ceann a Tuath na Hearadh)

Mealasta I.

Scarp

Taransay
(Taransaigh)

Shiant
Islands

WESTERN ISLES
(NA H-EILEANAN AN IAR)

South Harris
*(Ceann a Deas
na Hearadh)*

Scalpaigh
(Scalpay)

Shillay

Pabbay

Berneray

Boreray

Vallay

Outer Hebrides

Uibhist a' Tuath
(North Uist)

Heisker or
Monach Islands

BENBECULA

Ronay

Rona

Beinn na Faoghla
(Benbecula)

●Dunvegan Castle

Wiay

Raasay

Uibhist a' Deas
(South Uist)

Isle of Skye
(Eilean a' Cheo)

A87

Scalpay

A87

Soay

Eiriosgaigh
(Eriskay)

BARRA

Canna ●Canna House Gardens

Clan Donald ●

Barraigh
(Barra)

Rum

Bhatarsaigh
(Vatersay)

●Kisimul Castle

Pabaigh

Sanndraigh
(Sandray)

MAP 16

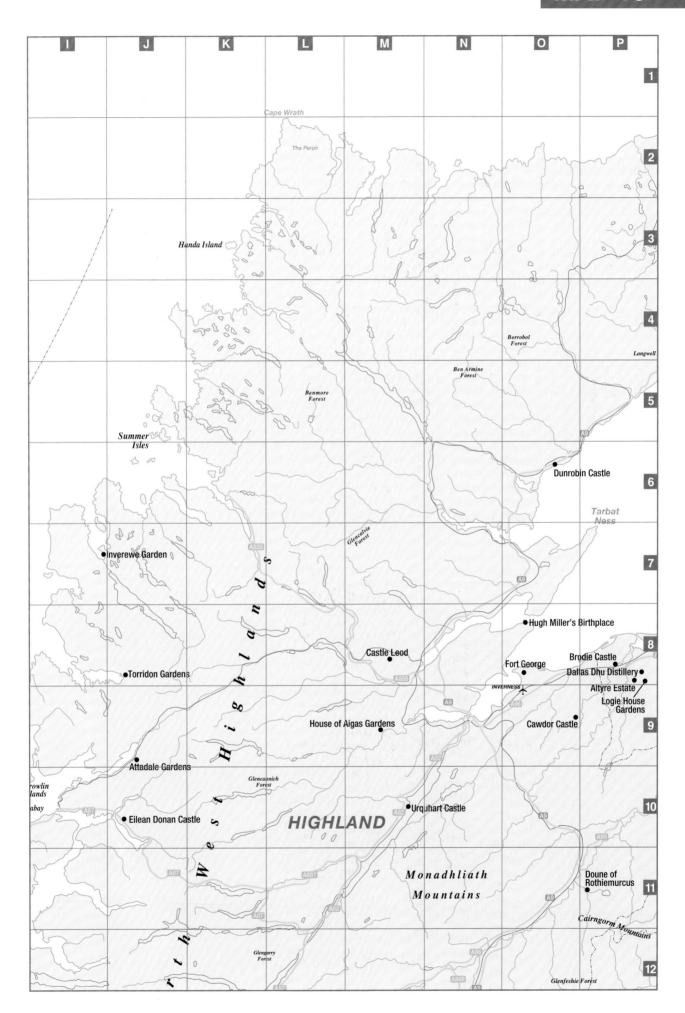

I J K L M N O P

1
2
3
4
5
6
7
8
9
10
11
12

Cape Wrath

The Parph

Handa Island

Borrobol
Forest

Langwell

Ben Armine
Forest

Benmore
Forest

Summer
Isles

Dunrobin Castle

Tarbat
Ness

Glencalvie
Forest

Inverewe Garden

Hugh Miller's Birthplace

Castle Leod

Brodie Castle

Fort George

Dallas Dhu Distillery

INVERNESS

Altyre Estate

Torridon Gardens

Logie House
Gardens

House of Aigas Gardens

Cawdor Castle

Attadale Gardens

Glencannich
Forest

rowlin
lands

abay

Eilean Donan Castle

Urquhart Castle

HIGHLAND

Monadhliath
Mountains

Doune of
Rothiemurcus

Cairngorm Mountains

Glengarry
Forest

Glenfeshie Forest

MAP 17

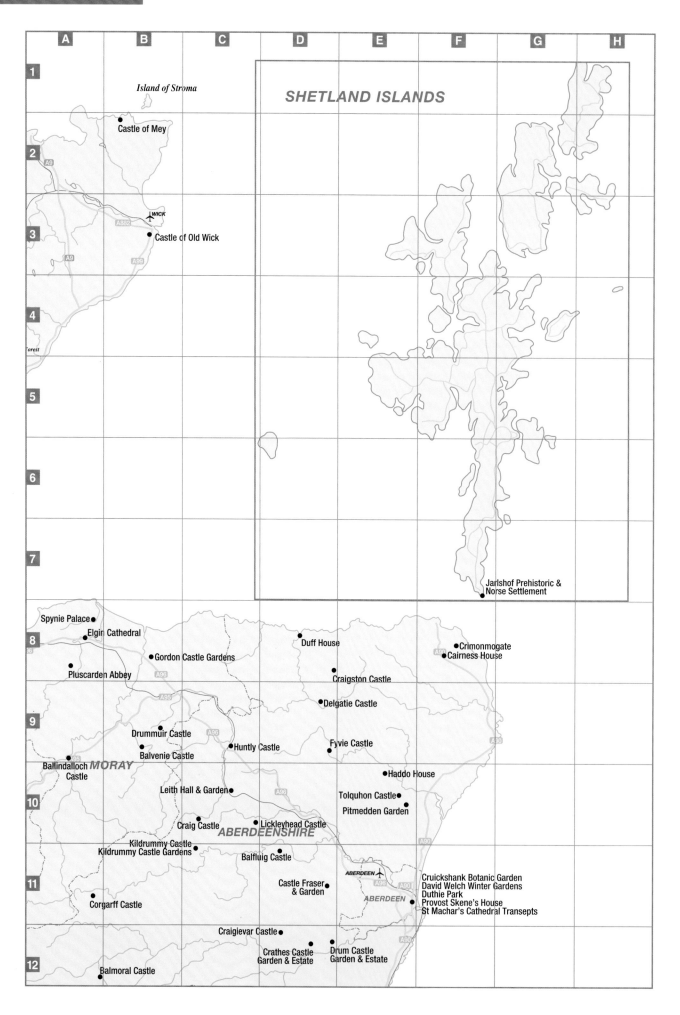

A **B** **C** **D** **E** **F** **G** **H**

1

Island of Stroma

SHETLAND ISLANDS

● Castle of Mey

2
A9

WICK
A882
3
● Castle of Old Wick
A9
A99

4
Forest

5

6

7

● Jarlshof Prehistoric &
Norse Settlement

Spynie Palace●
● Elgin Cathedral
8
● Duff House
●Crimonmogate
●Gordon Castle Gardens
●Cairness House
● Pluscarden Abbey
A96
●Craigston Castle

●Delgatie Castle

9
●Drummuir Castle
A96
●Fyvie Castle
●Huntly Castle
A90
●Balvenie Castle
●Ballindalloch *MORAY*
Castle
●Haddo House
●Leith Hall & Garden
●Tolquhon Castle
10
●Pitmedden Garden
●Craig Castle
●Lickleyhead Castle
ABERDEENSHIRE
●Kildrummy Castle
●Kildrummy Castle Gardens
●Balfluig Castle
ABERDEEN
11
Cruickshank Botanic Garden
●Castle Fraser
David Welch Winter Gardens
& Garden
Duthie Park
ABERDEEN
Provost Skene's House
●Corgarff Castle
St Machar's Cathedral Transepts

●Craigievar Castle
12
●Crathes Castle
●Drum Castle
Garden & Estate
Garden & Estate
● Balmoral Castle

MAP 18

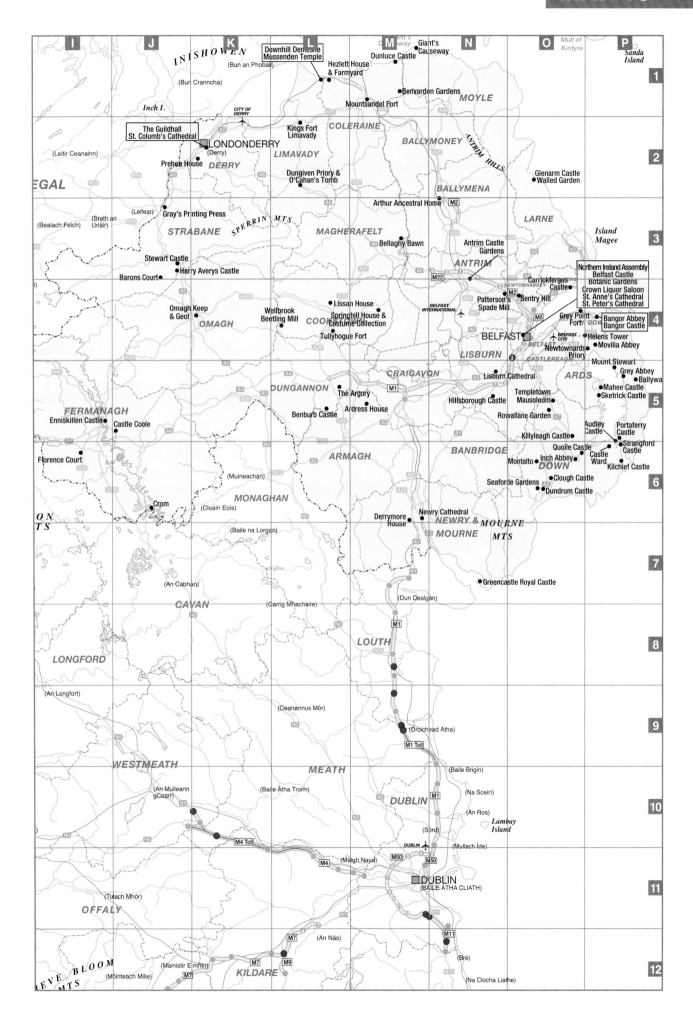

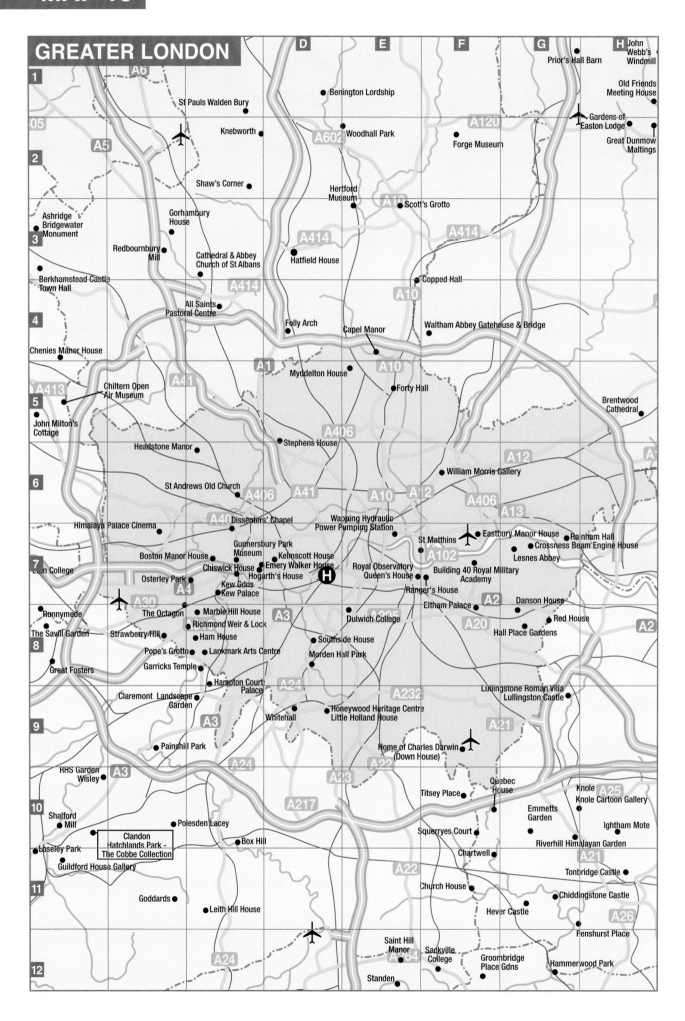

MAP 19

GREATER LONDON

1
05
2
3
4
5
6
7
8
9
10
11
12

D   E   F   G   H

John Webb's Windmill

Prior's Hall Barn

St Pauls Walden Bury

Benington Lordship

Old Friends Meeting House

A120

Gardens of Easton Lodge

Knebworth

Woodhall Park

A602

Forge Museum

Great Dunmow Maltings

Shaw's Corner

Hertford Museum

A10

Scott's Grotto

Ashridge Bridgewater Monument

Gorhambury House

A414

A414

Redbournbury Mill

Cathedral & Abbey Church of St Albans

Hatfield House

Copped Hall

Berkhamstead Castle Town Hall

A414

A10

All Saints Pastoral Centre

Chenies Manor House

Folly Arch

Capel Manor

Waltham Abbey Gatehouse & Bridge

A41

A1

Myddelton House

A10

A413

Chiltern Open Air Museum

Forty Hall

Brentwood Cathedral

John Milton's Cottage

A406

Headstone Manor

Stephens House

A12

A

St Andrews Old Church

A406

A41

A10

A12

William Morris Gallery

A406

A13

Himalaya Palace Cinema

A40

Dissenters' Chapel

Wapping Hydraulic Power Pumping Station

St Matthins

Eastbury Manor House

Rainham Hall

Gunnersbury Park Museum

A102

Crossness Beam Engine House

Boston Manor House

Kelmscott House

Lesnes Abbey

Chiswick House

Emery Walker House

Royal Observatory Queen's House

Building 40 Royal Military Academy

Eton College

Osterley Park

Hogarth's House

H

Kew Gdns

Ranger's House

Danson House

A4

Kew Palace

Eltham Palace

A2

The Octagon

A30

Marble Hill House

A3

Dulwich College

A20

Red House

Ronnymede

Richmond Weir & Lock

Hall Place Gardens

A2

The Savill Garden

Strawberry Hill

Ham House

Southside House

Pope's Grotto

Lankmark Arts Centre

Morden Hall Park

Lullingstone Roman Villa

Garricks Temple

Lullingston Castle

Great Fosters

Hampton Court Palace

A24

A232

Claremont Landscape Garden

Whitehall

Honeywood Heritage Centre Little Holland House

A21

A3

Painshill Park

Home of Charles Darwin (Down House)

A24

A22

RHS Garden Wisley

A3

A23

Titsey Place

Quebec House

Knole

A25

Shalford Mill

Polesden Lacey

Squerryes Court

Emmetts Garden

Knole Cartoon Gallery

Ightham Mote

Clandon Hatchlands Park – The Cobbe Collection

Box Hill

Chartwell

Riverhill Himalayan Garden

Loseley Park

Church House

A21

Guildford House Gallery

A22

Tonbridge Castle

Goddards

Leith Hill House

Chiddingstone Castle

Hever Castle

A26

Fenshurst Place

Saint Hill Manor

Sackville College

Groombridge Place Gdns

Hammerwood Park

A24

A64

Standen

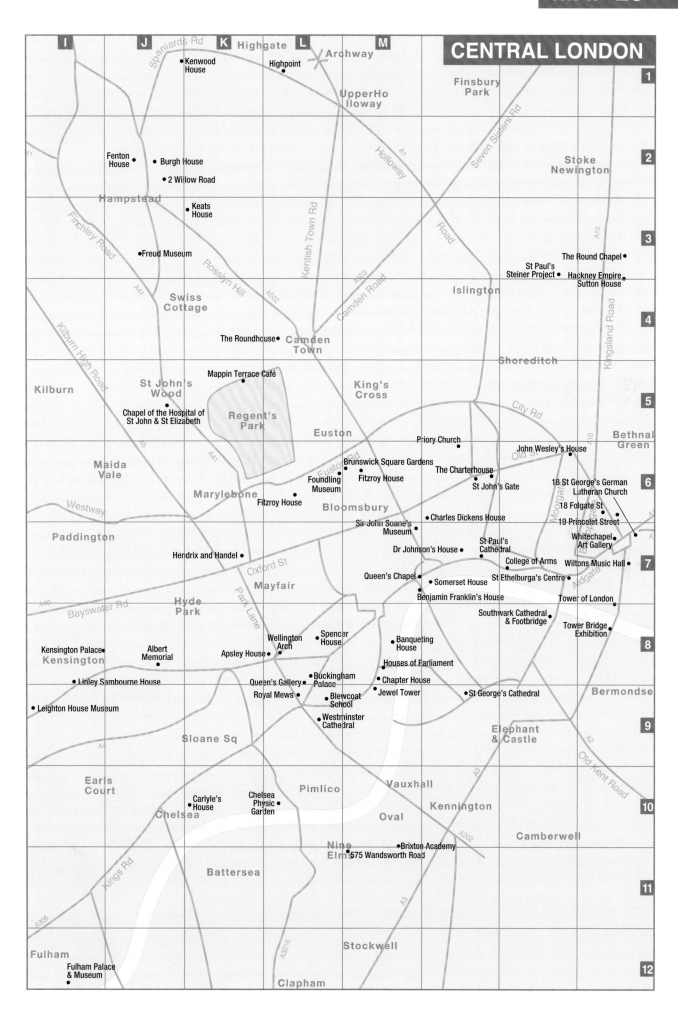

MAP 20

CENTRAL LONDON

I J **Spaniards Rd** K **Highgate** L **Archway** M

1

Kenwood House

Highpoint

Finsbury Park

UpperHo lloway

Holloway

Seven Sisters Rd

2

Fenton House

Burgh House

Stoke Newington

2 Willow Road

A1

Road

A10

Hampstead

Keats House

3

Finchley Road

Rosslyn Hill

Kentish Town Rd

A503

The Round Chapel

St Paul's Steiner Project

Hackney Empire

Sutton House

Freud Museum

A41

Camden Road

Islington

Kingsland Road

4

Swiss Cottage

A502

The Roundhouse

Camden Town

Shoreditch

Kilburn High Road

Mappin Terrace Café

5

A5

Kilburn

St John's Wood

King's Cross

City Rd

Bethnal Green

Chapel of the Hospital of St John & St Elizabeth

Regent's Park

A10

Euston

Priory Church

John Wesley's House

Moorgate

6

Maida Vale

A41

Westway

Euston Rd

Brunswick Square Gardens

Fitzroy House

The Charterhouse

St John's Gate

18 St George's German Lutheran Church

18 Folgate St

Marylebone

Foundling Museum

Fitzroy House

Bloomsbury

Charles Dickens House

19 Princelet Street

Bishopsgate

7

Paddington

Sir John Soane's Museum

Dr Johnson's House

St Paul's Cathedral

Whitechapel Art Gallery

Hendrix and Handel

Oxford St

College of Arms

Wiltons Music Hall

Mayfair

Queen's Chapel

Somerset House

St Ethelburga's Centre

Aldgate

A40

Bayswater Rd

Park Lane

Benjamin Franklin's House

Tower of London

8

Wellington Arch

Spencer House

Banqueting House

Southwark Cathedral & Footbridge

Tower Bridge Exhibition

Kensington Palace

Albert Memorial

Apsley House

Houses of Parliament

Hyde Park

Kensington

Linley Sambourne House

Queen's Gallery

Buckingham Palace

Chapter House

Bermondse

Leighton House Museum

Royal Mews

Blewcoat School

Jewel Tower

St George's Cathedral

A2

9

Westminster Cathedral

Elephant & Castle

Old Kent Road

Sloane Sq

A4

A3

Earls Court

Pimlico

Vauxhall

A202

10

Carlyle's House

Chelsea Physic Garden

Kennington

Camberwell

Chelsea

Oval

Kings Rd

A3216

Nine Elms

Brixton Academy

575 Wandsworth Road

A3

11

Battersea

A308

Stockwell

12

Fulham

Fulham Palace & Museum

Clapham

INDEX

Places listed by name in alphabetical order

INDEX

INDEX

INDEX

INDEX

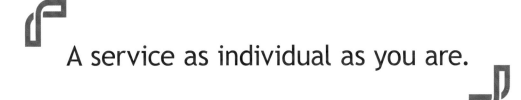

A service as individual as you are.

To find out more, please contact:

London
Andrew Lockwood
020 7131 4355

Edward Hendin
020 7131 4655

Bristol
James Shrives
0117 376 2193

Salisbury
Susan Shaw
01722 431 034

firstname.surname@smithandwilliamson.com

Uniquely placed in the industry for over a century, Smith & Williamson has been combining tax, accounting, financial planning and investment management services for owners of historic houses and landed estates.

As everyone's financial needs are different, we work closely with our clients to provide a bespoke service – with direct access to a team of professionals from each service area, who can give specialist advice on a wide range of financial issues.

smithandwilliamson.com

Smith & Williamson

Accountancy · Investment Management · Tax